80486
Programming

Penn Brumm

Systems Design Engineer
Amdahl Corporation

Don Brumm

Staff Systems Programmer
Operating System Development
Amdahl Corporation

Leo J. Scanlon

Freelance Writer
Software Consultant

FIRST EDITION
FIRST PRINTING

© 1991 by **Windcrest Books**, an imprint of TAB Books.
TAB Books is a division of McGraw-Hill, Inc.
The name "Windcrest" is a registered trademark of TAB Books.

Library of Congress Cataloging-in-Publication Data

Brumm, Penn.
    80486 programming / by Penn Brumm, Don Brumm, and Leo J. Scanlon.
      p.   cm.
    Includes bibliographical references (p. 489) and index.
    ISBN 0-8306-7577-9 (h)   ISBN 0-8306-3577-7 (p) :

    1. Intel 80486 (Microprocessor)—Programming.   I. Brumm, Don.
II. Scanlon, Leo J.   III. Title.
QA76.8.I2693B78   1991
005.265—dc20   91-10612
                                                             CIP

TAB Books offers software for sale. For information and a catalog, please contact TAB Software Department, Blue Ridge Summit, PA 17294-0850.

Acquisitions Editor: Roland S. Phelps
Book Editor: David M. McCandless
Production: Katherine G. Brown
Book Design: Jaclyn J. Boone

Paperbound cover photograph courtesy of Intel Corporation.   WPI

Contents

Appendices

Introduction

Intel Corporation's 80486 microprocessor is an enhanced version of the 80386, the 32-bit chip that brought microprocessors to the world of virtual systems and opened the door to commercial and scientific uses once excluded from desktop systems.

Like the 80386, the 80486 maintains binary compatibility with previous members of the Intel 86 family of microprocessor chips. However, the 80486 executes frequently-used instructions in one clock cycle, which lets it run programs twice as fast as the 80386 at the same clock rate. To get data and instructions from memory to the CPU execution fast enough to maintain this rate, the 80486 provides an on-chip cache memory and a burst bus.

The 80486 chip also incorporates an 80387 math coprocessor with its full instruction set. Because floating-point math data and instructions no longer need to travel from the processor to a separate math chip, math operations on the 80486 are more than four times faster than on the 80387 coprocessor.

Generally, four types of people pick up a book like this. One is a generalist who wishes to understand the history and architecture of a process or a physical entity such as the 80486 chip. Another is the programmer who, given a system by an original equipment manufacturer (OEM) designer, needs to program that system to function in the user world. Included in this second group are all those programmers who work for software houses that must keep up to date with the latest hardware revolution.

A third kind of person who reads this book is the OEM designer who has been given an assignment to take the chip and build a system. That designer first needs a good overview of the new chip's architecture. Finally, managers who must oversee one or all of the first three would read this book.

We found it difficult to structure material when writing about such an involved and interrelated subject as the 80486; what comes first, second, and so on? We finally decided to begin with basic building blocks (such as registers and data types) and go on from there.

We took one additional factor into consideration when planning this book. Often people are experts in one area and novices in another. In the areas of least knowledge, a quick refresher makes all the difference between a fast start-up and weeks of confusion.

Overall, we divided this book into sections to help each of its potential readers immediately identify where to go first. Chapters 1 through 5, the first section of the book, give the architectural overview of the 80486 to lead the reader from the internals of the chip outward to the associated subsystems that must work with the 80486. In addition, we explore some basic concepts.

Chapters 6 through 10, the second section of the book, are directed to the system-level programmer and/or programming manager, and describe the instruction set provided for the 80486 chip. Each instruction of the full instruction set is described, and most are demonstrated so you can understand in detail how the instruction interacts with the various registers and system flags. The demonstrations are written to exercise flag settings and register changes. The code does not represent the most efficient or complete way to perform a function and is not intended to be a tutorial on how to program.

Chapters 11 through 14, the third book section, are where the general overview comes in. Read these chapters if you need a quick refresher to some topic such as pipelining, interfacing concepts, and memory organization.

The appendices provide additional information that brings you up to date with this versatile and exciting new chip. Appendix A reviews background information about Intel Corporation and the design strategies that led to the 80486. Appendix B summarizes the various registers, bits, and flags that the 80486 uses. Appendix C assists when you run into a bit of jargon that is stated as letters you may not be familiar with. Appendix D reviews how the 80486 interacts with MULTIBUS I and II. Appendix E lists an assembly language program that demonstrates several of the instructions available in protected mode only (more on protected mode in Section 1).

The 80486 provides unprecedented power at a microcomputer level along with upward compatibility from earlier chips. Users can gain immediate performance improvements from current software without the expense of converting to a new system. Future software development will unlock the total power of the 80486.

1

Introduction to the 80486

Intel Corporation's 80486 microprocessor is the highest-performing member of the Intel 80X86 family. The 80486 runs DOS, Windows, the OS/2 operating system, the UNIX system, the Intel iRMX operating system, and iRMX kernel applications faster than any other processor.

Systems are said to be compatible if programs written on one will execute successfully on the other. If the compatibility extends in only one direction, from old to new, it is said to be *upward*. Upward compatibility at the object level supports an end-user's software investment as new systems replace older and slower ones. The 80486 is upwardly compatible with older generations of Intel microprocessors. That is, software written specifically for the 80486 and using 80486 features generally will not run on the older systems. However, since the 80486 instruction set and processing modules are a superset of the previous instructions sets, the older code is upwardly compatible to the 80386.

Like the earlier 80386, the 80486 features multitasking, on-chip memory management, virtual memory with paging, software protection, and a large address space. However, the 80486 also has both an 80387 numeric coprocessor and a cache memory on the chip. It also provides dynamic bus sizing that lets the 80486 work with 8-, 16-, or 32-bit external devices.

Intel implemented the 80486 using their CHMOS III technology, which is a semiconductor process that combines the high frequency of HMOS (*High Density Metal-Oxide Semiconductor*) with the modest power consumption of CMOS (*Complementary Metal-Oxide Semiconductor*). The 80486 can switch between programs running under different operating systems, such as MS-DOS and UNIX. This switching allows software designers to incorporate standard 16-bit applications directly onto the 32-bit system.

The processor defines an address space as one or more segments, any size from 1 byte to 4 gigabytes (four billion bytes). The segments can be individually protected by privilege levels and thus selectively shared between tasks. The protection mechanism is based on the notion of a privilege hierarchy—a graded or ranked series. That is, various tasks or programs can be assigned certain levels that are used exclusively for that task. (See FIG. 1-1.)

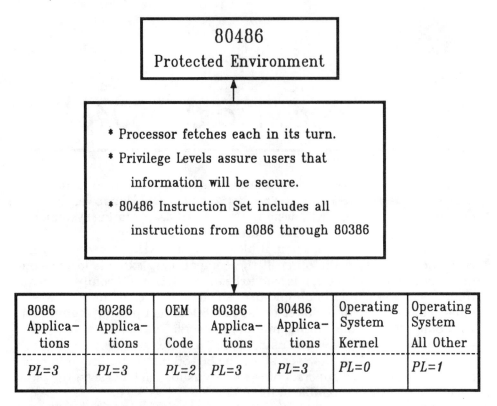

Memory Segments with Different Privilege Levels
1-1 80486 support.

In the illustrations in this book, note that certain register bits are undefined or are shown as reserved for future Intel use. Treat these bits as undefined because future processors may change them—perhaps without notice. Do not depend on the states of any of these undefined bits when testing the values of defined register bits. Mask them out when testing. Also, do not depend on the ability to retain information written into any of the undefined or reserved bits. When loading registers, always load these bits as zero or as unchanged from their stored values.

Basic definitions

Before proceeding, I need to define a few basic terms. These concepts are often referred to both in this book and in articles about the 80486. Many of the terms have Intel and/or 80486-based specific meanings.

SEGMENT—Beginning with the 8086, Intel introduced the concept of segments, which are defined as units of contiguous (adjacent) address space. In the 8086, a segment has a maximum of 64K or 65536 bytes. In the 80386 and 80486, that limitation no longer applies. Programmers can now view segments as one-dimensional subspaces, each having a length of up to 4 gigabytes.

GATES—A gate is a logic element that allows only certain processes to pass through it. The 80486 provides protection for control transfers among executable segments at differing privilege levels by use of gate descriptors. There are four kinds of gates (Call, Trap, Interrupt, and Task), all described in Chapter 6.

DESCRIPTOR—A descriptor is a data structure defining the characteristics of a program element. For example, descriptors describe a data record, a segment, or a task.

TABLE—A table is a collection of data laid out in rows and columns for reference or stored as an array. Elements of a table can be obtained by direct calculation from a known selector or base address.

LINEAR ADDRESS SPACE—An address indicates the location of a register, a particular place in storage, or some other data source or destination. In the 80486, linear address space runs from byte 0 to 4 gigabytes. A linear address points to a particular byte within this space.

LOGICAL ADDRESS—First, there is no conceptual parallel from linear address space to the space used by logical addressing. A logical address consists of a selector and offset. The selector points to some segment descriptor (part of which is that segment's linear base address). The offset tells how far into the segment the required byte is. The various terms used in this preliminary description are all described in detail within the first section of this book. Logical address is mentioned here to introduce the concept and its difference from the other types of addresses.

PHYSICAL ADDRESS—The address that actually selects the memory where a required byte is located. In the 80486, linear and physical addresses differ only when paging is in effect.

TASK—A task is a basic, unique function of a program or system. It can be one instance of the execution of a program. Tasks are also referred to as *processes*.

TASK STATE SEGMENT—TSS. A TSS is a data structure delineated and pointed to by a descriptor, wherein the (interrupted) state of a task is stored. Systems software creates the TSSs and places the initial information in them, such as correct stack pointers for interrupt handlers.

MICROCODE—A list of small program steps, also a set of control functions performed by the instruction decoding and executing logic of a computer system. It's code that is "below" the level of assembly language.

PAGING—Paging refers to a procedure that transmits the consecutive bytes called a page between locations, such as between main storage and memory. Paging simplifies the operating system swapping algorithms because it provides a uniform mechanism for managing the physical structure of memory.

FLAG—A flag is an indicator whose set/not set state is used to inform a later section of a program whether or not a condition has occurred.

32-bit processor overview

Integration of functions link elements into a single structure that cannot be divided without destroying the stated functions. The 80486 chip has an integrated memory management and protection architecture that includes address translation registers, multitasking hardware, and a protection mechanism to support a number of operating systems. This memory management and protection mechanism translates logical addresses to physical addresses and enforces the protection necessary for maintaining task integrity in a multitasking environment. (See FIG. 1-2.)

Basic units

The 80486 consists of nine units that operate in parallel. These units are the Bus Interface Unit (BIU), Instruction Prefetch Unit, Cache Unit, Instruction Decode Unit, Control Unit, Integer Unit, Floating-Point Unit (FPU), Segmentation Unit, and Paging Unit.

Bus Interface Unit An interface is a device (physical or logical) that connects adjacent components, circuits, equipment, or system elements. The BIU provides the interface between the 80486's internal units and its environment. Internally, the BIU communicates with the Cache and Instruction Prefetch Units via three 32-bit buses (data bus, control bus, and address bus), as shown in FIG. 1-3. Externally, the BIU provides the data, control, and address signals for communicating with external memory and I/O devices.

Instruction Prefetch Unit "Lookahead" is a feature that permits a system to obtain instructions or data before actually using it. The Instruction Prefetch Unit performs the program lookahead function of the 80486. When the BIU is not performing bus cycles to execute an instruction, the Instruction Prefetch Unit uses the BIU to fetch sequentially along the instruction byte stream. By reading instructions before they are needed, the 80486 rarely needs to wait for an instruction prefetch cycle on the processor bus.

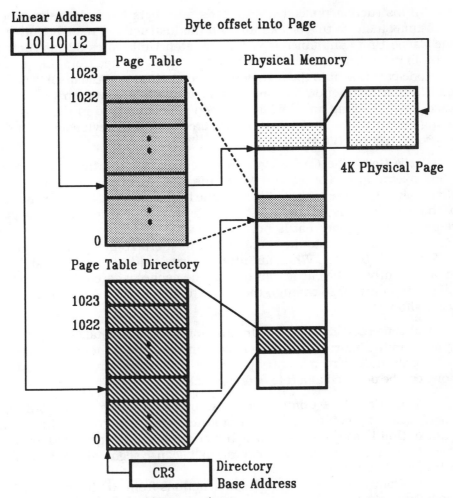

1-2 Linear to physical address mapping.

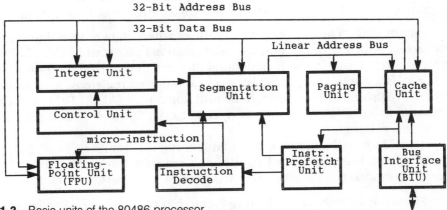

1-3 Basic units of the 80486 processor.

An instruction prefetch cycle reads a 16-byte block of instructions each time; it stores this block into both the Instruction Prefetch Unit and the Cache Unit simultaneously. The Prefetch Unit stores 32 instruction bytes in its prefetch queue. As each instruction is fetched from the queue, the code part is sent to the Instruction Decode Unit and the displacement part (if that instruction has one) is sent to the Segmentation Unit to be used for calculating an address. If a loop is encountered in the program being executed, the Prefetch Unit gets a copy of the previously executed instructions from the cache.

Cache Unit   The Cache Unit stores copies of recently-read instructions, operands, and other data. When the processor requests information that is already in the cache (called a cache hit), it can read this information without performing a processor-bus cycle. However, when the processor requests information that is not in the cache (called a cache miss), the information is read into the cache in one or more 16-byte data transfers, called *cache line fills*. When an internal write request is generated to an area currently in the cache, not only is the cache updated, but the write information is passed through the cache to memory. This is called *cache write-through*.

Instruction Decode Unit   The Instruction Decode Unit takes instruction bytes from the Instruction Prefetch Unit and translates them into instruction words and microcode entry points for the Control Unit. Most instructions can be decoded at a rate of one per clock.

Control Unit   The Control Unit interprets the instruction word and microcode entry points it receives from the Instruction Prefetch Unit. The Control Unit has outputs with which it controls the Integer and Floating-Point Units. It also controls segmentation, because segment selection may be specified by instructions.

The Control Unit executes the instructions from the Instruction Prefetch Unit using its built-in microcode. To speed up the execution of memory reference instructions, the Control Unit starts executing any memory reference instruction while the previous instruction is still executing.

Integer Unit   The Integer Unit identifies where data is stored and performs all of the arithmetic and logical operations provided by the 80386's instruction set, plus a few instructions that are new with the 80486. The Integer Unit contains eight 32-bit general-purpose registers, several specialized registers, and an Arithmetic and Logic Unit (ALU). This unit also contains a barrel shifter used to speed the shift, rotate, multiply, and divide operations.

Two 32-bit bidirectional buses connect the Integer and Floating-Point Units. These buses are used together to transfer 64-bit operands. The same buses also connect the processing units with the Cache Unit.

Floating-Point Unit   The Floating-Point Unit executes the same instruction set as the 80387 math coprocessor. The FPU contains a push-down register stack and dedicated hardware for interpreting the 32-, 64-, and 80-bit formats specified in IEEE Standard 754.

Segmentation Unit A segment is a protected, independent address space. Segmentation enforces isolation between application programs to invoke recovery procedures and isolate the effects of programming errors.

The Segmentation Unit translates a segmented address issued by a program (a logical address) into an unsegmented address (a linear address). The locations of segments in the linear address space are stored in data structures called *segment descriptors*. The Segmentation Unit forwards linear addresses to the Paging and Cache Units. When a segment is accessed for the first time, its segment is copied into a processor register. A program can have up to 16,383 segments, and a processor register can hold up to six segment descriptors at the same time.

Paging Unit The Paging Unit allows access to data structures larger than the available memory by keeping the structure partly in memory and partly on disk. Paging divides the linear address space into 4K blocks called pages and uses page tables in memory to map a linear address to a physical address. Physical addresses are used by the cache and put on the processor bus.

The Paging Unit also identifies problems—such as an attempted access to a page not in resident memory—and raises exceptions called page faults.

The Paging Unit includes a Translation Lookaside Buffer (TLB) that stores the 32 most recently used page table entries. The Paging Unit looks up linear addresses in the TLB; if it can't find an address, it generates requests to fill the TLB with the correct physical address contained in a page table in memory. A bus cycle takes place only when the correct address is in the TLB.

The 80486 is a 32-bit processor that uses separate 32-bit registers and data paths to support 32-bit addresses and data paths. The processor addresses up to four gigabytes (four billion bytes) of physical memory and 64 terabytes (64 trillion bytes) of virtual memory.

Memory Management Unit (MMU)

To handle segmentation, the Memory Management Unit (MMU) consists of a segmentation unit and a paging unit. The *segmentation unit* provides four levels of protection (zero through three) to both isolate and protect applications and the operating system from each other. This component also allows easy code and data relocatability and efficient sharing.

The MMU's *paging unit* operates beneath (and transparent to) the segmentation process. This transparency allows the physical address space to be managed separate and independent from the segment management. Each segment is mapped into a linear address space that, in turn, is mapped onto one or more 4K pages. To implement an efficient virtual memory system, the 80486 supports full restartability for all page and segment faults.

Real and protected mode architecture

The 80486 has two modes of operation: real address mode (called real mode) and Protected Mode. *Real mode* is required primarily to set up the processor for the protected mode operation and to allow execution of previous chip generation software. *Protected mode* provides access to the advanced paging, memory management, and privilege capabilities of the 80486. These design features allow object-code compatibility with previous Intel chips. Real mode, protected mode, and virtual 8086 environment are overviewed here and discussed in detail in Chapter 8.

Real mode   When the processor is reset or powered up, it starts in real mode. Here, the 80486 operates as a very fast 8086, but with 32-bit extensions if the programmer desires. Real mode has the same base architecture as the 8086 (see Appendix A for more information on the 8086), but also allows access to the 32-bit register set of the 80486. The 8086 addressing mechanism, memory size, and interrupt handling (and their consequent limitations) are all identical to the real mode on the 80486.

Real mode uses two components to form the logical address. A 16-bit selector determines the linear base address of a segment. The base address is then used as the 32-bit physical address. The difference between the two modes depends on how the base address is calculated.

Relocatability is a property of programs or data that allows them to be located in different places in memory at different times without requiring modification to system or application software. Segment relocation in the 80486 real mode is identical to the 8086 process. The 16-bit value in a segment selector is shifted left by four bits (multiplied by 16) to form the 20-bit base address of a segment. The effective address is extended with four high-order zeros (to give a 20-bit value) and added to the base to form a linear address. This linear address is equivalent to the physical address because paging is not used in real-address mode.

Interrupts and exceptions are breaks in the normal flow of a system or routine. Interrupts and exceptions in 80386 real-address mode work exactly as they do on the 8086. (See Chapter 3 for a list of the interrupts recognized by the 80486.) In real mode, the Interrupt Descriptor Table (IDT) is an 8086 real interrupt vector table, starting at real zero and extending through real 1024 (4 bytes per interrupt with 256 possible entries).

The only way to leave real-address mode is to explicitly switch to protected mode. The 80486 enters the protected mode when a MOV to CR0 (Move to Control Resister Zero) instruction sets the protection enable (PE) bit in CR0. For compatibility with the 80286, the LMSW (Load Machine Status Word) instruction may also be used to set the PE bit.

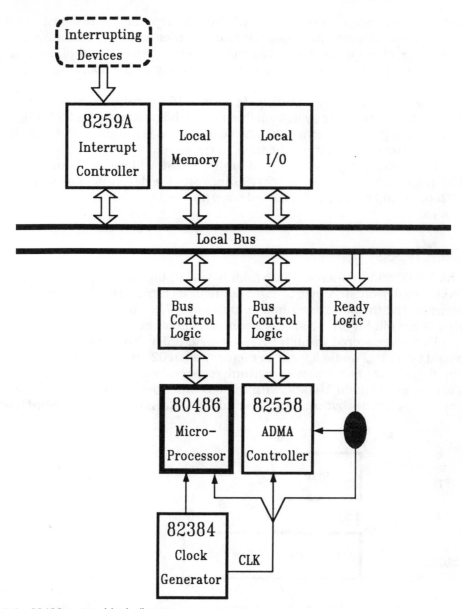

1-4 80486 system block diagram.

The processor re-enters real-address mode if software clears the PE bit in CR0 with a MOV to CR0 instruction.

Protected mode The complete capabilities of the 80486 are available when it operates in protected mode. Software can perform a task switch to enter tasks designated as virtual 8086 mode tasks. Each such task behaves with 8086 semantics (the relationship between symbols and their intended meanings independent of their interpretation devices). This allows 8086 software—an application program or an entire operating system—to execute on the 80486. At the same time, the virtual 8086 tasks are isolated and protected from one another and from the host 80486 operating system.

Like real mode, protected mode uses a 16-bit selector to specify an index into an operating system-defined table that contains the 32-bit base address of a given segment. The physical address is formed by adding the base address obtained from the table to the offset.

In general, programs designed for the 80286 will run without modification on the 80486. Also, the 80486 supports the descriptors used by the 80286, as long as the Intel-reserved word (low-order word) of the descriptor is zero.

Data types

The 80486 divides memory into 8-bit bytes, 16-bit words, and 32-bit double words (DWords). A byte is eight contiguous bits starting at any logical address; and the bits are numbered 0 through 7, with bit zero as the least significant bit. Figure 1-5 shows a comparison of the basic data types.

Words are stored in high-byte, low-byte order. The value that in AX would be 0201_{16} would appear in memory as 0102. (It seems that byte-oriented transfers and reverses to/from registers will be with us forever.) Thus, words contain 16 bits, with the low-order byte at the lower address and the high-order byte at the higher address. Each byte within a word has

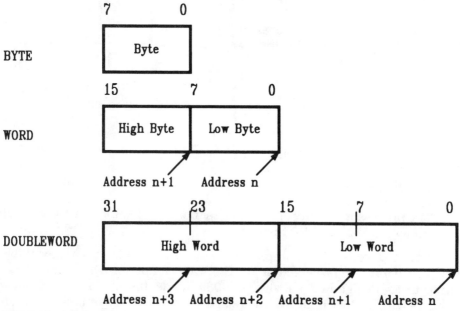

1-5 Basic data types.

its own address. The address of the word or DWord is the byte address of the low-order byte.

Note: This method for storing multi-byte data, with the high-order bits in the highest-address byte, is sometimes called the *little endian* format. Some systems require multi-byte data to be stored in the opposite order: with the high-order bits in the lowest-address byte. This is called the *big endian* format. The 80486 has two instructions that can convert between the big and little endian formats; BSWAP (Byte Swap) handles four-byte values, and XCHG (Exchange) handles two-byte values.

To allow maximum flexibility in data structures and efficient memory utilization, words need *not* be aligned at even-numbered addresses. Nor do doublewords need to be aligned at addresses evenly divisible by four. However, when used in a system configuration with a 32-bit bus, data transfers between processor and memory take place in units of doublewords, beginning at addresses evenly divisible by four. The processor converts the requests for misaligned words or doublewords into the sequence of requests that is acceptable to the memory interface. Thus, a misalignment of data reduces performance by increasing the number of memory cycles. For the best performance, align data structures and stacks so that word operands start at even addresses and doubleword operands start at addresses evenly divisible by four.

Because prefetching and queuing occur within the CPU, instructions needn't be aligned on word or doubleword boundaries. There is a slight increase in speed if they *are,* however.

In addition to bytes, words, and doublewords, the 80486 also supports these additional data types:

UNPACKED BINARY CODED DECIMAL (BCD)—An unpacked byte representation of a decimal digit in the range 0 through 9. Unpacked decimal numbers are stored as unsigned byte values, with one digit in each byte. The magnitude of the number is determined from the low-order half-byte (or *nibble*). The high-order half-byte must be zero for division and multiplication, but it may contain any value for subtraction or addition.

PACKED BCD—A packed byte representation of two decimal digits, each in the range of 0 through 9. One digit is stored in each half-byte. The digit in the high-order half-byte is the most significant. The range of a packed decimal byte is 0 through 99.

BIT FIELD—A contiguous sequence of bits in which the position of each binary digit is considered as an independent unit. A bit field may begin at any bit location of any byte and may be up to 32 bits long.

BIT STRING—Like a bit field, a bit string is a contiguous sequence of bits. A bit string may begin at any bit position of any byte and may be up to $2^{32} - 1$ bits long.

NEAR POINTER—A 32-bit logical address that represents the offset within a segment. Near pointers are used in either a flat or a segmented model of memory organization.

FAR POINTER—A 48-bit logical address of two components: a 16-bit segment selector and a 32-bit offset. Far pointers are used by programmers only when system designers choose a segmented memory organization.

INTEGER—A signed binary value contained in a 32-bit doubleword, a 16-bit word, or an 8-bit byte. All operations assume a 2's complement representation. The sign bit is located in bit 7 in a byte, bit 15 in a word, and bit 31 in a doubleword. It is zero for positive integers and one for negative. Because this high-order bit is used as the sign, an 8-bit (byte) integer can range from -128 to $+127$, a 16-bit (word) integer may range from $-32,768$ through $+32,767$, and a 32-bit integer (doubleword or Dword) ranges from -2^{31} to $+2^{31} - 1$. The value zero has a positive sign.

ORDINAL—An unsigned binary value contained in an 8-bit byte, a 16-bit word or a 32-bit doubleword. All bits are considered in determining the magnitude of the number. The value range of a byte is 0 through 255. A word can range from 0 through 65536 and a doubleword form 0 through $2^{32} - 1$.

STRING—A contiguous sequence of bytes, words or double words. A string may contain from zero through $2^{32} - 1$ bytes, or 4 gigabytes.

FPU data types

The Floating-Point Unit (FPU) within the 80486 supports these data types:

PACKED BCD—The FPU supports only 80-bit packed BCD data types. The most-significant bit, bit 79, holds the sign of the number (0 for positive or zero, 1 for negative). The remaining bit positions in this byte, bits 72–78, are unused and ignored by the FPU. The low-order 72 bit positions, bits 0–71, hold 18 decimal digits packed two per byte. An 80-bit packed BCD operand can range from -10^{18} to $+10^{18}$.

INTEGER—A signed binary value contained in a 16-bit word, 32-bit doubleword, or 64-bit quadword. All operations assume a 2's complement representation. The sign bit holds 0 for positive or zero, or 1 for negative. It is located in bit 15 in a word, bit 31 in a doubleword, and bit 63 in a quadword. A 16-bit (word) integer can range from $-32,768$ to $+32,767$, a 32-bit (doubleword) integer ranges from -2^{31} to $+2^{31} - 1$, and a 64-bit (quadword) integer ranges from -2^{63} to $+2^{63} - 1$.

FLOATING-POINT—Floating-point data types in the FPU contain three fields: *sign*, *exponent*, and *significand*. The one-bit sign is in the most-significant bit of the number. The significand field gives the significant bits of the number. The exponent field contains the power of 2 needed to scale the significand. The FPU supports three types of floating-point numbers:

- *Single-precision real:* 32 bits, with a 23-bit significand and an 8-bit exponent.

- *Double-precision real:* 64 bits, with a 52-bit significand and an 11-bit exponent.

- *Extended-precision real:* 80 bits, with a 64-bit significand and a 15-bit exponent.

The exponent can be negative (to represent fractional numbers) as well as positive, but it is not a signed number. Instead, it is *biased*. That is, a number (called the bias) is added to the true value of the exponent to obtain the exponent field of that value's floating-point representation in the FPU. To determine the true exponent, you must subtract the bias from the given exponent. For example, the single real format has a bias of 127. If the 8-bit exponent field contains 131 (decimal), the true exponent is 131 − 127, or 4. The exponent bias is 1023 for the double real format and 16383 for the extended real format.

The 80486 generally stores nonzero real numbers in normalized floating-point form, with a one in the leading (leftmost) bit position of the significand. Because leading zeroes are eliminated, normalized storage allows the maximum number of significant digits to be held in a significand.

Special numeric values In addition to the real or integer values that result from normal calculations, the FPU can also deal with a variety of special values. These special values can express relevant information about the operations that produced them. Some of these values generate FPU exceptions (discussed later in this chapter). Here are brief descriptions of the special types:

DENORMAL REAL NUMBERS—As just mentioned, the 80486 generally stores real numbers in normalized form, with a 1 in the significand's leading bit position. However, the 80486 can operate on reals that are not normalized (that is, reals with significands that have one or more leading zeroes).

These so-called denormals typically arise when a calculation produces a "tiny" result, one whose exponent would be too negative to store in the destination format. The 80486 provides the Underflow exception to detect cases where denormals would be created. It also provides the Denormalized Operand exception to detect cases where denormals enter into subsequent calculations.

ZERO—The value zero in the real and decimal integer formats may be signed either positive or negative. It always behaves identically in both cases. If you need to know a zero value's sign, you can determine it with the FXAM instruction. Dividing a nonzero value by zero produces a result of infinity and generates a Zero Divisor exception. Dividing zero by zero generates an Invalid Operation exception.

INFINITY—The real formats support positive and negative infinity. They are represented by an exponent of all ones and a significand with a leading one and trailing zeroes. A programmer can code an infinity or the FPU can create it in response to an Overflow or Zero Divide exception. Infinity in a register is tagged special in the register's tag word.

NaN (NOT-A-NUMBER)—A NaN is a member of a class of special values that exists in the real formats. A NaN may have either sign, and has a biased exponent of all ones and any significand except a leading one and trailing zeroes (which represents infinity). There are two kinds of NaNs: signaling and quiet.

A *signaling* NaN (SNaN) has a leading zero in its significand; the remaining bits can have any value. SNaNs can be used as operands, but the FPU never generates them. An arithmetic operation on an SNaN triggers an Invalid Operation exception (except for load operations from the stack, FXCH, FCHS, and FABS).

For example, a programmer could use signaling SNaNs to trap to the Invalid Operation exception handler. The handler could then decode the SNaN's significand to determine what kind of condition triggered the exception.

A *quiet* NaN (QNaN) has a leading one in its significand. The 80486 creates a QNaN as the result of performing a real operation in which at least one operand is a NaN. The 80486 also produces a special quiet NaN, called the *real indefinite*, in response to performing an invalid operation that does not involve NaNs. A real indefinite has a negative sign, all ones in the biased exponent, and a significand with two leading ones and trailing zeroes. A real indefinite in a register is tagged special in the register's tag word.

INDEFINITE—For each numeric data type, a unique encoding is reserved for representing the special value indefinite. The 80486 produces the indefinite value in response to a masked Invalid Operation exception. The 80486 produces the indefinite value in response to a masked Invalid Operation exception.

The indefinite for reals is described in the discussion of quiet NaNs. For packed decimals, indefinite may be stored with a FBSTP instruction. However, attempting to load indefinite from a packed decimal integer (using FBLD) will produce an undefined result. In the binary integers, the same encoding may represent either indefinite or the largest possible negative number $(-2^{15}, -2^{31}, \text{ or } -2^{63})$. The indefinite value cannot be loaded from a binary integer.

UNSUPPORTED FORMATS—The extended format permits many bit patterns that do not fall into any of the preceding categories. Many of these patterns were used by the 80287 but are not supported by the 80387 math coprocessor or the 80486 FPU.

For example, the encodings formerly known as pseudo-NaNs, pseudo-infinities, and un-normal numbers are not supported. The 80486 raises the Invalid Operation exception if it encounters them as operands. However, the 80486 can correctly use the encodings formerly known as pseudo-denormal numbers, but it raises the Denormalized Operand exception.

Registers

A register is a temporary storage device that facilitates arithmetical, logical, and transfer operations. The 80386 and 80486 registers are a superset of the previous 8086, 80186, and 80286 registers. All the previous generations' 16-bit registers are contained within the 32-bit architecture.

The 80486 includes six directly accessible segment selector registers, which contain values that point to the segments. These selector values can be loaded as a program executes and also are task-specific, which means that the segment registers are automatically reloaded when the 80486 switches tasks. (*Note:* In "back" of the segment selector registers are actual segment cache registers containing the description of the segment indicated by the selector. This is done in the hardware to avoid an additional memory fetch when segment description is needed.

There are a few differences regarding the availability of the registers in real and protected mode. Figure 1-6 summarizes them.

REGISTER	USE IN REAL MODE		USE IN PROTECTED MODE		USE IN VIRTUAL 8086 MODE	
	LOAD	STORE	LOAD	STORE	LOAD	STORE
General Registers	YES	YES	YES	YES	YES	YES
Segment Registers	YES	YES	YES	YES	YES	YES
Flag Register (EFLAGS)	YES	YES	YES	YES	IOPL	IOPL
Control Registers	YES	YES	PL=0	PL=0	NO	YES
GDT Register (GDTR)	YES	YES	PL=0	YES	NO	YES
LDT Register (LDTR)	NO	NO	PL=0	YES	NO	YES
IDT Register (IDTR)	YES	YES	PL=0	YES	NO	NO
Task Register	NO	NO	PL=0	YES	NO	NO
Debug Control	YES	YES	PL=0	PL=0	NO	NO
Test Registers	YES	YES	PL=0	PL=0	NO	NO

PL=0   The register can be accessed only when the current privilege level (CPL) is zero.

IOPL   The PUSHF and POPF instructions are made I/O Privilege Level sensitive in virtual 8086 mode.

1-6 Register availability.

General registers

The eight general-purpose registers are 32 bits long and hold addresses or data. They support data operands of 1, 8, 16, 32 and (by using two regis-

| | 31 | 23 | 15 | 7 | 0 |

```
           31            23            15           7            0
        ┌──────────────────────────┬────────────────────────────┐
  EAX   │                          │ AH          │ AL           │
        │                          │          AX                │
        ├──────────────────────────┼────────────────────────────┤
  EDX   │                          │ DH          │ DL           │
        │                          │          DX                │
        ├──────────────────────────┼────────────────────────────┤
  ECX   │                          │ CH          │ CL           │
        │                          │          CX                │
        ├──────────────────────────┼────────────────────────────┤
  EBX   │                          │ BH          │ BL           │
        │                          │          BX                │
        ├──────────────────────────┼────────────────────────────┤
  EBP   │                          │          BP                │
        ├──────────────────────────┼────────────────────────────┤
  ESI   │                          │          SI                │
        ├──────────────────────────┼────────────────────────────┤
  EDI   │                          │          DI                │
        ├──────────────────────────┼────────────────────────────┤
  ESP   │                          │          SP                │
        └──────────────────────────┴────────────────────────────┘
```

1-7 General registers.

ters) 64 bits; bit fields of 1 to 32 bits; and 16- and 32-bit address operands. These registers are named EAX, EBX, ECX, EDX, ESI, EDI, EBP, and ESP.

The least significant 16 bits of the registers are separately accessible. Most assemblers use the 16-bit names of the registers: AX, BX, CX, DX, SI, DI, BP, and SP. Figure 1-7 shows the format of the general registers.

8-bit operations can individually access the low byte (bits 0 – 7) and the high byte (bits 8 – 15) of the general registers AX, BX, CX, and DX. The low bytes are named AL, BL, CL, and DL, respectively, while the high bytes are named AH, BH, CH, and DH. Again, this selection is done by most assemblers by using the register names.

System flags register

The EFLAGS register controls I/0, maskable interrupts, debugging, task switching, and enabling of virtual 8086 execution in a protected, multi-tasking environment (all in addition to providing status flags that represent the result of instruction execution). Figure 1-8 shows the EFLAGS register contents. The low 16 bits (0 – 15) of EFLAGS contain the 80286

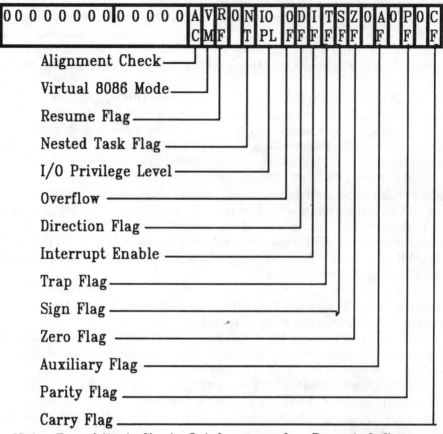

Alignment Check

Virtual 8086 Mode

Resume Flag

Nested Task Flag

I/O Privilege Level

Overflow

Direction Flag

Interrupt Enable

Trap Flag

Sign Flag

Zero Flag

Auxiliary Flag

Parity Flag

Carry Flag

Note: Zero bits indicate Intel reserved.   Do not define.

1-8   EFLAGS register.

16-bit status or flag register named FLAGS, which is most useful when executing 8086 and 80286 code.

In the following descriptions, the term "set" means "set to 1," and "reset" means "clear to zero."

AC (ALIGNMENT CHECK) BIT 18—Setting AC lets the 80486 check the alignment of operands when you make references to memory. The 80486 issues an alignment-check exception when reference is made to an unaligned operand, such as a word that starts at an odd-numbered address or a doubleword that starts at an address that is not a multiple of four. Alignment-check exceptions are generated only in user mode (privilege level 3).

This bit is new with the 80486.

VM (VIRTUAL 8086 MODE) BIT 17—The VM bit provides Virtual 8086 Mode within the protected mode. If set while the processor is in protected mode, the 80486 switches to Virtual 8086 operation. The VM bit can be set *only* two ways: in protected mode by the IRET instruction and only if Current Privilege Level is zero, and by task switches at any privilege level.

RF (RESUME FLAG) BIT 16—This flag temporarily disables debug exceptions (breaks to normal program flow) so that an instruction can be restarted after a debug exception without immediately causing another one.

NT (NESTED TASK) BIT 14—The 80486 uses this flag to control chaining of interrupted and *CALL*ed tasks. A CALL transfers the program execution sequence on a temporary basis to a subroutine or subprogram. On termination of that subroutine, execution is resumed at the instruction following the CALL. NT influences the operation of the IRET instruction.

IOPL (INPUT/OUTPUT PRIVILEGE LEVEL) BITS 12–13—This two-bit field applies to protected mode. IOPL shows the highest current privilege level (CPL) value permitted to execute I/O instructions without generating an exception 13 fault or consulting the I/O Permission Bitmap. It also shows the highest CPL value that allows change of the IF (INTR Enable Flag) bit when new values are *popped* into the EFLAGS register (See POP and PUSH in Chapter 10).

OF (OVERFLOW FLAG) BIT 11—OF is set if the operation resulted in carry/borrow into the sign bit (high-order bit) of the result but did not result in a carry/borrow out of the high-order bit, or vice-versa.

DF (DIRECTION FLAG) BIT 10—DF defines whether the ESI and/or EDI registers are to decrement or increment during string operations. If DF = 0, the registers increment; if DF = 1, they decrement.

IF (INTERRUPT-ENABLE) BIT 9—Setting IF allows the CPU to recognize external (maskable) interrupt requests. Clearing this bit disables these interrupts. IF has no effect on either nonmaskable external interrupts or exceptions.

TF (TRAP FLAG) BIT 8—Setting TF puts the processor into single-step mode for debugging. The CPU automatically generates an Exception 1 after each instruction, which allows a program to be inspected as it executes each instruction. When TF is reset, exception 1 traps occur only as a function of the breakpoint addresses loaded into debug registers DR0–DR3. Further information is given in an upcoming discussion of the debug registers.

SF (SIGN FLAG) BIT 7—SF is set if the high-order bit of the result is set. It is reset otherwise. For 8-, 16-, and 32-bit operations, SF reflects the state of bit 7, 15, and 31, respectively.

ZF (ZERO FLAG) BIT 6—ZF is set if all bits of the result are 0. Otherwise, it is reset.

AF (AUXILIARY CARRY FLAG) BIT 4—This flag simplifies the addition and subtraction of packed BCD quantities. Regardless of the operand length (8, 16 or 32 bits), AF is set if the operation resulted in a borrow into bit 3 (which is a subtraction) or a carry out of bit 3 (which is an addition).

Otherwise, AF is reset. Remember that BCD uses bits 0 through 3 to represent decimal digits.

PF (PARITY FLAG) BIT 2—PF is set if the low-order eight bits of the operation contains an even number of "1's" (even parity). PF is reset if the low-order eight bits have odd parity. PF is always a function of only the low-order eight bits, regardless of operand size.

CF (CARRY FLAG) BIT 0—CF is set if the operation resulted in a carry out of the high-order bit (an addition), or a borrow into the high-order bit (a subtraction). Otherwise, CF is reset. For 8-, 16-, or 32-bit operations, CF is set according to the carry/borrow at bit 7, 15, or 31, respectively.

Segment registers

Six 16-bit segment registers hold the segment selector values that identify the currently addressable memory segments. The registers are:

CODE SEGMENT (CS)—CS points to the segment that contains the currently executing sequence of instructions. The 80486 fetches all instructions from this segment, using the contents of the instruction pointer as an offset. CS is changed as the result of inter-segment control-transfer instructions, interrupts and exceptions. The CS cannot be explicitly loaded.

STACK SEGMENT (SS)—Subroutine calls, parameters and procedure activation records usually require a region of memory that is allocated for a stack. All stack operations use SS to locate that stack. Unlike the CS register, the SS register can be loaded explicitly by program instructions.

The next four registers are data segment registers (DS, ES, FS, GS), each of which is addressable by the currently executing program. Having access to four separate data areas aids program efficiency by allowing them to access different types of data structures. These four registers can be changed under program control.

To use the data segment registers, the 80486 associates a base address with each segment selected. To address a data unit within a segment, a 32-bit offset is added to the segment's base address. Once a segment is selected (by loading the segment selector into a segment register), a data manipulation instruction needs only to specify the offset.

Registers that hold Segment descriptors are not programmer visible. Inside the 80486, a descriptor register is associated with each programmer-visible segment register. Each descriptor register holds a 32-bit segment base address, a 32-bit segment limit, and the other necessary segment attributes.

When a selector value is loaded into a segment register, the processor automatically updates the associated descriptor register. In protected mode, the base address, the limit (the field that defines the size of the segment), and the attributes are all updated according to the contents of the segment descriptor indexed by the selector. In real address mode, only the base address is updated directly, by shifting the selector value four bits to the left (because the segment maximum limit and attributes are fixed in real mode).

Segmented memory management registers

These registers are also known as *System Address Registers.* Four registers locate the data structures that control segmented memory management. These registers are defined to reference the tables or segments supported by the 80286/386/486 protection model.

The addresses of these tables and segments are stored in special System Address and System Segment Registers. Chapter 2 describes the Global Descriptor Table, the Local Descriptor Table, and the Interrupt Descriptor Table in detail.

GDTR (GLOBAL DESCRIPTOR TABLE REGISTER)—This register holds the 32-bit linear base address and the 16-bit limit of the Global Descriptor Table.

LDTR (LOCAL DESCRIPTOR TABLE REGISTER)—This register holds the 16-bit selector for the Local Descriptor Table. Because the LDT is a task-specific segment, it is defined by selector values stored in the system segment registers. There is a programmer-invisible segment descriptor register associated with the LDT.

IDTR (INTERRUPT DESCRIPTOR TABLE REGISTER)—This register points to a table of entry points for interrupt handlers (the IDT). The register holds the 32-bit linear base address and the 16-bit limit of the Interrupt Descriptor Table.

TR (TASK REGISTER)—This register points to the information needed by the processor to define the current task. The register holds the 16-bit selector for the Task State Segment descriptor (See Chapter 2 for further information). Because the TSS segment is task-specific, it is defined by selector values stored in the system segment registers. Note that a programmer-invisible segment descriptor register is associated with each system segment register.

Instruction pointer

The Extended Instruction Pointer (EIP) is a 32-bit register. EIP contains the offset address of the next sequential instruction to be executed. This offset is relative to the start (or base address) of the current code segment. The EIP is not directly visible to programmers but is controlled explicitly by control-transfer instructions, interrupts, and exceptions.

The low-order 16 bits of EIP are named IP and can be used by the processor as a unit. This feature is useful when executing instructions designed for the 8086 and 80286 processors, which only have an IP.

Control registers

The 80486 has three 32-bit control registers (CR0, CR2, and CR3—CR1 is reserved by Intel) to hold machine states or statuses of a global nature. A global status is one that can be accessed by (or that controls) any of the logical units of the system. Along with the System Address Registers, these registers hold machine state information that affects all tasks in the system. Load and store instructions have been defined to access the control registers.

Control registers are accessible to systems programmers only via variants of the MOV instruction that allows them to be loaded from or stored in general registers. Figure 1-9 shows the formats of the four control registers.

3 1		1 8	1 6		1 1		5 4 3 2 1 0	
Page Directory Base Register (PDBR)			Reserved			P C D / P W T	0 0 0	CR3
Page Fault Linear Address								CR2
Reserved								CR1
P G / C D / N W	Reserved		A M	W P	Reserved		N E T / E T / T S / E M / M P / P E	CR0

1-9 Control register formats.

CR0—Contains flags that control or indicate conditions applying to the system as a whole, not to an individual task. The low-order 15 bits of this register is the Machine Status Word (MSW), bits 0 – 15, for compatibility with 80286 protected mode.

PG (PAGING) BIT 31—PG indicates whether the 80386 uses page tables to translate linear addresses into physical addresses.

CD (CACHE DISABLE) BIT 30—CD enables the internal cache when set and disables it when clear. (See TABLE 1-1.) Cache hits cannot be disabled,

Table 1-1   Internal cache control modes.

CD	NW	Operating Mode
1	1	Cache fills disabled, write-through and invalidates disabled.
1	0	Cache fills disabled, write-through and invalidates enabled.
0	1	Invalid. Loading CR0 with this bit combination generates a General-Protection fault.
0	0	Cache fills enabled, write-through and invalidates enabled.

however; to disable the cache completely, it must be flushed. Chapter 4 gives more information about the cache and how it operates. This bit assignment is new with the 80486.

NW (NOT WRITE-THROUGH) BIT 29—NW enables (when clear) or disables (when set) write-throughs and cache invalidation cycles. (See TABLE 1-1.) Chapter 4 gives more information about the cache and how it operates. This bit assignment is new with the 80486.

AM (ALIGNMENT MASK) BIT 18—AM enables (when set) or disables (when clear) checking the alignment of memory operands. This bit assignment is new with the 80486.

WP (WRITE-PROTECT) BIT 16—When set, WP write-protects user-level pages against supervisor-mode access. When WP is clear, read-only user-level pages can be written by a supervisor process. This feature is useful for implementing the copy-on-write method of creating a new process ("forking") used by some operating systems, such as UNIX. This bit assignment is new with the 80486.

NE (NUMERIC ERROR) BIT 5—When set, NE enables the standard mechanism for reporting floating-point numeric errors. When NE is clear and the IGNNE# input is active, numeric errors are ignored. When NE is clear and IGNNE# is inactive, a numeric error causes the processor to stop and wait for an interrupt. The interrupt is generated by using the FERR# pin to drive an input to the interrupt controller. This bit assignment is new with the 80486.

ET (EXTENSION TYPE) BIT 4—This bit is set to indicate support of the 80387 math coprocessor instructions. On the 80386, ET indicates the type of coprocessor in the system: 80287 or 80387.

TS (TASK SWITCHED) BIT 3—The processor sets TS with every task switch and tests it when interpreting floating-point arithmetic instructions. You can reset TS by loading into the CR0 register or by executing a CLTS instruction.

EM (EMULATION) BIT 2—When set, EM makes the processor generate an exception 7 (Device Not Available) when it executes an ESC, WAIT, or numeric instruction.

MP (MATH PRESENT) BIT 1—On the 80286 and 80386, the MP bit controls the function of the WAIT instruction, which is used to coordinate a coprocessor. When running programs on the 80486, this bit should be set.

PE (PROTECTION ENABLE) BIT 0—Setting PE causes the processor to begin executing in protected mode. Resetting PE returns to real-address mode.

CR1—Reserved for future Intel processors.

CR2—Used for handling exceptions generated during paging, or page faults, when the PG (Paging) flag in CR0 is set. In CR2, the 80486 stores the 32-bit linear address that triggered the page fault. The error code pushed onto the page fault handler's stack when it is invoked provides additional status information about this page fault.

CR3—Used when the PG (Paging) flag in CR0 is set. CR3 contains the physical base address of the page directory table for the current task. The page directory must be aligned to a page (4 K-aligned), so the low 12 bits of CR3 are ignored. On the 80486 processor, Intel has assigned external cache functions to two of these bits:

PCD (PAGE-LEVEL CACHE DISABLE) BIT 4—When paging is enabled, the state of this bit is driven on the PCD pin during bus cycles that are not paged, such as interrupt acknowledge cycles. When paging is disabled, it is driven during all bus cycles. The PCD pin controls caching in an external cache on a cycle-by-cycle basis.

PWT (PAGE-LEVEL WRITE-THROUGH) BIT 3—When paging is enabled, the state of this bit is driven on the PWT pin during bus cycles that are not paged, such as interrupt acknowledge cycles. When paging is disabled, it is driven during all bus cycles. The PCD pin controls write-through in an external cache on a cycle-by-cycle basis.

A task switch through a TSS that changes the value in CR3 (or as an explicit load to CR3) invalidates all cached page table entries in the paging unit cache. Note that if the value in CR3 does not change during the task switch, the cached page table entries are not flushed.

Floating-Point registers

Figure 1-10 shows the floating-point register set. The on-chip Floating-Point Unit (FPU) contains eight data registers, a tag word, a control register, a status register, an instruction pointer, and a data pointer.

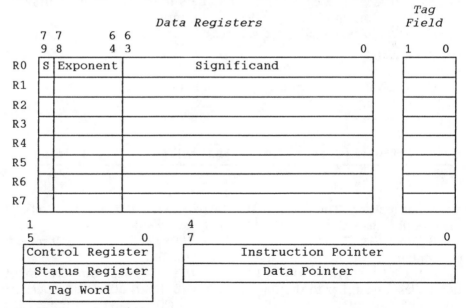

1-10 Floating-point registers.

The 80486's on-chip FPU operates exactly the same as the 80387 math coprocessor. Software written for the 80387 will run unmodified on the FPU.

Data registers Floating point computations use the 80486's FPU data registers. There are eight data registers (R0–R7), each 80 bits long. The data registers are divided into three fields (Sign, Exponent, and Significand) that correspond to the FPU's extended-precision data type.

The 80486 has instructions that operate on the FPU's data registers explicitly, but it also has instructions that access these registers as a stack. Those instructions operate on the top one or two stack elements. Here, the Top field in the FPU status word identifies the current top-of-stack register. A *push* operation decrements Top by one and loads a value into the new top register. A *pop* operation stores the value from the current top register and increments Top by one. Like other 80486 stacks in memory, the FPU register stack grows downward, toward lower-numbered registers.

Some instructions address the data registers implicitly, while others address them explicitly. Many instructions operate on the register at the top of the stack by implicitly addressing the register at which Top points. Other instructions let the programmer specify which register to use relative to Top.

Tag word The 16-bit Tag Word contains eight 2-bit tags, where each tag reports on the content of a numeric data register (see FIG. 1-11). Primarily, the tag word optimizes the FPU's performance and stack handling by making it possible to distinguish between empty and nonempty register locations. It also enables exception handlers to check the contents of a stack location without having to decode the actual data.

A tag can have the following values:

00	=	Valid
01	=	Zero
10	=	QNaN, SNaN, infinity, denormal and unsupported formats
11	=	Empty

15   0

Tag(7)	Tag(6)	Tag(5)	Tag(4)	Tag(3)	Tag(2)	Tag(1)	Tag(0)

1-11 FPU Tag word.

Status register The 16-bit Status Register, shown in FIG. 1-12, reflects the overall state of the FPU. The bits are as follows:

B (BUSY) BIT 15—This bit is included for 8087 compatibility. It reflects the contents of the ES (Error Summary) status bit.

C0–C3 (CONDITION CODES) BITS 14, 10, 9, 8—These numeric condition codes are similar to the flags in EFLAGS. Instructions that perform arithmetic operations report the outcome in C0–C3, as summarized in TABLE 1-2. Additional information is in TABLE 1-3 and TABLE 1-4.

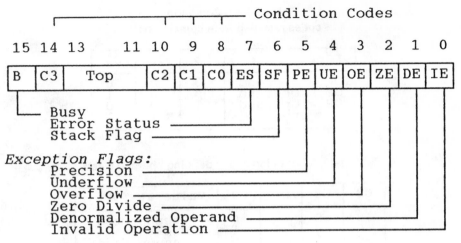

1-12 FPU Status register.

Table 1-2   FPU condition codes.

Instruction	C0	C3	C1	C2
FPREM, FPREM1	Three least-significant bits of quotient			Reduction 0 = complete 1 = incomplete
	Q2	Q0	Q1 or O/U#	
FCOM, FCOMP, FCOMPP, FTST, FUCOM, FUCOMP, FUCOMPP, FICOM, FICOMP	Result of comparison (See Table 1-3)		Zero or O/U#	Operand is not comparable if C2 = 1
FXAM	Operand class (See Table 1-4)		Sign or O/U#	Operand class (Table 1-4)
FINCTOP, FDECTOP, Constant loads, FXTRACT, FLD, FILD, FBLD, FSTP (ext real)	Undefined		Zero or O/U#	Undefined
FIST, FBST, FRNDINT, FST, FSTP, FADD, FMUL, FDIV, FDIVR, FSUB, FSUBR, FSCALE, FSQRT, FPATAN, F2XM1 FYL2X, FYL2XP1	Undefined		Roundup or O/U#	Undefined
FPTAN, FSIN, FCOS, FSINCOS	Undefined		Roundup or O/U#, undefined if C2 = 1	Reduction 0 = complete 1 = incomplete
FLDENV, FRSTOR	Each bit loaded from memory			
FINIT	Clears these bits			
FLDCW, FSTENV, FSTCW, FSTSW, FCLEX, FSAVE	Undefined			

**Table 1-3   Condition
codes resulting from comparison.**

Order	C3	C2	C0
TOP > Operand	0	0	0
TOP < Operand	0	0	1
TOP = Operand	1	0	0
Unordered	1	1	1

Table 1-4   Condition codes defining operand class.

C3	C2	C1	C0	Value at TOP
0	0	0	0	+ Unsupported
0	0	0	1	+ NaN
0	0	1	0	− Unsupported
0	0	1	1	− NaN
0	1	0	0	+ Normal
0	1	0	1	+ Infinity
0	1	1	0	− Normal
0	1	1	1	− Infinity
1	0	0	0	+ 0
1	0	0	1	+ Empty
1	0	1	0	− 0
1	0	1	1	− Empty
1	1	0	0	+ Denormal
1	1	1	0	− Denormal

Table 1-2 includes the following terms:

O/U#—When Status Register bits IE (Invalid Operation Exception) and SF (Stack Flag) are both set, indicating a stack exception, this bit distinguishes between stack overflow (C1 = 1) and stack underflow (C1 = 0).

Reduction—If FPREM or FPREM1 produces a remainder that is less than the modulus, reduction is complete. When reduction is incomplete, the value at the top of the stack is a partial remainder, which can be used as input to further reduction.

For FPTAN, FSIN, FCOS, and FSINCOS, the reduction bit (C2) is set if the operand at the top of the stack is too large. In this case, the original operand remains at the top of the stack.

Roundup—When the Status Register's PE (Precision Exception) bit is set, the C1 bit indicates whether the last rounding in the instruction was upward.

TOP (TOP-OF-STACK) BITS 13 – 11—Points to the FPU register that is the current top-of-stack. That is, Top = 000 means that R0 is the top-of-stack, Top = 001 means that R1 is the top-of-stack, and so on.

ES (ERROR SUMMARY) BIT 7—This bit is set if any Unmasked Exception bit (bits 0 – 5 in the Status Register) is set; otherwise; ES is clear. The 80486 asserts the FERR# (Floating-point Error) signal when ES is set.

SF (STACK FLAG) BIT 6—This bit distinguishes invalid operations due to stack overflow or underflow. When SF is set, C1 (bit 9) indicates stack overflow (C1 = 1) or stack underflow (C1 = 0).

EXCEPTION FLAGS, BITS 5 – 0—These flags are set to indicate that the FPU has detected an exception while executing an instruction. Each flag can be masked by setting a bit in the FPU Control Register. TABLE 1-5 lists the exception conditions and their causes, in order of precedence. It also tells what action the FPU takes if the corresponding exception flag is masked.

Table 1-5   FPU exception.

Exception	Cause	Default action (if exception is masked)
Invalid Operation (IE, bit 0)	Operation on a signaling NaN, unsupported format, indeterminate form (e.g., 0/0), or stack overflow/underflow.	Result is a quiet NaN, integer indefinite, or BCD indefinite.
Denormalized Operand (DE, bit 1)	At least one of the operands is denormalized; that is, it has the smallest exponent but a nonzero significand.	Normal processing continues.
Zero Divisor (ZE, bit 2)	The divisor is zero, the dividend is a noninfinite, nonzero number.	Result is infinity.
Overflow (OE, bit 3)	The result is too large to fit in the specified format.	Result is largest finite value or infinity.
Underflow (UE, bit 4)	The result is too small to be represented in the specified format and, if this exception is masked, denormalization causes loss of accuracy.	Result is denormalized or zero.
Inexact Result (Precision) (PE, bit 5)	The true result is not exactly representable in the specified format (e.g., 1/3); the result is rounded according to the rounding mode.	Normal processing continues.

If an exception is not masked by the Control Register, the 80486 will set both the exception flag and the ES (Error Summary) flag in the Status Register and assert the FERR# output signal. Then, when the 80486 tries to execute WAIT or another floating-point instruction, an exception 16 (Floating-point Error) occurs or, if the NE (Numeric Error) bit is set in CR0, an external interrupt. The exception condition must be resolved by an interrupt service routine. In the FPU's instruction and data pointers (described next), the FPU saves the address of the floating-point instruction that caused the exception and the address of any memory operand required by the instruction.

Instruction and data pointers Because the FPU operates in parallel with the 80486's Arithmetic and Logic Unit (ALU), an error the FPU detects may be reported after the ALU executes the instruction that caused the error. To allow a failing numeric instruction to be identified, the

80486 contains two pointer registers that supply the address of the failing instruction and (if appropriate) the address of its numeric operand.

These instruction and data pointers are provided for user-written error handlers, and can be accessed with four instructions: FLDENV (Load Environment), FSTENV (Store Environment), FSAVE (Save State), and FRSTOR (Restore State). Whenever the 80486 decodes a floating-point instruction, it saves the instruction (including any prefixes), the address of the operand (if present), and the opcode. This allows exception handlers to determine the precise nature of any numeric exceptions that may be encountered.

When stored in memory, the instruction and data pointers appear in one of four formats, depending on the processor's operating mode (protected or real-address) and the operand size attribute (32- or 16-bit operands). In virtual-8086 mode, the real-address mode formats are used. Figures 1-13 and 1-14 show these pointers as they are stored following an FSAVE or FSTENV instruction.

Protected Mode

31	15	0	
Reserved	Control Word		0H
Reserved	Status Word		4H
Reserved	Tag Word		8H
IP Offset			CH
Reserved	CS Selector		10H
Data Operand Offset			14H
Reserved	Operand Selector		18H

Real-Address Mode

31		15		0	
Reserved		Control Word			0H
Reserved		Status Word			4H
Reserved		Tag Word			8H
Reserved		Instruction Pointer 15..0			CH
0 0 0 0	Instruction Pointer 31..16	0	Opcode 10..0		10H
Reserved		Operand Pointer 15..0			14H
0 0 0 0	Operand Pointer 31..16	0 0 0 0 0 0 0 0 0 0 0 0			18H

1-13 Numeric instruction and data pointer images in memory, 32-bit format.

As in the 80287 and 80387 math coprocessors, the instruction address saved points to any prefixes that preceded the instruction. This is different from the 8087, where the instruction address points only to the ESC instruction opcode.

Protected Mode		Real-Address and Virtual-8086 Mode		

15		0	15		0	
Control Word			Control Word			0H
Status Word			Status Word			2H
Tag Word			Tag Word			4H
IP Offset			Instruction Pointer 15..0			6H
CS Selector			IP19.16 | 0 | Opcode 10..0			8H
Operand Offset			Operand Pointer 15..0			AH
Operand Selector			OP19.16 | 0 0 0 0 0 0 0 0 0 0 0 0			CH

1-14 Numeric instruction and data pointer images in memory, 16-bit format.

Control word The FPU provides several processing options that are selected by loading the Control Register with a control word from memory. Figure 1-15 shows the format of the control word.

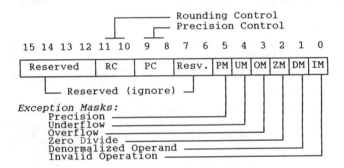

1-15 FPU control word.

Bits 0-5 of the control word contain mask bits for the six floating-point exception conditions. The high-order byte of the control word configures the FPU processing options, including precision control and rounding control.

The PC (Precision Control) bits—8 and 9—can be used to set the FPU's operating precision at less than the default precision (64-bit significand). These control bits can provide compatibility with earlier arithmetic processors that have less precision than the 80486 processor or the 80387 math coprocessor. The Precision Control bits affect only the following arithmetic instructions: FADD, FSUB, FSUBR, FMUL, FDIV, FDIVR, and

FSQRT. For all other instructions, either the precision is determined by the opcode or extended precision is used.

The RC (Rounding Control) bits, 10 and 11, provide for the common "round-to-nearest" mode as well directed rounding (up or down) and true chop. Rounding Control affects only those instructions that perform rounding at the end of an operation and thus can generate a precision exception. Specifically, these are FST, FSTP, FIST, all arithmetic instructions (except FPREM, FPREM1, FXTRACT, FABS, and FCHS), and all transcendental instructions.

Debug registers

The six programmer-accessible debug registers (DR0–DR3, DR6, and DR7) bring advanced debugging capabilities to the 80486, including data breakpoints and the ability to set instruction breakpoints without modifying code segments. Registers DR0–DR3 specify the four linear breakpoints. DR4 and DR5 are reserved by Intel for future development. DR6 displays the current state of the breakpoints. DR7 is used to set the breakpoints.

Translation Lookaside Buffer (TLB)

The Translation Lookaside Buffer (TLB) is a cache used for translating linear addresses to physical addresses.

Warning: The TLB testing mechanism is unique to the 80386 and 80486 and may not be continued in the same way in future processors. Software that uses this mechanism as it currently is may be incompatible with future processors.

The TLB is a four-way, set-associative memory. A set is a collection of elements that have some feature in common or bear a certain relation to one another. Figure 1-16 shows the TLB structure.

The TLB has the following:

CONTENT-ADDRESSABLE MEMORY—CAM. CAM holds 32 linear addresses and associated tag bits, which are used for data protection and cache implementation.

RANDOM ACCESS MEMORY—RAM. RAM holds the upper 20 bits of the 32 physical addresses that correspond to the linear addresses in the CAM.

Logic implements the four-way cache and includes a 2-bit replacement pointer that decides which of the four sets into which a new entry is directed during a write to the TLB.

Addresses and commands are written to the TLB through the command register, while *data* is read from or written to the TLB through the data register. Test Register Six (TR6) is the command register for TLB accesses while Test Register Seven (TR7) is used as the data register.

Test registers Two test registers are used to control the testing of the RAM/CAM (Content Addressable Memories) in the Translation Lookaside

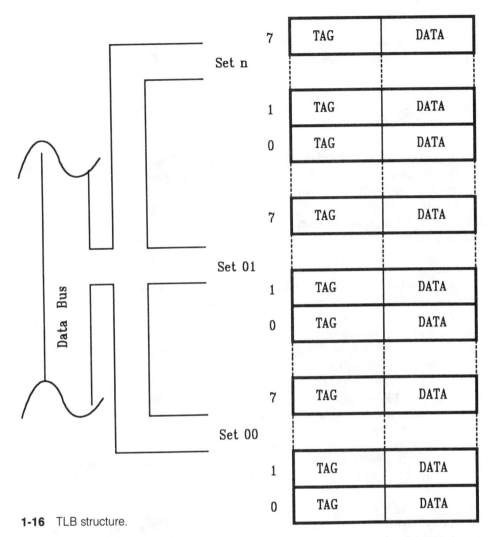

1-16 TLB structure.

Buffer (TLB), the cache used for storing information from page tables. TR6 is the command test register, and TR7 is the data register that contains the data of the TLB test.

These registers are accessed by variants of the MOV instruction, which is defined in both real-address mode and protected mode. In the protected mode, the MOV instruction that accesses them can be executed only at privilege level 0. Any attempt to read or write either of the TRs when executing in any other privilege level causes a general protection exception. Figure 1-17 presents the formats of the test registers TR6 and TR7.

Fields for TR6 are as follows:

LINEAR ADDRESS—BITS 12–31. On a TLB write, a TLB entry is allocated to this linear address. The rest of the TLB entry is set depending on

	31			12	11	10	9 8 7	6 5	4	3 2	1 0	
Physical Address					P C D	P W T	LRU	0 0	P L	R E P	0 0	TR7
Linear Address					V	D	D# U U#	W W#	0	0 0	0 C	TR6

1-17 TLB test register formats.

the value of TR7 and the value just written into TR6. On a TLB lookup, the TLB is interrogated per this value. If one and only one TLB entry matches, the rest of the fields of TR6 and TR7 are set from the matching TLB entry.

V—BIT 11. This is the valid bit. The TLB uses it to identify entries that contain valid data. Valid means a successful translation has been made. Entries in the TLB that have not been assigned values have zero in the valid bit. All valid bits can be cleared by writing to Control Register 3 (CR3).

D, D#—BITS 10 AND 9. Bit 10 is the dirty bit (the entry has been changed) and bit 9 is its complement for/from the TLB entry.

U, U#—BITS 8 AND 7. Bit 8 is the U/S (User accessible) bit and bit 7 is its complement for/from the TLB entry.

W, W#—BITS 6 AND 5. Bit 6 is the R/W (Writeable) bit and bit 5 is its complement for/from the TLB entry.

C—BIT 0. TR6 contains a command and an address tag. To cause an immediate TLB lookup, move a doubleword into TR6 that contains a 1 in this bit. To cause an immediate write to the TLB, move a doubleword that has a 0 in this bit.

The fields of TR7 are as follows:

PHYSICAL ADDRESS—BITS 12–31. This is the data field of the TLB. On a write to the TLB, the TLB entry allocated to the linear address in TR6 is set to this value. On a TLB lookup (read), the data field (physical address) from the TLB is loaded into this field.

PCD—BIT 11. This corresponds to the PCD bit of a page table entry.

PWT—BIT 10. This corresponds to the PWT bit of a page table entry.

LRU—BITS 7–9. On a TLB read, this field corresponds to the bits used in the cache replacement algorithm. The values that are reported are the states of these bits before the TLB lookup. TLB lookups that result in hits and TLB writes can change these bits.

PL—BIT 4. On a TLB write, a set PL bit causes the REP field of TR7 to be used to select which of the TLB entry's four associative blocks will be loaded. If PL is clear, the internal pointer of the paging unit is used to select the block. On a TLB lookup, the PL bit indicates whether the lookup was a hit (PL = 1) or a miss (PL = 0).

REP—BITS 2 AND 3. For a TLB write, REP selects which of the four associated blocks of the TLB will be written. For a TLB read, if PL is set,

REP reports which of the four associate blocks contains the tag. For a TLB read, if PL is clear, REP is undefined.

Test operations   Following are generalized descriptions of TLB operations.

To write a TLB entry,

1. Load the TR7 register with the desired physical address, PCD, PWT, PL, and REP values. If PL (bit 4) is set, the REP field selects the associative block in which to place the entry. If PL is clear, the internal pointer is used.

2. Load the TR6 register with the appropriate linear address and values for the V, D, U, and W bits. The C bit must be clear.

To look up (read) a TLB entry,

1. Load the TR6 register with the appropriate linear address and attributes. The C bit must be set.

2. Read the TR7 register. If PL (bit 4) is set, the rest of the register contents report the TLB contents. If PL is clear, the other values in the TR7 register, except the LRU bits, are undefined.

Internal cache

A cache (pronounced "cash") is a high-speed memory component in the memory hierarchy between main memory and the processor. It acts as temporary storage and is designed to improve transfer rates and raise the processor speed.

Warning: The cache testing mechanism is unique to the 80486 and may not be continued in the same way in future processors. Software that uses this mechanism as it currently is may be incompatible with future processors.

The cache is a four-way, set-associative memory. This means that a data block from a given location in main memory can be stored in any of four locations in the cache. The cache consists of three blocks:

The *data block* contains up to 8K of data and instructions. It is divided into four arrays, each containing up to 128 cache lines. Each cache line holds data from 16 successive memory locations, starting at an address that is divisible by 16. (In other words, each cache line holds 16 bytes, 8 words, or 4 doublewords of data.) Corresponding to each group of four cache lines, one from each array, is a 7-bit index into the arrays. Four cache lines that have the same index are called a *set*.

The *tag block* contains a 21-bit tag for each line of data in the cache. Thus, the tag block is also divided into four arrays, each containing 128 tags. The tag consists of the high-order 21 bits of the physical address of the data stored in the corresponding cache line.

The *valid/LRU block* contains a 7-bit quantity for each of the 128 sets of cache lines. Four bits are used to mark the cache lines in the set individually as "valid" or "invalid." The other three bits track the use of the data in the set; they are checked when a cache line-fill is needed (and all lines in the set are valid).

The 80486 accesses the cache by splitting the physical address into three parts:

- The high-order 21 bits are the tag field. It distinguishes the cached data from any other 16-byte data line that could have been stored in the same set.
- The next-highest 7 bits are the index field. It determines the set in which the data can be stored.
- The low-order 4 bits select the byte within the specified cache line.

Test registers   Three test registers are used to control the testing of the cache: TR3 is the test data register, TR4 is the test status register, and TR5 is the test control register.

These registers are accessed by variants of the MOV instruction, which is defined in both real-address mode and protected mode. In protected mode, the MOV instructions that access the cache test registers can be executed only at privilege level 0 (most-privileged). Attempting to read or write the test registers from any other privilege level causes a general-protection exception.

Figure 1-18 shows the formats of test registers TR3, TR4, and TR5.

3 1		1 1 1 0 9 8 7 6 5 4 3 2 1 0			
Reserved		Set Select	E N T	C T L	TR5
Linear Address	V	LRU	Valid	0 0 0	TR4
Data					TR3

1-18   Cache test register formats.

TR3, the cache test data register, contains a doubleword to write to the cache fill buffer or a doubleword read from the cache read buffer. The fill and read buffers can each hold four doublewords. A specific doubleword in either buffer is selected by using the 2-bit Entry Select field in the TR5 register.

The fields for TR4, the cache test status register, are as follows:

TAG ADDRESS—BITS 11–31. On a cache write, this is the entry that becomes the tag.

V—BIT 10. This is the Valid bit for the entry that was accessed. On a cache lookup, it is a copy of one of the bits reported in bits 3–6.

LRU—BITS 7–9. On a cache lookup, these are the three LRU bits of the set that was accessed. On a cache write, these bits are ignored.

VALID—BITS 4–6. On a cache lookup, these are the four Valid bits of the set that was accessed.

The fields for TR5, the cache test control register, are as follows:

SET SELECT—BITS 4–10. This field selects one of the 128 sets in the cache data block.

ENT—BITS 2 and 3. This is the Entry Select field. During a cache read or write, it selects one of the four entries in the set specified by the Set Select. During fill-buffer writes or read-buffer reads, it selects one of the four doublewords in a line.

CTL—BITS 0 and 1. This is the Control field; it determines what kind of operation occurs. To do a cache read or write, load this field with binary 10 or 01, respectively. To flush the cache (mark all entries as invalid), load it with binary 11. To write to the cache fill buffer or read from the cache read buffer, load it with binary 00.

Note that writing to TR5 with either bit 0 or bit 1 set causes a cache access. TR5 cannot be read.

Test operations   Following are generalized descriptions of cache operations.

Important: Before cache testing, you must disable caching by setting the CD bit in the CR0 register.

To write to the cache fill buffer,

1. Load the TR5 register with a value in the Entry Select field (bits 2–3) that specifies one of the four doublewords in the cache fill buffer. The value of the Control field (bits 0–1) must be binary 00.
2. Load the TR3 register with the data to be written to the doubleword in the cache fill buffer. Loading TR3 writes the doubleword to the buffer.
3. Repeat steps 1 and 2 for the remaining three doublewords in the cache fill buffer.

To write to the cache,

1. Load the cache fill buffer as just described.
2. Load the TR4 register with the Tag Address (bits 11–31) and a Valid bit (bit 10). The other bits of TR4 (0–9) have no effect on the cache write operation.
3. Load the TR5 register with the Control (bits 0–1), Entry Select (bits 2–3), and Set Select (bits 4–10) values. The value of the Control field must be binary 01. Loading TR5 triggers the cache write operation.

To read from the cache, load the TR5 register with the Control (bits 0–1), Entry Select (bits 2–3), and Set Select (bits 4–10) values. The value of the Control field must be binary 10. Loading TR5 triggers the cache read operation.

The cache read operation loads the TR4 register with the tag for the entry that was read and the LRU and Valid bits for the entire set that was read. The cache read operation also loads the cache read buffer with 128 bits of data.

To read from the cache read buffer,

1. Load the TR5 register with a value in the Entry Select field (bits 2–3) that specifies one of the four doublewords in the cache read buffer. The value of the Control field (bits 0–1) must be binary 00.
2. Read a doubleword from the cache read buffer by unloading the TR3 register.
3. Repeat steps 1 and 2 for the remaining three doublewords in the cache read buffer.

To flush the cache, load the Control field (bits 0–1) of the TR5 register with binary 11. None of the other fields have any meaning in this case. Loading TR5 with 11 flushes the cache and clears all of its LRU and Valid bits.

2
Selectors and descriptors

In the 80486, selectors and descriptors are those items that provide the hardware with the software's expected image of what is located where.

Selectors

A selector is a 16-bit pointer that, when loaded into a register or used with certain instructions, selects certain descriptors. In a logical address, the selector portion identifies an individual descriptor by first specifying the descriptor table and then indexing to the descriptor within that table. Figure 2-1 shows a general selector format. The various terms (such as Global Descriptor Table and descriptor) are defined later in this chapter.

The fields are as follows:

INDEX—Selects one of up to 8192 descriptors in a descriptor table. The 80486 multiplies this index value by eight (the length of a descriptor) and then adds the result to the base address of the descriptor table. This accesses the correct entry in the table.

TABLE INDICATOR (TI)—This bit specifies the descriptor table to which the selector refers: a zero points to the GDT (Global Descriptor Table) and a one indicates the current LDT (Local Descriptor Table).

REQUESTED PRIVILEGE LEVEL (RPL)—Used by the system protection mechanism. See Chapter 6 for more on protection and privilege.

The first entry of the GDT is not used by the processor. A selector that has an index of zero and a table indicator of zero (that is, a selector that points to the first entry in the GDT) is called a *null selector*. The 80486 does not cause an exception when a segment register, other than CS or SS, is loaded with a null selector. It *does* cause an exception when the segment register is used to access memory. You could find this useful to trap accidental references.

```
  15                         3 2 1 0
┌─────────────────────────────┬──┬───┐
│                             │T │ R │
│           Index             │I │ P │
│                             │  │ L │
└─────────────────────────────┴──┴───┘
```

TI   Table Indicator
RPL Requested Privilege Level

2-1 Selector format.

Segment descriptors

Descriptors are those objects to which the segment selector point. They are 8-byte quantities that contain attributes about a given linear address space (that is, about a segment). These attributes include the segment 32-bit base linear address, the segment's 20-bit length and granularity, the protection level, read, write or execute privileges, the default size of the operands (16- or 32-bit), and the type of segment.

All descriptor attribute information is contained in 12 bits of the segment descriptor. Segments on the 80386 have three attribute fields in common: the *P* (Present) bit, the *DPL* (Descriptor Privilege Level) bits, and the *S* (Segment Descriptor) bit.

Segment descriptors are stored in either a Global Descriptor Table (GDT) or Local Descriptor Table (LDT). The 80486 locates the GDT and the current LDT in memory by means of the GDTR and LDTR registers.

A segment descriptor provides the 80486 with the data it needs to map a logical address into a linear address. These descriptors are not created by programs, but by compilers, linkers, loaders, or the operating system. Figure 2-2 shows the general segment-descriptor format.

The fields are as follows:

BASE—This defines the location of the segment within the 4 gigabyte linear address space. The 80486 concatenates the three fragments of the base address to form a single 32-bit value.

LIMIT—This field defines the size of the segment. The 80486 links the two parts of the LIMIT field, to form a 20-bit result. The processor then interprets the LIMIT field in one of two ways, depending on the setting of the Granularity Bit:

- In units of one byte, to define a LIMIT of up to 1 megabyte.
- In units of 4 Kilobytes (one page), to define a LIMIT of up to 4 giga-bytes.

The LIMIT is shifted left by 12 bits when loaded, and low-order one-bits are inserted.

GRANULARITY BIT—This bit specifies the units with which the LIMIT field is interpreted. When G = 0, LIMIT is interpreted as units of one byte. If G = 1, LIMIT is interpreted in units of 4K.

Descriptor Used for Special System Segments

3 1				2 3	1 9	1 5	1 1		8 7	0
Base 31..24	G	D	0	A V L	Segment Limit 19..16	P	D P L	S	Type	Base 23..16
Base Address 15..0						Segment Limit 15..0				

Descriptor Used for Application Code and Data Segments

3 1				2 3	1 9	1 5	1 1		9 8 7	0
Base 31..24	G	D	0	A V L	Segment Limit 19..16	P	D P L	S	Type A	Base 23..16
Base Address 15..0						Segment Limit 15..0				

G	Granularity		P	Segment Present
D	Default Operation Size		DPL	Descriptor Privilege Level
	(code segment descriptors)		S	Segment
	0 = 16 bits; 1 = 32 bits			0 = System; 1 = Code/Data
AVL	Available for programmer use		A	Accessed

2-2 General segment descriptor format.

D (DEFAULT OPERATION SIZE)—This bit indicates whether operands and effective addresses default to 16 bits (D=0) or 32 bits (D=1) in length.

DPL (DESCRIPTOR PRIVILEGE LEVEL)—This field defines the privilege level of the segment. It controls access to the segment, using the protection mechanism described in Chapter 6.

S (SEGMENT)—This bit determines whether a given segment is a system segment (S=0) or a code or data segment (S=1)

TYPE—This field differs between the two kinds of descriptors. System segments use the following set of values in TYPE:

0 = Reserved	8 = Reserved
1 = Available 80286 TSS	9 = Available 80386/486 TSS
2 = LTD	A = Reserved
3 = Busy 80286 TSS	B = Busy 80386/486 TSS
4 = 80286 Call Gate	C = 80386/486 Call Gate
5 = 80286/386 Task Gate	D = Reserved
6 = 80286 Interrupt Gate	E = 80386/486 Interrupt Gate
7 = 80286 Trap Gate	F = 80386 Trap Gate, 80486 Task Gate

In application code and data descriptors, TYPE specifies the kind of access that can be made to the segment, as summarized in TABLE 2-1. Note that the high-order bit of TYPE indicates whether the segment is data (T=0) or code (T=1). The other three bits differ between the two segment types.

Table 2-1   Application segment types.

Value	T	E	W	A	Descriptor Type	Description
0	0	0	0	0	Data	Read-only
1	0	0	0	1	Data	Read-only, accessed
2	0	0	1	0	Data	Read/Write
3	0	0	1	1	Data	Read/Write, accessed
4	0	1	0	0	Data	Read-only, expand-down
5	0	1	0	1	Data	Read-only, expand-down, accessed
6	0	1	1	0	Data	Read/Write, expand-down
7	0	1	1	1	Data	Read/Write, expand-down, accessed

Value	T	C	R	A	Descriptor Type	Description
8	1	0	0	0	Code	Execute-only
9	1	0	0	1	Code	Execute-only, accessed
A	1	0	1	0	Code	Execute/Read
B	1	0	1	1	Code	Execute/Read, accessed
C	1	1	0	0	Code	Execute-only, conforming
D	1	1	0	1	Code	Execute-only, conforming, accessed
E	1	1	1	0	Code	Execute/Read-only, conforming
F	1	1	1	1	Code	Execute/Read-only, conforming, accessed

For data segments, the three low bits of the TYPE field can be interpreted as Expand-down (E), Write-enable (W), and Accessed (A). For code segments, these bits can be interpreted as Conforming (C), Read-enable (R), and Accessed (A).

Data segments can be read-only or read/write. Stack segments are data segments that must be read/write. If the stack segment needs to change size, it must be an expand-down data segment. For an expand-down data segment, the segment limit has the reverse of its usual meaning. In standard, "expand-up" segments, valid offsets range from 0 to the segment limit. By contrast, offsets into expand-down segments must be greater than the segment limit. This interpretation of the segment limit causes memory space to be allocated at the bottom of the segment when the segment limit is increased. This is appropriate for stack segments because they grow toward lower addresses. If the stack is given a segment that does not change size, it need not be an expand-down segment.

Code segments can be execute-only or execute/write. An execute/read segment might be used, for example, when constants have been placed with instruction code in a ROM. In this case, the constants can be read by either using an instruction with a CS override or placing a segment selector for the code segment in a segment register for a data segment.

Code segments are also classified as conforming or non-conforming. Transferring execution into a more-privileged conforming segment keeps the current privilege level. Transferring into a non-conforming segment at a different privilege level generates an exception, unless a task gate is used (see Chapter 6 for a discussion of multitasking).

For both data and code segments, an Accessed (A) bit in the TYPE field reports whether the segment has been accessed. Operating systems that implement virtual memory at the segment level may monitor the frequency of segment usage by testing and clearing this bit periodically.

P (SEGMENT PRESENT)—If this bit holds a 0 value, the descriptor is not valid for use in address translation. The 80486 signals an exception when a selector for the descriptor is loaded into a segment register. Figure 2-3 shows the format of a "not-present" descriptor.

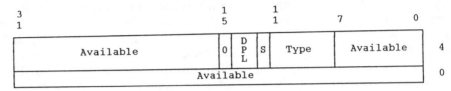

P = 0   For this descriptor, the Segment Present bit = 0

DPL   Descriptor Privilege Level

S   Segment Type

2-3 Format of not-present descriptor.

In addition to the selector value, every segment register has an "invisible" segment descriptor cache register associated with it. When the segment register's contents are changed, the 8-byte descriptor associated with that selector is automatically loaded (cached). Once loaded, all references to that segment use the cached descriptor information instead of re-accessing the descriptor.

To provide operating system compatibility between the 80286 and 80386/486, the 80386 and 80486 processors support all the 80286 segment descriptors. The only differences between the two formats are that the values of the type fields and the limit and base address fields have been expanded for the 80386/486.

The 80286 system segment descriptors contain a 24-bit address and a 16-bit limit. The 80386/486 system descriptors, on the other hand, have a 32-bit base address, a 20-bit limit and a granularity bit (G Bit). To tell the difference, if the upper word of the descriptor is zero, then it is an 80286-type descriptor.

The only other difference between 80286 and 80386/486 style descriptors is the interpretation of the word count field of call gates and the B bit. The word count field specifies the number of 16-bit quantities to copy for 80286 call gates and the 32-bit quantities for 80386/486 call gates. The B bit controls the size of PUSHes when using a call gate. If B = 0, the PUSHes are 16 bits; if B = 1, the PUSHes are 32 bits.

Descriptor tables

Descriptor tables define all the segments used in the 80486 system. The three types of tables are the Global Descriptor Table (GDT), the Local Descriptor Table (LDT), and the Interrupt Descriptor Table (IDT). The registers that point to these tables (and contain the 32-bit linear base address and the 16-bit limit of each table) are, respectively, the GDTR, LDTR, and IDTR. These registers were initially discussed in Chapter 1.

Descriptor tables are variable length memory arrays, with 8-byte entries that contain descriptors. In the 80486, they range in size from 8 bytes to 64K, and each table holds up to 8192 8-byte descriptors. The upper 13 bits of a selector are used as an index into the descriptor table. Because the operating system maintains these tables, Load Descriptor Table instructions are privileged instructions. The first entry of the GDT (where INDEX=0) is not used by the 80486.

The 80486 stores descriptor information in segment registers. This way, the processor does not have to index into a table each time it refers to the information. There are two classes of instructions to do this: Implied load instructions (such as CALL and JMP) and Direct load instructions (such as POP, MOV, LDS, LFS).

Each register has a programmer-visible portion and a programmer-invisible portion. Using either the direct load or the implied load instructions, the visible portions of these segment address registers are manipulated by programs as if they were simply 16-bit registers. The invisible portions are manipulated by the processor; it fetches the base address, limit, type, and other information from a descriptor table and loads them into the invisible portion of the segment register.

Global Descriptor Table (GDT)

Every 80486 system contains a Global Descriptor Table (GDT). The GDT holds descriptors that are available to all the tasks in a system. Except for descriptors that control interrupts or exceptions, the GDT can contain any other kind of segment descriptor.

Generally, the GDT contains three types of descriptors: code and data segments used by the operating system, descriptors for the Local Descriptors in a system, and task state segments. The first slot of the GDT is not used; it corresponds to the null selector, which defines a null pointer value.

Local Descriptor Table (LDT)

Operating systems are generally designed so that each task has a separate Local Descriptor Table (LDT). LDTs provide a way for isolating a given task's code and data segments from the rest of the operating system. The GDT contains descriptors for segments that are common to all tasks. The LDT is associated with a given task and may contain only code, data, stack, task gate and call gate descriptors.

A segment cannot be accessed by a task if its segment descriptor does not exist in either the current LDT or the GDT. This both isolates and protects that task's segments, while still allowing global *data* to be shared among tasks.

The GDT and IDT registers consist of a 16-bit limit value and a 32-bit linear address. (The 16 plus the 32 add to 48 bits, or 6 bytes.) Unlike the 6-byte GDT or IDT registers that contain both the base address and limit, the programmer-visible portion of the LDT register contains only a 16-bit selector. This selector refers to an LDT descriptor in the GDT.

Interrupt Descriptor Table (IDT)

The Interrupt Descriptor Table (IDT) contains the descriptors that point to the location of up to 256 interrupt service routines. The IDT can only contain trap gates, task gates, and interrupt gates. (*Gates* are circuits having one output and several inputs, the output remaining unenergized until certain input conditions have been met.) The IDT should be at least 256 bytes in size so it can hold the descriptors for the 32 Intel-Reserved Interrupts. *Every interrupt used by the system must have an entry in the IDT.*

3
Interrupts and exceptions

Both hardware- and software-generated interrupts can alter the programmed execution of the 80486. A hardware-generated interrupt occurs in response to an active input on one of two 80486 interrupt inputs: NMI, which is non-maskable, or INTR, which is maskable. A software-generated interrupt (a fault, trap, or abort) occurs in response to an INT instruction or an exception, a software condition that requires servicing. Figure 3-1 shows a schematic representation of maskable and non-maskable interrupts.

Maskable interrupts (INTR)

The 80486 INTR input allows external devices to interrupt the executing program. To ensure recognition, the INTR input must be held high until the 80486 acknowledges the interrupt by performing the interrupt acknowledge sequence. Also, maskable interrupts must be enabled in software for interrupt recognition.

The INTR signal is usually supplied by the 8259A Programmable Interrupt Controller. The Controller is, in turn, connected to devices that require interrupt servicing. The 8259A appears to the 80486 as a set of I/O ports. It accepts interrupt requests from devices connected to it, determines the priority of those requests, activates the INTR input, and then supplies the appropriate service routine vector when requested. The service routine vector is the entry in the IDT that points to a service routine for handling the interrupt. The mechanism is the same as that used in the INT instruction.

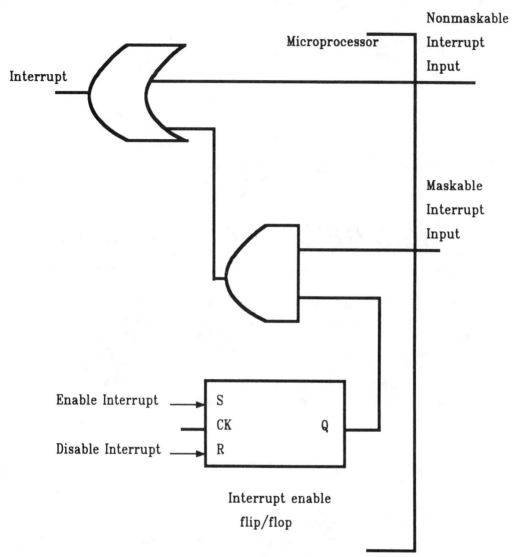

3-1 Representation of maskable and nonmaskable interrupts.

Nonmaskable interrupts (NMI)

The 80486 NMI input generally signals a catastrophic event such as an imminent power loss, a memory error, or a bus parity error. NMI is edge-triggered (on a low-to-high transition) and asynchronous. A valid signal is low for eight CLK2 periods before the transition and high two CLK periods after the transition.

An NMI automatically causes the 80486 to execute the service routine that corresponds to location 2 in the IDT. The 80486 will not service sub-sequent NMI requests until the current one has been serviced. The 80486 disables INTR requests in real mode, although these can be re-enabled in the service routine. In protected mode, the disabling of the INTR request depends on the gate in IDT location 2.

The NMI and the software exceptions recognized by the processor are assigned predetermined identifiers in the range zero (0) through 31. At the present time, some numbers are reserved by Intel for future use.

In the case of maskable interrupts, external interrupt controllers (such as Intel's 8259A Programmable Interrupt Controller) determine the identifier and communicate it to the processor during the processor's interrupt-acknowledge sequence. In response to an interrupt request, the 80486 accepts and then services the interrupt. That is, it transfers pro-gram execution to an interrupt service routine. Any number from 32 through 255 can be assigned to the service routines. Table 3-1 shows the assigned and unassigned identifiers.

Interrupt Descriptor Table

The entry point descriptors to the service routines or the interrupt tasks are stored in memory in a table, the Interrupt Descriptor Table or IDT. The IDT associates each interrupt or exception identifier with a descriptor for the instructions that service the associated event.

To access a particular service routine, the 80486 obtains a vector, or index, to the table location that contains the descriptor. The source of this vector depends on the type of interrupt. If the interrupt is maskable (INTR input active), the vector is supplied by the 8259A Interrupt Controller. If the interrupt is nonmaskable (NMI input is active), location 2 in the IDT is used.

The IDT is an array of 8-byte descriptors. The first entry of the IDT can contain a descriptor, unlike the first entry of the Global Descriptor Table (GDT) or the Local Descriptor Table (LDT). To locate the correct descriptor, the processor multiplies the identifier by eight. The IDT can contain up to 256 identifiers and can reside in any location in memory. The processor finds it by using the IDT register (IDTR). The instructions LIDT (Load Interrupt Descriptor Table Register) and SIDT (Store Interrupt Descriptor Table Register) operate on the IDTR.

LIDT loads the IDT register with the linear base address and limit val-ues contained in the memory operand. This instruction is executed only when the CPL is zero. It is used normally by the initialization of the operat-ing system when it creates the IDT. The operating system can use the instruction to change from one IDT to another.

SIDT copies the base and limit value stored in the IDTR to a memory location. SIDT can be executed at any privilege level.

Table 3-1   Interrupt and exception ID assignments.

Identifier	Description
0	Divide Error
1	Debug Exceptions
2	Nonmaskable Interrupt
3	Breakpoint
4	Overflow
5	Bounds Check
6	Invalid Opcode
7	Device Not Available
8	Double Fault
9	Reserved by Intel. (On pre-80486 CPUs, "Coprocessor Segment Overrun")
10	Invalid Task State Segment
11	Segment Not Present
12	Stack Exception
13	General Protection
14	Page Fault
15	Reserved by Intel.
16	Floating-Point Error (On pre-80486 CPUs, "Coprocessor Error")
17	Alignment Check
18-31	Reserved by Intel.
32-255	Available for user-defined maskable interrupts

Exceptions

Exceptions are classified as *faults*, *aborts*, or *traps*, depending on the way they are reported and also whether restart of the instruction that caused the exception is supported. Faults are exceptions that are either detected before the instruction begins to execute or during execution. If detected during execution, the fault is reported with the machine restored to a state that permits the instruction to be restarted. The CS (Code Segment) Register and EIP (Instruction Pointer) values, saved when a fault is reported, point to the instruction causing the fault.

A trap is reported at the instruction boundary immediately after the instruction in which the exception was detected. The CS and EIP values, stored when the trap is reported, point to the instruction after the instruction causing the trap. The reported values of CS and EIP reflect alterations of program flow if a trap is detected during an instruction that alters that program flow. If a trap is detected in a JMP (JUMP) instruction, for example, the CS and EIP values pushed onto the stack point to the *target* of the JMP, *not* to the instruction immediately after the JMP.

An abort allows neither the restart of the program that caused the exception nor the identification of the precise location of the instruction causing the exception. Aborts are used to report severe errors such as illegal and/or inconsistent values in system tables or hardware errors.

The time that elapses before an interrupt request is serviced depends on several factors. The interrupt source must take this delay into account. The following all can affect elapsed time:

- If the interrupt is masked, an INTR request will not be recognized until interrupts are re-enabled.
- If a nonmaskable interrupt is currently being serviced, an incoming nonmaskable interrupt request will not be recognized until the 80486 encounters the IRET (interrupt return) instruction.
- Saving the Flags register and other registers requires time.
- If interrupt servicing requires a task switch, time must be allowed for saving and restoring the task state.
- If the 80486 is currently executing an instruction, the instruction must be completed. With certain exceptions (such as a string move, which allows an interrupt after each block move), an interrupt request is recognized *only* on an instruction boundary.

The longest delay occurs when the interrupt request arrives while the 80486 is executing a long instruction such as multiplication, division, or a task-switch in the protected mode. If the instruction sets the interrupt flag, thereby enabling interrupts, an interrupt is not processed until *after* the next instruction.

Interrupt controller

The 8259A Programmable Interrupt Controller manages interrupts for an 80486 system. The programmable features allow it to be used in a variety of ways to fit the interrupt requirements of a particular system. A single 8259A can accept interrupts from up to eight external sources, and up to 64 requests can be accommodated by cascading several 8259A chips.

The 8259A resolves priority between active interrupts, then interrupts the processor and passes it a code to identify the interrupting source.

Interrupt and exception priorities

If more than one interrupt or exception is waiting at an instruction boundary, the processor services them in a preset sequence based on their priorities. Going from highest to lowest priority, the classes of exception and interrupt sources are as follows:

- Debug Trap Exceptions from the last instruction (TF flag set, T bit in TSS set, or data breakpoint).
- Debug Fault Exceptions for the next instruction (code breakpoint).
- Nonmaskable Interrupt (NMI).
- Maskable Interrupt.
- Faults from fetching next instruction (Segment Not Present or General Protection Fault).
- Faults from instruction decoding (Invalid Opcode, instruction too long, or privilege violation). If WAIT instruction, Device Not Available.
- Exception with TS and MP bits of CR0 set. If ESC instruction, Device Not Available.
- Exception with EM or MP bits of CR0 set. If WAIT or ESC instruction, Floating-Point Error.
- Exception with ERROR# pin asserted.
- Segment Not Present Faults, Stack Faults, and General Protection Faults for memory operands.
- Alignment Check Faults for memory operands.
- Page Faults for memory operands.

When the processor selects an interrupt to service, any exceptions of lower priority are delayed until their priority is reached. These low-priority exceptions will be rediscovered when the interrupt handler returns control to the point of interruption. Lower-priority interrupts are retained and held pending.

Interrupt tasks and procedures

An interrupt or exception can call an interrupt handler that is either a procedure or a task. An interrupt gate or trap gate points indirectly to a procedure that executes in the context of the currently executing task. The gate selector points to an executable-segment descriptor in either the GDT or the current LDT. The offset field of the gate points to the beginning of the interrupt or exception handling procedure. The 80486 invokes an interrupt or exception handling procedure in much the same manner as it

CALLs a procedure. Figure 3-2 shows the formats of the IDT Gate Descriptors.

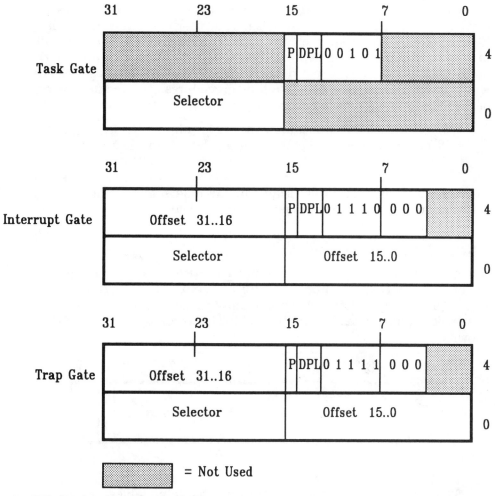

3-2 IDT gate descriptors for the 80486.

An interrupt procedure differs from a normal procedure in the method used to leave the procedure. The IRET (Interrupt Return) instruction is used to exit from an interrupt procedure. IRET is similar to RET (Return), except that IRET increments the ESP by an extra four bytes because the flags are on the stack. IRET then moves the saved flags into the EFLAGS register.

An interrupt that vectors through an interrupt gate resets IF (Interrupt-Enable Flag). This prevents other interrupts from impacting or tampering with the current interrupt handler. The IRET instruction at the end of the interrupt procedure restores IF to the value in the EFLAGS image on the stack. In contrast, an interrupt through a trap gate does *not* change the IF.

The processor does not permit an interrupt to transfer control to a procedure in a segment of lesser privilege (that is, one with a numerically higher privilege level than the current level). Violation of this rule results in a general protection exception. Because it is difficult to predict the occurrence of an interrupt, restrictions are placed on the privilege levels at which interrupt and exception handling procedures can execute. Use one of the following methods to ensure that privilege levels are not violated.

- Place the handler procedure in a privilege level zero segment.
- Place the handler in a conforming segment. This method suits handlers for certain exceptions, such as divide error. Such an interrupt handler must use only the data available to it from the stack. If it needs data from a data segment, the data segment must have a privilege level of three, making it unprotected.

Error codes

When the processor finds an exception that relates to a specific segment, the 80486 pushes the appropriate error code onto the exception handler stack. The error code format looks like that of a selector, except that it has two one-bit items instead of an RPL field. The format of the error code is shown in FIG. 3-3.

3-3 Error code format.

The fields are as follows:

SELECTOR INDEX—Indexes into the error handling tables.

TI—BIT 2. Table Indicator. If the I-bit is not set and TI=0, TI indicates the error code refers to the Global Descriptor Table (GDT). If I-bit is not set, and TI=1, TI refers to the Local Descriptor Table (LDT).

I—BIT 1. The 80486 sets this IDT (Interrupt Descriptor Table) bit if the index portion of the error code refers to a gate descriptor in the IDT.

EXT—BIT 0. The 80486 sets the External (EXT) bit if the exception was caused by an event external to the program.

The 80486 recognizes sixteen defined error codes.

Interrupt 0—Divide Error The divide-error occurs during a DIV (Unsigned Divide) or IDIV (Signed Divide) instruction when the divisor is zero.

Interrupt 1—Debug Exceptions The 80486 generates this interrupt for five general conditions:

- Task-switch breakpoint trap.
- General detect fault.
- Data address breakpoint trap.
- Instruction address breakpoint fault.
- Single-step trap.

Whether the exception is a trap or a fault depends on the condition. The 80486 does not push an error code onto the stack for this exception. Create an exception handler that checks the debug registers (DR0–DR7) to determine which condition triggered the exception.

Interrupt 3—Breakpoint INT 3 (Call to Interrupt Procedure) causes this trap. INT 3 is one byte long, which makes it easy to replace an opcode in an executable segment with the breakpoint opcode. The saved CS:EIP (Code Segment, Instruction Pointer) points to the byte following the breakpoint.

Interrupt 4—Overflow When the processor executes an INTO (Call to Interrupt Procedure for Overflow) *and* the OF (Overflow) flag is set, this interrupt is triggered. Both signed and unsigned arithmetic use the same arithmetic instructions. The 80486 cannot judge which one is meant. Therefore, it does not cause overflow exceptions automatically.

It does set the OF flag when the results would be out of range if interpreted as signed numbers.

Interrupt 5—Bounds Check While executing a BOUND (Check Array Index Against Bounds) instruction, if the 80486 finds that the operand is greater than the limit, the processor signals this fault. Software can also use BOUND to check a signed array index against signed limits that are defined in a block of memory.

Interrupt 6—Invalid Opcode This fault occurs if an invalid opcode is found by the execution unit. That exception is not detected until the processor attempts to execute it. In other words, prefetching an invalid opcode does not trigger this interrupt. Also, no error code is pushed on the stack. An exception can be handled within the same task.

Another problem can cause this exception. If the type of operand is invalid for a given opcode, this fault is triggered. For example, an interrupt will occur if an LES (Load Full Pointer into ES Register) uses a register source operand.

Interrupt 7—Device Not Available This exception is generated by either of two conditions:

- The processor executes a WAIT or ESC instruction and the TS (Task Switched) bit of Control Register Zero (CR0) is set. *Note:* On the 80286 and 80386 processors, the MP (Math Present) bit in the CR0 register must also be set if the WAIT instruction is to generate an interrupt. On the 80486, the MP bit should always be set.

- The processor executes an ESC instruction, and the EM (Emulation) bit of CR0 is set.

Interrupt 8—Double Fault Generally, the 80486 handles exceptions serially. If it cannot, it signals a double-fault exception. To be able to determine if the error is a double-fault condition, the 80486 divides exceptions into three classes: benign exceptions, contributory exceptions, and page faults. The 80486 always pushes an error code onto the stack of the double-fault handler. That error code is *always* zero. The faulting instruction may not be restarted. If another exception occurs while the processor is attempting to handle a double fault, the processor shuts down. Figure 3-4 shows the three classes.

Class	Identification	Description
Benign Exceptions	1	Debug Exceptions
	2	Nonmaskable Interrupt
	3	Breakpoint
	4	Overflow
	5	Bounds Check
	6	Invalid Opcode
	7	Device Not Available
	16	Floating-Point Error
Contributory Exceptions	0	Divide Error
	10	Invalid TSS
	11	Segment Not Present
	12	Stack Exception
	13	General Protection
Page Fault	14	Page Fault

3-4 Three classes of double-faults.

Interrupt 10—Invalid Task State Segment (TSS) An attempt to switch to an invalid TSS causes this exception. Twelve conditions, listed in FIG. 3-5, can cause a TSS to be considered invalid. An error code is pushed onto the stack to help identify which cause it is. The EXT (External) bit indicates if the exception was caused by a condition outside the control of the program, such as an external interrupt via a task gate that triggered the switch to the invalid TSS. To ensure a correct TSS to process this condition, the exception handler must be a task called via a task gate.

Interrupt 11—Segment Not Present This exception occurs when the 80486 finds that the P (Present) bit of a descriptor is zero. This fault is restartable. The exception handler makes the segment present and

Error Code	Conditions
TSS id + EXT	The limit in the TSS Descriptor is less than 103
LTD id + EXT	Invalid LDT selector, or LDT not present
SS id + EXT	Stack segment selector is outside table limit
SS id + EXT	Stack segment is not a writeable segment
SS id + EXT	Stack segment selector RPL not equal to CPL
CS id + EXT	Code segment selector is outside table limit
CS id + EXT	Code segment selector does not refer to code segment
CS id + EXT	DPL of non−conforming code segment is not equal to the new CPL
CS id + EXT	DPL of conforming code segment is greater than new CPL
DS/ES/FS/GS id + EXT	DS, ES, FS, or GS segment selector is outside table limits
DS/ES/FS/GS id + EXT	DS, ES, FS, or GS is not a readable segment

3-5 Conditions invalidating a TSS.

returns. The interrupted program then resumes execution. Generally, an operating system uses this exception to implement virtual memory at the segment level.

Interrupt 12—Stack Exception Interrupt 12 occurs in either of two conditions:

- When the processor attempts to load the SS register with a descriptor that is marked as not-present but is otherwise valid. This can occur in an interlevel CALL, an interlevel return, in a task switch, an LSS instruction, or a MOV or POP instruction to SS.

- In any operation that refers to the SS register and has a limit violation. This includes stack-oriented instructions such as ENTER, LEAVE, POP, and PUSH. It also includes other memory references that imply use of SS.

An instruction that causes this interrupt is restartable in all cases. The return pointer pushed onto the exception handler's stack points to the instruction to be restarted.

Interrupt 13—General Protection Exception This exception is the "catch-all." All protection violations that do not cause another exception cause a general exception. The following are sample causes:

- Exceeding segment limit when referencing a descriptor table.
- Writing into a read-only data segment or into a code segment.
- Reading from an execute-only segment.
- Loading DS, ES, FS, GS or SS with the descriptor of a system segment.
- Switching to a busy task.
- Violating privilege rules.
- Loading CR0 with PG = 1 (Paging is enabled) and PE = 0 (Protection Enable is not).
- Exceeding segment limit when using CS, DS, ES, FS, or GS.
- Transferring control to a segment that is not executable.

Interrupt 14—Page Fault Interrupt 14 occurs when paging is enabled (PG = 1) and the processor finds one of the two following conditions while translating a linear address to a physical address:

- The current procedure does not have enough privilege to access the indicated page.
- The page-table entry or page-directory that is needed for the address translation has a zero in its present bit.

The 80486 makes available to the page fault handler two pieces of information to aid diagnosis of the error and how to recover from it:

- Control Register 2 (CR2). The 80486 stores the linear address, used in the access that caused the exception, into CR2. The exception handler uses this to locate the corresponding page table and page directory entries.
- An error code on the stack. This error code has a different format from other exceptions. The code tells the exception handler whether the exception is due to a not-present page or to an access rights violation, whether the memory access that caused the exception was a read or a write, and whether the 80486 was executing at user or supervisor level at the time of the exception.

Interrupt 16—Floating Point Error   A floating-point error fault signals an error generated by a floating-point arithmetic instruction. Interrupt 16 can only occur if the NE (Numeric Error) bit in the CR0 register is set.

Interrupt 17—Alignment Check   This fault can be generated for access to unaligned operands. For example, a word stored at an odd byte address or a double word stored at an address that is not a multiple of four. TABLE 3-2 lists the alignment requirements by data type.

Table 3-2   Alignment requirements by data type.

Data Type	Address Must be Divisible By
WORD	2
DWORD	4
Short REAL	4
Long REAL	8
TEMPREAL	8
Selector	2
48-bit Segmented Pointer	4
32-bit Flat Pointer	4
32-bit Segmented Pointer	2
48-bit "Pseudo-Descriptor"	4
FSTENV/FLDENV save area	4 or 2, depending on operand size
FSAVE/FRSTOR save area	4 or 2, depending on operand size
Bit String	4

To enable alignment checking, the 80486 must be in user mode (CPL = 3), the AC flag must be set, and the AM (Alignment Mask) bit in CR0 must be set.

Exception summary

Figure 3-6 summarizes the exceptions recognized by the 80486 processor.

Number	Description	Return to faulting instruction?	Caused by
0	Divide Error	Yes	DIV and IDIV
1	Debug Exceptions	*	Any code or data reference
3	Breakpoint	No	INT 3 instruction
4	Overflow	No	INTO instruction
5	Bounds Check	Yes	BOUND instruction
6	Invalid Opcode	Yes	Reserved opcodes
7	Device Not Available	Yes	ESC and WAIT
8	Double Fault	Yes	Any instruction
10	Invalid TSS	Yes	JMP, CALL, IRET, or an interrupt

3-6 Exception summary.

Number	Description	Return to faulting instruction?	Caused by
11	Segment Not Present	Yes	Any instruction that modifies segments
12	Stack Exception	Yes	Stack operations
13	General Protection	Yes	Any code or data reference
14	Page Fault	Yes	Any code or data reference
16	Floating-Point Error	Yes	ESC and WAIT
17	Alignment Check	Yes	Any data reference
0-255	Software Interrupt	No	INT n instruction

*Debug exceptions are either traps or faults. The exception handler can distinguish between traps and faults by examining the contents of the DR6 register.

3-6 Continued.

4

Memory

Memory is a basic component of a computer system; it stores information for future use. Not only must the memory unit store large amounts of information, it must be designed to allow rapid access to any particular portion of that information. Speed, size, and cost are the crucial criteria in any storage unit. This chapter digs further into the 80486 and describes memory organization, memory interfacing, and cache memory.

Memory organization

Internal memory forms an integral physical part of any computer and is controlled by the processor (with some assists by direct memory access facilities). Organizational techniques for dividing memory aid programmers in making the best possible use of the total computer system. Two common organizational models, flat and segmented, are discussed below.

Segmentation

Segmentation is the division of memory into logical blocks for use by a computer. Memory segmentation allows efficient management of the logical address space. Segments are used to enclose regions of memory that have common attributes.

Memory is organized into one or more variable-length segments, from one byte up to four gigabytes in size. Every task in an 80486 can have up to 16,381 segments (each up to four gigabytes long), thus providing 64 terabytes of virtual memory. Any given region of the linear address space (a segment of the physical memory) has several attributes associated with it. These include its size, location, type (stack, code, or data), and protection characteristics.

The memory organization model seen by programmers is determined at system design. The 80486 architecture gives the designers the freedom to choose a model for each task. The most common models are as follows:

FLAT—An address space consisting of a single array of up to 4 gigabytes. In this model, the processor maps the 4 gigabyte flat space onto the physical address space by address translation mechanisms. A pointer into this space is a 32-bit number that may range from 0 to $2^{32} - 1$. Relocation of separately-compiled modules in this space must be performed by systems software, such as loaders, linkers, binders, and so on.

SEGMENTED—An address space that consists of a collection of up to 16,383 linear address spaces of up to 4 gigabytes each. The total space, as viewed by a program, can be up to 2^{46} bytes (64 terabytes). The processor maps the logical address space onto the physical address space by address translation mechanisms.

Programmers view the segmented model (also called logical address space) as a collection of up to 16,383 one-dimensional subspaces, each with some specified length. Each of these linear subspaces is a *segment*, a unit of contiguous address space. A complete pointer into this address space consists of two parts: a *segment selector*, which is a 16-bit field that identifies a segment, and an *offset*, which is a 32-bit value that points to a byte within the segment.

Address space

As noted above, physical memory is organized as a sequence of 8-bit bytes. Each byte is assigned a unique address that ranges from zero to $2^{32} - 1$, or 4 gigabytes. The 80486 has three distinct address spaces: physical, logical, and linear.

Physical addresses are the actual addresses used to select the physical memory chips that contain the data. A logical address consists of a segment selector and an offset into that segment. A linear address is the address formed by adding the offset to the base address of the segment. In a segmented memory model, logical address space is much larger space as viewed by a program and can be up to 2^{46} bytes, or 64 terabytes. The 80486 maps the logical space onto the physical space by address translation mechanisms.

The 80486 converts logical addresses into physical addresses in two steps. First, it performs a segment translation by converting a logical address consisting of a segment selector and segment offset into a linear address. Second, it does a page translation by converting a linear address into a physical address. The second step is optional, depending on how the system was designed to run.

Paging and page translation

Paging is another type of memory management useful in a multitasking operating system. Paging operates only in protected mode and provides a means of managing the very large segments of the 80486. Paging divides programs into uniformly sized pages, unlike segmentation (which modularizes programs and data into variable length segments). In a real sense, paging operates beneath segmentation. That is, the paging mechanism translates the protected linear address, which comes from the segmentation unit, into a physical address. Figure 4-1 illustrates the 80486 paging mechanism.

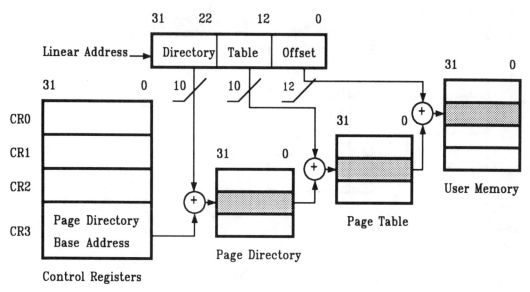

4-1 Memory paging mechanism.

In the second phase of address translation, the 80486 changes a linear address into a physical address by specifying a page table, a page within that table, and an offset within that page. The page-translation step is optional. Page translation is in effect only when the PG bit of CR0 (Control Register Zero) is set. This bit is generally set by the operating system during software initialization. This PG bit must be set if the operating system is to use multiple virtual 8086 tasks, page- oriented virtual memory, or page-oriented protection.

A linear address is composed of three fields: DIR, PAGE, and OFFSET. Figure 4-2 shows how the 80486 converts the linear address into the physical address. The addressing mechanism uses the DIR field as an index into a page directory and uses the OFFSET field to address a byte within the page determined by the page table.

A *page frame* is a block of 4K in physical memory. Pages begin on 4K boundaries and are fixed in size. The pages bear no direct relation to the logical structure of a program. The page frame address specifies the physical starting address of a page and the low-order 12 bits are always zero. In a page directory, the page frame address is the address of a page table. In a

Linear Address

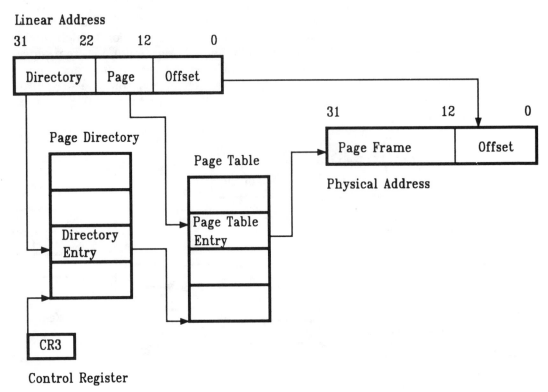

4-2 Page translation.

second-level page table, the page frame address is the address of the page frame that contains the desired memory operand.

Page tables A page table is an array of 32-bit page specifiers. The table is, itself, a page and contains 4K of memory or up to 1K 32-bit entries. Figure 4-3 shows the format of a page table entry.

The fields are as follows:

D (DIRTY) BIT 6, AND A (ACCESSED) BIT 5—These bits provide data about page usage and are set by hardware. The processor sets the accessed bits in both levels of page tables to the value of one before a read or write operation to a page. Then the processor sets the dirty bit in the second-level page table to the value of one before a write to an address covered by that page table entry. The dirty bit in directory entries is undefined.

In an operating system that supports paged virtual memory, these bits are used to determine which pages can be eliminated from physical memory when the demand for memory exceeds the available physical memory. The operating system holds the responsibility for testing and clearing these two bits.

Page Frame Address 31..12	AVL	0	0	D	A	P C D	P W T	U / S	R / W	P

AVL	Available for systems or programmer use
D	Dirty bit
A	Accessed bit
PCD	Page Cache Disable
PWT	Page Write-through
U/S	User/Supervisor bit
R/W	Read/Write bit
P	Present bit
0	Intel reserved. Do not use.

4-3 Format of a page table entry.

PCD (PAGE CACHE DISABLE) BIT 4 and PWT (PAGE WRITE-THROUGH) BIT 3—These bits, new with the 80486, are used for page-level cache management. Software can use them to control the caching of individual pages or second-level page tables. Caching is discussed later in this chapter.

U/S (USER/SUPERVISOR) BIT 2 and R/W (READ/WRITE) BIT 1—These bits are used for page-level protection that the 80486 performs at the same time as address translation.

P (PRESENT) BIT 0—The Present bit indicates whether a page table entry can be used in address translation. If so, P = 1. If P = 0, in either level of page tables, the entry is *not* valid for address translation and the remainder of the entry is available for software use.

If P = 0 in either level of page tables and an attempt is made to use a page-table entry for address translation, the 80486 signals a page exception.

Page translation and segment combinations   It may be expedient to turn off the 80486 segmentation when the 80486 executes software designed for special architectures that do not have segments. The processor does not have a specific mode to disable segmentation. However, the same effect is achieved by initially loading the segment registers with selectors for descriptors that encompass the entire 32-bit linear address space. Once the descriptors are loaded, the segment registers are not changed. The 80486 instructions' 32-bit offsets address the entire linear-address space.

Segments can be larger or smaller than a page (4K). If the required data structure is larger than a page and the operating system supports paged virtual memory, the operating system (OS) divides the structure into pages, any number of which may be present at any one time. This is transparent to the applications programmer. If the required information is smaller than a page, the OS may be designed to combine several data structures within a page.

The 80486 architecture does not force any one-to-one relationship between the boundaries of pages and segments. Thus, a segment can contain the end of one page and the beginning of another. Similarly, a page can contain the end of one segment and the beginning of another. Memory management software may be of simpler design, however, if it enforces some correlation between page and segment boundaries. For example, the logic for segment and page allocation can be combined if segments are allocated only in units of one page. In this case, there is no need for logic to account for partially used pages.

DMA controller

A Direct Memory Access (DMA) controller performs DMA transfers between main memory and an I/O device, typically a hard disk, floppy disk, or communications channel. In a DMA transfer, a large block of data can be copied from one place to another without the intervention of the CPU.

The 82258 Advanced DMA (ADMA) Controller offers four channels and provides all the signals necessary to perform DMA transfers. The main features of the 82258 are as follows:

- One of the four high-speed channels can be replaced with as many as 32 lower-speed, multiplexed channels.
- Command chaining to perform multiple commands.
- Data chaining to scatter data to separate memory locations—for example, separate pages—and to gather data from separate locations.
- Compare, translate, and verify functions.
- Automatic assembly and disassembly to convert from 16-bit memory to 8-bit I/O, or vice versa.

Memory interfacing

To achieve the performance potential of the 80486, a system must use relatively fast memory. Unfortunately, the faster the memory, the more the machine costs. The cost-performance tradeoff can be settled by dividing functions and using a combination of both fast and slow memories. By placing the most frequently used functions in fast memory and all other functions in slow memory, high performance for most operations can be achieved at a cost much less than that of a fast memory subsystem.

In high-performance systems, overall system delivery is linked closely to how well memory subsystems perform. To get all the potential promised by the 80486, fast memory must be used in spite of its higher cost. To get the best cost-performance tradeoff, a mix of fast and slower memory is used.

Main memory is a basic part of a microcomputer and stores program instructions and data. Generally, the main memory is random access and made up of a number of words, each consisting of a number of bits. An address is assigned to each word so that it may be uniquely accessed.

Basic memory interface

Configuring a memory system from memory units may be thought of as filling a memory space. The space can be viewed as a rectangular area divided into rows corresponding to possible address combinations. Each row consists of the number of bits making up a data word. Once the memory units have been placed into the space, the necessary interconnections must be specified.

The data lines of every memory unit are each connected to the corresponding line of the processor data bus. The address lines are used to first select a memory unit or a parallel group of units and then a word location within the selected unit or units.

The block diagram in FIG. 4-4 shows how bus control logic provides the control signals for data buffers, the memory latches, and memory devices. It also returns RDY# active to end the 80486 bus cycle and NA# to control address pipelining. Based on the address outputs of the 80486, the address decoder generates chip-select signals and the BS#8 and BS16# signals.

Static RAM (SRAM) interface

Static RAMs (SRAMs) store information until power is cut off. A SRAM consists of two transistor states that are cross-coupled to operate in a bi-stable manner; that is, they stay in either of two stable states—on or off.

Two complementary data lines in each column convey information to or from the element in the selected row. The memory elements in each column are coupled to the data lines with n-channel, normally off MOS transistors. The gates of the coupling transistors for each row connect to a corresponding row-select line. The row-select lines are the output lines of an address decoder. Therefore, only those coupling transistors in the selected row (as determined by the specified address to the decoder) are turned on. In this way, information is channeled between data lines and the selected element in each column.

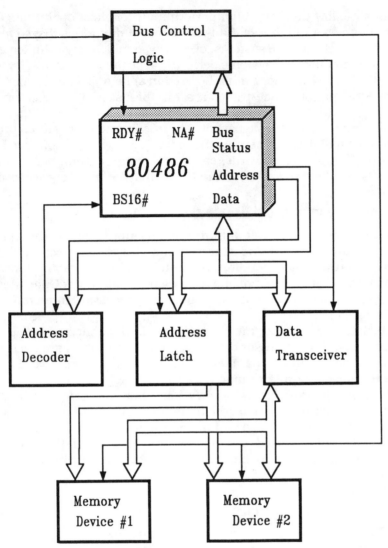

4-4 Block diagram of a basic memory interface.

Dynamic RAM (DRAM) interface

Dynamic RAM (DRAM) memory subsystems provide relatively fast access times at a low cost per bit. On the other hand, DRAMs require a brief idle time between accesses to recharge or refresh the data. Refreshing is done by performing a read and/or write operation. Each refresh operation restores the contents of several word locations in a memory unit. If this time is not allowed, data stored in the DRAM can be lost. If back-to-back accesses are needed to the same bank of DRAMs, the second access is delayed by this recharge time. To avoid this delay, arrange memory so that each subsequent access is most likely to be directed to a different DRAM bank.

For most DRAMs, periodic activation of each of the row address signals internally refreshes the data in every column of the row. Most DRAMs allow a RAS-only (Row Address Select) refresh cycle, the timing of which is the same as a read cycle, except that only the RAS signals are activated (no Column Address Select—CAS—signals) and all the data pins are in the high impedance state.

The frequency of refreshing and the number of rows to be refreshed depend on the type of DRAM. For the DRAMs 64K x N and larger, only the lower eight multiplexed address bits (A7-A0, 256 rows) must be supplied for the refresh cycle. The upper address bits are ignored. Larger DRAMs generally require refresh every 4 milliseconds. Once the system is initialized, the integrity of the DRAM data and states is maintained (even during an 80486 HALT or shutdown state or hardware reset) because all DRAM system functions are performed in hardware external to the CPU.

Some DRAMs require a number of warm-up cycles before they can operate. Generally, there are two ways to provide these cycles:

- Using external logic, activate the RFRQ signal for a preset amount of time. This causes the DRAM control hardware to run several refresh cycles.
- As part of the 80486 initialization process, perform several dummy DRAM cycles. One way to do these dummy cycles is to set up the 80486 registers and perform a REP LODS instruction.

80486 internal cache

This section gives a general introduction to caching and then describes the internal cache of the 80486.

Introduction to caching

A *cache memory* is a mechanism interposed in the memory hierarchy between main memory and the processor. Its purpose is to improve effective memory transfer rates and raise processing speeds. The term "cache" refers to the fact that the mechanism is transparent to program operation.

By maintaining a copy of the data in cache memory, the cache concept anticipates how the CPU is likely to use the data in main memory. The concept is extended to include data adjacent already used data. Often a block of several words is transferred from memory to the cache even though only one word is immediately needed. If the required word is part of a stream of sequential instructions, it is likely that subsequent instructions will be retrieved with the required first word, which makes repeated access to main memory unnecessary.

All data is stored in main memory. With a cache system, some of that data is duplicated in the cache. When the processor needs to read or write information in memory, it checks first in the cache. If the required data is there, the CPU can use it quickly, because cache is comprised of the fastest memory available. If the data is not in the cache when the processor needs it, the data is fetched from main memory and also written to cache.

Operation of the internal cache

The 80486 processor has an on-chip internal cache that can store 8K of instructions and data. This cache is implemented as an associative memory. An associative memory has extra storage for each unit of memory, called a *tag*.

When an address is applied to an associative memory, each tag compares itself to the address simultaneously. If a tag matches the address, access is provided to the unit of memory associated with the tag; this is called a *cache hit*. If no match occurs, the cache signals a *cache miss*. A cache miss requires a bus cycle to access main memory.

To make the internal cache more efficient, storage is allocated in blocks of 128 bits (i.e., four doublewords), called *cache lines*. The 80486's cache does not support partially-filled cache lines, so caching a single doubleword requires caching four doublewords. This would be inefficient if it were not for the fact that the processor rarely accesses random locations in memory. Instead, over a short period of time, the processor usually accesses a small number of areas in memory (such as the code segment or the stack), and it usually accesses many neighboring locations in these areas.

To simplify the hardware implementation, cache lines can only be mapped to aligned 128-bit blocks of main memory. (An aligned 128-bit block begins at an address that has zero in its four low bits.) When a new cache line is allocated, the processor loads a block from main memory into the cache line. This operation is called a *cache line fill*. Allocated cache lines are said to be valid; unallocated cache lines are invalid.

Caching can be write-through or write-back. On reads, both forms of caching operate as just described. On writes, write-through caching updates both cache memory and main memory; write-back caching updates only the cache memory. Write-back caching updates main memory when a write-back operation is performed. Write-back operations are triggered when cache lines need to be de-allocated, which can occur when new cache lines are being allocated in a cache that is already full.

The internal cache of the 80486 is of the write-through variety. However, it can be used with external caches that are write-through, write-back, or a combination of both types.

Operating Modes   Software controls the operating mode of the cache. Caching can be either

- Enabled, its state following reset.
- Disabled while valid cache lines exist (a mode in which the cache acts like a fast, internal RAM).
- Fully-disabled.

These modes are controlled by bits 30 and 29 of the CR0 register—CD (Cache Disable) and NW (Not Write-through)—as summarized in TABLE 4-1.

Table 4-1   Cache operating modes.

CD	NW	Description
1	1	Caching is disabled, but valid cache lines continue to respond. To disable the cache completely, enter this mode and perform a cache flush (with an INVD or WBINVD instruction). To use the cache as a fast internal RAM, preload the cache with valid cache lines by carefully choosing memory locations or by using the test registers. In this mode, writes to valid cache lines update the cache but do not update main memory.
1	0	No new cache lines are allocated, but valid cache lines continue to respond.
0	1	Invalid setting. Generates a general-protection exception with an error code of zero.
0	0	Caching is enabled.

Be careful when disabling the cache. Whenever CD is set to 1, the 80486 will not read external memory if a copy is still in the cache. When NW is set to 1, the 80486 will not write to external memory if the data is in the cache. This means that "stale" data can develop in the 80486 cache. This stale data will not be written to external memory if NW is later cleared to 0 or that cache line is later overwritten as the result of a cache miss. In general, the cache should be flushed when disabled.

It is possible to freeze data in the cache by loading it using test registers while CD and NW are set (for details, see Chapter 1). This is useful to provide guaranteed cache hits for time-critical interrupt code and data.

Note that all segments should start on 16-byte boundaries to allow programs to align code/data in cache lines.

Cache management instructions The instructions INVD (Invalidate Cache) and WBINVD (Write-Back and Invalidate Cache) are used to invalidate the contents of the internal and external caches. INVD flushes the internal cache and generates a special bus cycle to indicate that external caches should also be flushed. (How hardware responds to a cache-flush bus cycle is implementation dependent.)

WBINVD is similar to INVD, but before flushing the internal cache, it generates a special bus cycle to indicate that external, write-back caches should write-back modified data to main memory.

Page-level cache management

The 80486 has two bits in the CR3 register, the page directory, and the second-level page tables that can be used to manage the caching of pages. The PCD (Page-level Cache Disable) bit affects the operation of the internal cache. Both the PCD bit and the PWT (Page-level Write-through) bit drive processor output pins (also called PCD and PWT) for controlling external caches. How external hardware treats these signals is implementation-dependent. For example, a hardware system may control the caching of pages by decoding some of the high address bits.

As just mentioned, there are three potential sources of the bits used to drive the 80486's PCD and PWT outputs: the CR3 register, the page directory, and the second-level page tables. These outputs are driven by the following:

- The CR3 register for bus cycles where paging is not used to generate the address, such as loading an entry in the page directory.
- A page directory entry when an entry from a second-level page table is accessed.
- A second-level page table entry when instructions or data in memory are accessed.

PCD bit When a page table entry has a set PCD bit, caching of the page is disabled even if hardware is requesting caching by asserting the KEN# input. When the PCD bit is clear, hardware may request caching on a cycle-by-cycle basis.

Disabling caching is necessary for pages that contain memory-mapped I/O ports. It is also useful for pages in which caching would provide no performance benefit (for example, for pages that contain initialization software).

Regardless of the page-table entries, the 80486 will assert the PCD output whenever the CD (Cache Disable) bit in CR0 is set.

PWT bit When a page table entry has a set PWT bit, a write-through caching policy is specified for data in the corresponding page. Clearing the PWT bit makes it possible to use a write-back policy for the page. Because the 80486 internal cache is a write-through cache, it is unaffected by the state of the PWT bit. PWT is only useful for external, write-back caches.

In multiprocessor systems, enabling write-through may be useful for shared memory, especially for memory locations that are written infrequently by one processor but read often by many processors.

5
Interfacing: local bus and Input/Output

The 80486 features 32-bit wide internal and external data paths and eight general-purpose 32-bit registers. The processor outputs 32-bit physical addresses directly, for a physical memory of four gigabytes. This chapter explores more of the sub-systems that surrounds the 80486, by discussing local bus interface, Input/Output and I/O interfacing.

Local bus interface

A bus is a path over which data are transferred, from any of several sources to any of several destinations. It acts as a common connection among a number of locations such as between the CPU, memory, and peripheral devices. Bus lines act as the means of communications. Figure 5-1 shows a block diagram of a general bus interface.

The 80486 performs a variety of bus operations in response to internal and external conditions; for example, it services interrupt requests. The 80486 communicates with external memory, I/O, and other devices through a parallel bus interface. This interface consists of data and address buses, a clock, and signals for the following functions:

- Data parity
- Bus status, control, and arbitration
- Burst control
- Interrupts
- Cache control
- Floating-point error status
- Address mask

DATA BUS. There are 32 pins ($D_{31} - D_0$) on which 8, 16, or 32 bits of data can be transferred at once. Data transfers to 8- or 16-bit devices is

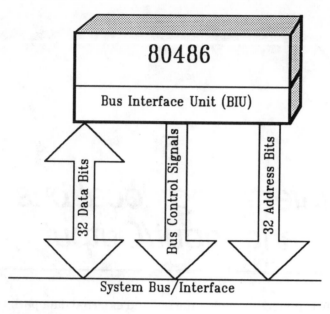

5-1 General bus interface.

possible using the data bus sizing feature controlled by the BS8# and BS16# input pins.

Note: The # symbol at the end of a signal name indicates that the active, or "asserted," state occurs when the signal is at a low voltage. Conversely, when a signal name has no # suffix, the signal is active at the high voltage level.

ADDRESS BUS. This bus generates 32-bit addresses on 30 address pins $(A_{31} - A_2)$ and has four byte-enable pins (BE3#–BE0#), one pin for each byte of the 32-bit data bus. The 30 address pins point to a block of four bytes. The bus-enable pins identify which bytes within the block are involved in the current transfer.

CLOCK. The CLK signal provides the fundamental timing and internal operating frequency of the 80486 microprocessor. CLK is a 1X clock, as opposed to a 2X clock in the 80386. Thus, a 25-Mhz 80486 uses a 25-MHz clock, whereas a 25-MHz 80386 requires a 50-MHz clock. A 1X clock allows simpler system design because it cuts in half the clock speed required in the external system.

DATA PARITY—There are two data parity signals:

- DP0-DP3 (Data Parity Input/Outputs)—There is a bi-directional data parity pin for each byte of the data bus.
- PCHK# (Parity Error)—The 80486 asserts this output pin to signal a parity error. The 80486 checks parity during code, memory, and I/O reads. It does not check parity during interrupt acknowledge cycles.

BUS STATUS. These output pins report on the current bus cycle, as follows:

- LOCK# (Bus Lock)—The current bus cycle is locked.
- PLOCK# (Pseudo-Lock)—The current bus transaction requires more than one bus cycle to complete. This occurs when the 80486 is reading or writing a memory operand larger than 32 bits, such as a 64-bit segment table descriptor.
- ADS# (Address Status)—The address bus lines and bus cycle definition signals (M/IO#, D/C#, and W/R#) are valid.
- M/IO# (Memory/I/O)—Memory or I/O cycle.
- D/C# (Data/Control)—Data or Control cycle.
- W/R# (Write/Read)—Write or Read cycle.

TABLE 5-1 lists the bus cycle definitions as a function of M/IO#, D/C#, and W/R#.

Table 5-1   Bus cycle definitions.

M/IO#	D/C#	W/R#	Bus Cycle Initiated
0	0	0	Interrupt Acknowledge
0	0	1	Halt/Special Cycle
0	1	0	I/O Read
0	1	1	I/O Write
1	0	0	Code Read
1	0	1	Reserved
1	1	0	Memory Read
1	1	1	Memory Write

BUS CONTROL. These input pins allow external logic to control the bus on a cycle-by-cycle basis:

- RDY# (Ready)—Indicates that the current bus cycle has been completed.
- BS8# (Bus Size 8) and BS16# (Bus Size 16)—Cause the processor to run multiple bus cycles to satisfy data transfers for 8- and 16-bit devices. Doubleword transfers are converted to the appropriate number of byte or word transfers.

BUS ARBITRATION. This is the mechanism by which the 80486 relinquishes control of its local bus when requested by another bus master:

- BREQ (Bus Request)—The 80486 asserts BREQ whenever a bus cycle is pending internally. External logic can use BREQ to arbitrate among several processors.

- HOLD (Bus Hold Request)—This signal can be generated by another bus master to ask the 80486 to release control of its local bus. The 80486 asserts HLDA (Bus Hold Acknowledge) as it gives up control of the bus.
- BOFF# (Backoff Input)—Similar to HOLD, but BOFF# *forces* the 80486 to release control of its bus in the next clock. The 80486 does not assert HLDA in response to BOFF#.

BURST CONTROL. The 80486's burst bus mechanism enables high-speed cache fills from external memory. Burst cycles can strobe data into the processor at a rate of one item per clock. (Non-burst cycles have a maximum rate of one item every two clocks.) Burst cycles are not limited to cache fills, however; all bus cycles requiring more than a single data cycle can be burst. The burst control signals are

- BRDY# (Burst Ready)—This signal performs the same function during a burst cycle that RDY# performs during a non-burst cycle.
- BLAST# (Burst Last Output)—This signal indicates that the next time BRDY# is returned, it will be treated as a normal RDY#, terminating the line fill or other multiple-data-cycle transfer.

INTERRUPTS. These signals can interrupt or suspend execution of the processor's current instruction stream:

- RESET—This input forces the 80486 to begin execution at a known state.
- INTR (Maskable Interrupt Request) and NMI (Nonmaskable Interrupt Request)—These inputs cause the processor to interrupt its current instruction stream and begin executing an interrupt service routine.

CACHE CONTROL. These input signals control the 80486's on-chip cache:

- AHOLD (Address Hold Request) and EADS# (External Address Valid)—These signals are used during cache invalidation cycles. AHOLD conditions the 80486 address lines, $A_4 - A_{31}$, to accept an address input. EADS# indicates that an external address is actually valid on the address inputs and makes the 80486 read that address and perform an internal cache invalidation cycle.
- KEN# (Cache Enable)—Used to determine whether the data being returned by the current cycle is cacheable. When KEN# is active and the 80486 generates a cycle that can be cached (almost any memory read cycle), the cycle will be transformed into a cache line fill cycle.
- FLUSH# (Cache Flush)—Forces the 80486 to flush its entire internal cache.

FLOATING-POINT ERROR STATUS. The 80486 provides two pins to report floating-point errors:

- FERR# (Floating-point Error)—The 80486 asserts FERR# whenever an unmasked floating-point error occurs. FERR# is similar to the ERROR# pin on the 80387 numeric coprocessor.
- IGNNE# (Ignore Numeric Error)—When external logic asserts IGNNE#, the 80486 will ignore non-control floating point instructions.

Figure 5-2 summarizes the 80486 signal pins. See Chapter 7 for a complete list of these pins.

Each bus cycle starts when the address is valid on the address bus, and the bus cycle definition pins (W/R#, D/C#, and M/IO#) reflect the type of bus cycle being performed. Memory read and write cycles can be locked to prevent another bus master from using the local bus and to also allow for indivisible read-modify-write operations. (See Chapter 12 and Appendix D for more information on MULTIBUS masters and slaves.)

Address pipelining allows bus cycles to be overlapped, which increases the amount of time for the memory or I/O device to respond. The first bus cycle after an idle bus state is always non-pipelined. To initiate address pipelining, this cycle must be extended by at least one CLK cycle so that the address and status can be output before the end of the cycle. Subsequent cycles can be pipelined as long as no idle bus cycles occur.

ADDRESS MASK—When the A20M# (Address Bit 20 Mask) input pin is asserted, the 80486 masks physical address bit 20 (A_{20}) before performing a cache lookup or driving a memory cycle on the bus. A20M# emulates the address wraparound at one megabyte that occurs on the 80286.

Bus states

The 80486 processor uses a single-frequency (1x) clock input. All operations across the bus (except for the two asynchronous inputs, NMI and IGNNE#) are times with respect to the rising edge of the CLK input.

There are two advantages to using a 1x clock as opposed to the 2x clock used in the 80386:

- The 1x clock simplifies system design by cutting in half the clock frequency required by external devices.
- The 1x clock keeps RF emissions to a minimum and simplifies clock generation.

The bus can pass through five states during its operations. A transition between states is made in every clock cycle, even when the transition is back to the preceding state. The bus states are as follows:

Signal Name	Signal Function	Active State	Input/ Output	Input Sync or Async to CLK
Address and Data Buses				
A_2-A_3	Address Bus	High	O	--
A_4-A_{31}	Address Bus	High	I/O	--
A20M#	Address Bit 20 Mask	Low	I	A
D_0-D_{31}	Data Bus	High	I/O	S
BE0#-BE3#	Byte Enable	Low	O	--
BS8#	Bus Size 8	Low	I	S
BS16#	Bus Size 16	Low	I	S
DP0-DP3	Data Parity	High	I/O	--
PCHK#	Parity Error	Low	O	--
Cycle Definition and Control				
ADS#	Address Status	Low	O	--
M/IO#	Memory I/O indicator	--	O	--
D/C#	Data/Control indicator	--	O	--
W/R#	Write/Read indicator	--	O	--
RDY#	Transfer Acknowledge	Low	I	S
BRDY#	Burst Ready	Low	I	S
BLAST#	Burst Last Output	Low	O	--
KEN#	Cache Enable	Low	I	S
Bus Control				
CLK	Clock	--	I	--
RESET	Reset	High	I	A
NMI	Nonmaskable Interrupt Request	High	I	A
INTR	Maskable Interrupt Request	High	I	A
BREQ	Bus Request	High	O	S
HOLD	Bus Hold Request	High	I	S
HLDA	Bus Hold Acknowledge	High	O	--
BOFF#	Backoff Input	Low	I	S
LOCK#	Bus Lock indicator	Low	O	--
PLOCK#	Pseudo-Lock indicator	Low	O	--
Cache Control				
EADS#	External Address Valid	Low	I	S
AHOLD	Address Hold Request	High	I	S
FLUSH#	Cache Flush	Low	I	A
Floating-Point Error Control				
FERR#	Floating-point Error	Low	O	--
IGNNE#	Ignore Numeric Error	Low	I	A

5-2 Summary of 80486 signal pins.

- **Ti**—The bus is idle. Address and status signals may be driven to undefined, or the bus may be floated to a high-impedance state. The bus stays in this state when no bus cycle is executing or when HOLD or BOFF# (Backoff) is asserted.
- **T1**—First clock cycle of a bus cycle. Address and status signals are valid and ADS# is asserted.

Signal Name	Signal Function	Active State	Input/ Output	Input Sync or Async to CLK
CLK	Clock	--	I	--
D_0-D_{31}	Data Bus	High	I/O	S
BE0#-BE3#	Byte Enable	Low	O	--
A_2-A_{31}	Address Bus	High	O	--
W/R#	Write/Read indicator	--	O	--
D/C#	Data/Control indicator	--	O	--
M/IO#	Memory I/O indicator	--	O	--
LOCK#	Bus Lock indicator	Low	O	--
PLOCK#	Pseudo-Lock indicator	Low	O	--
ADS#	Address Status	Low	O	--
RDY#	Transfer Acknowledge	Low	I	S
BS8#	Bus Size 8	Low	I	S
BS16#	Bus Size 16	Low	I	S
BREQ	Bus Request	High	O	S
HOLD	Bus Hold Request	High	I	S
HLDA	Bus Hold Acknowledge	High	O	--
BOFF#	Backoff Input	Low	I	S
BRDY#	Burst Ready	Low	I	S
BLAST#	Burst Last Output	Low	O	--
RESET	Reset	High	I	A
INTR	Maskable Interrupt Request	High	I	A
NMI	Nonmaskable Interrupt Request	High	I	A
AHOLD	Address Hold Request	High	I	S
EADS#	External Address Valid	Low	I	S
KEN#	Cache Enable	Low	I	S
FLUSH#	Cache Flush	Low	I	A
A20M#	Address Bit 20 Mask	Low	I	A
FERR#	Floating-point Error	Low	O	--
IGNNE#	Ignore Numeric Error	Low	I	A

5-2 Continued.

- **T2**—Second and subsequent clock cycles of a bus cycle. Data is driven for a write cycle; data is expected for a read cycle. RDY# and BRDY# are sampled.
- **T1b**—First clock cycle of a restarted bus cycle. Address and status signals are valid and ADS# is asserted. Externally, this state cannot be distinguished from T1.
- **Tb**—Second and subsequent clock cycles of an aborted bus cycle. The bus enters this "backoff" state if BOFF# is asserted within a T1 or T2 cycle. It remains in this state while HOLD, AHOLD, or BOFF# is asserted, and proceeds to state T1b when all three signals are de-asserted.

TABLE 5-2 shows the six conditions under which the processor can float its bus signals.

Like other Intel 8086-family processors, the 80486 supports an address space in memory that is separate from the address space for I/O

Table 5-2   Conditions for floating the processor bus.

When this occurs	The processor does this
HOLD is asserted during the Ti (idle) state.	Floats the bus and asserts HLDA in the next clock.
HOLD is asserted in the Tb (backed off) state.	Stays in Tb. The bus is not floated.
HOLD is asserted. RDY# is asserted and BOFF# is de-asserted in the T2 state.	Floats the bus and asserts HLDA in the next clock.
HOLD is asserted. BRDY# is asserted and BOFF# is de-asserted in the T2 state either for the last transfer of a burst or non-burst transfer.	Floats the bus and asserts HLDA in the next clock.
BOFF# is asserted.	Floats the bus in the next clock, without asserting HLDA.
AHOLD is asserted.	Floats A2-A31 in the next clock.

ports. The 80486 can address up to four gigabytes (2^{32} bytes, addresses 00000000H to FFFFFFFFH) of memory and up to 64K (2^{16}) bytes, addresses 00000000H to 0000FFFFH) of I/O. Both the memory and I/O address space has hardware support for protection and multitasking.

A programmer can access memory locations and I/O ports as 8-bit bytes, 16-bit words, 32-bit doublewords, and as a variety of other data structures. The hardware, however, views memory and I/O on the data bus as a sequence of doublewords (2^{32}) 32-bit memory locations and 2^{14} 32-bit I/O ports, maximum). Each 32-bit memory location starts at a physical address that is a multiple of four (0, 4, 8, 12, and so on).

From the processor's viewpoint, each doubleword location has four individually-addressable bytes at consecutive memory locations. On the data bus, the least-significant (low-order) byte of a doubleword is transferred on bits $D_0 - D_7$; the most-significant (high-order) byte is transferred on bits $D_{24} - D_{31}$. When the processor reads a doubleword, it accesses one byte from each section.

$A_2 - A_{31}$ are the most-significant bits of the physical address; these signals address doublewords of memory. The two least-significant bits of the physical address are used internally to drive the appropriate Byte Enable outputs, BOE# – BE3#.

Data transfers

Data transfers, also called *data cycles*, move instructions, operands, and other data across the processor bus. Each data item (byte, word, or doubleword), is identified by an address and the Byte Enable signals.

Bus cycles control data transfers through a series of signal changes on the bus. The beginning of data transfer bus cycles is marked by the assertion of the Address Status (ADS#) output. A single bus cycle may involve multiple data transfers; for example, "burst cycles" (described next) transfer several data items in a single cycle. The converse is also true for 8- or 16-bit bus sizes: a single 32-bit data transfer involves multiple bus cycles.

Non-burst and burst cycles   Data transfers can be made in the following ways:

- **Non-burst Cycles**
  Non-cacheable memory or I/O reads or writes
  Cacheable memory reads, including instruction prefetches.

- **Burst Cycles**
  Non-cacheable memory or I/O reads or (for small bus sizes) writes.
  Cacheable memory reads, including instruction prefetches.

Non-burst cycles that transfer a single data item are called *single-cycle transfers*. A continuous series of non-burst single-cycle transfers is called a *multiple-cycle sequence*. Cacheable cycles provide the processor with internal copies of recently-read instructions, operands, and other data. When the processor generates a read request, it first checks its cache for the data being addressed. Here is what happens:

- If data at the specified address was read into the cache previously and is still valid (a "cache hit"), no bus cycle is required.
- If the requested data is not in the cache or not valid (a "cache miss"), the processor reads it from memory. During memory reads that result from a cache miss, the processor transfers 16 bytes into the cache (a "cache line fill"), if caching is enabled. Only memory reads are convertible into cache line fills; write data is only put into the cache if data at the address of the write is currently cached.

Burst cycles are the fastest way to transfer more than one data item. They are the most important type of cycle for high-performance systems. Burst cycles transfer up to 16 bytes of contiguous data at a maximum rate of one data item per clock cycle. Burst cycles are designed primarily for 16-byte cache fills, but they can also be used for non-cacheable transfers that involve fewer bytes.

Interrupts

The 80486's execution can be altered by both hardware- and software-generated interrupts. A hardware interrupt occurs when an active input is placed on one of two 80486 interrupt request inputs (NMI—Nonmaskable Interrupts, and INTR—Maskable Interrupt). The software interrupt occurs when the 80486 encounters either an INT (Interrupt) instruction or finds a software condition (an exception) that needs servicing.

Interrupt Latency is the elapsed time before an interrupt request is serviced. Any of the following causes can affect interrupt latency:

- If the interrupt service routine saves registers that are not automatically saved by the 80486. These instructions also delay the beginning of interrupt servicing.
- Saving the Flags Register (EFLAGS) and CS:EIP (Code Segment, Instruction Pointer) register that contains the return address.
- If interrupts are masked, an INTR will be recognized only after interrupts are re-enabled.
- If the processor is currently executing an instruction, the instruction must be completed. An interrupt request is recognized only on an instruction boundary, with the single exception that Repeat String instructions are interruptible after each iteration.
- If the interrupt servicing needs a task switch, registers must be saved and others restored.

Interrupt acknowledge cycle As part of the acknowledge cycle, an unmasked interrupt causes the 80486 processor to suspend execution of the current program and perform some instructions from another program. This second program is called a *service routine* (or sometimes *handler*).

The 80486 performs two back-to-back interrupt acknowledgment cycles in response to an active INTR input. These interrupt acknowledgment cycles, special bus cycles, activate the 8259A programmable interrupt controller which, in turn, supplies the interrupt vector on D0–D7 of the data bus.

System logic must delay RDY# to extend the cycle to the minimum pulse width requirements of the 8259A. Additionally, the 80486 inserts four idle clocks between the two cycles, to match the recovery time of the interrupt controller.

Bus size

The 80486 performs data transfers for 8-, 16-, and 32-bit data buses. Two sets of signals work together to control the flow of cycles across these buses:

- Bus Size—The BS8# and BS16# inputs.
- Bus Enables—The BE0#–BE3# outputs.

The bus size inputs are useful for interfacing to I/O or ROM. The BS8# and BS16# inputs allow the external system to specify, on a cycle-by-cycle basis, whether the external device being addressed can supply 8 or 16 bits of data. BS8# and BS16#, together with the address of data being accessed, control the sequence in which the byte enable outputs (BE0#–BE3#) are driven. BE0#–BE3# tell the external device which of the bytes on the 32-bit data bus are valid in any cycle or transfer. The only exception to this is during the first transfer of a cacheable read cycle (cache line fill), when BE0#–BE3# should be ignored and the external system should supply valid data as if BE0#–BE3# were all asserted.

Without BS8# or BS16# asserted, the data bus size is 32 bits. BS8# and BS16# can be used in burst or non-burst cycles. If both BS8# and BS16# are asserted, only BS8# is recognized. Asserting BS8# or BS16# can cause the processor to run additional bus cycles to complete a transfer.

This interface to smaller bus sizes is very different from the interface used in the 80386 processor. Unlike the 80386, the 80486 expects to find data on all four addressed bytes of the data bus. External logic must interface to all four bytes, using the BE0#–BE3# outputs and detection of the first transfer of a cache line fill to steer the external byte swapper.

The processor might not use all of the enabled bytes when the BS8# or BS16# input is asserted. TABLE 5-3 shows which bits positions the processor uses for all of the valid combinations of the byte enable signals and for all bus sizes. The implied rule is that when multiple bytes are enabled, return only the lowest byte(s) that the device on the data bus can provide.

Table 5-3   Data bus signals and bus size.

BE3#	BE2#	BE1#	BE0#	No selects (32-Bit Bus)	BS16# (16-Bit Bus)	BS8# (8-Bit Bus)
1	1	1	0	D0–D7	D0–D7	D0–D7
1	1	0	0	D0–D15	D0–D15	D0–D7
1	0	0	0	D0–D23	D0–D15	D0–D7
0	0	0	0	D0–D31	D0–D15	D0–D7
1	1	0	1	D8–D15	D8–D15	D8–D15
1	0	0	1	D8–D23	D8–D15	D8–D15
0	0	0	1	D8–D31	D8–D15	D8–D15
1	0	1	1	D16–D23	D16–D23	D16–D23
0	0	1	1	D16–D23	D16–D31	D16–D23
0	1	1	1	D24–D31	D24–D31	D24–D31

Special bus cycles

The 80486 initiates special bus cycles in the same way as data transfers, except that the cycle-definition signals have the values shown in TABLE 5-4.

Table 5-4   Special bus cycles.

Operation	MI/O#	D/C#	W/R#	BE3#	BE2#	BE1#	BE0#
Halt	0	0	1	1	0	1	1
Shutdown	0	0	1	1	1	1	0
Cache Flush	0	0	1	1	1	0	1
Cache Write-Back and Flush	0	0	1	0	1	1	1

Shutdown cycle The shutdown condition occurs when the 80486 is processing a double fault and encounters a protection fault. The 80486 cannot recover from this, and shuts down. That is, it stops performing bus operations. The processor will remain shut down until either the NMI or RESET input is asserted.

Shutdown indicates an error in operating system data structures, such as task state segment (TSS) descriptors (if tasks are used for exception handling), segment descriptors, or page table entries. It may be advantageous to invoke an NMI interrupt handler to record diagnostic information.

Halt cycle The 80486 halts in response to a HLT instruction. This instruction can be used to respond to an unrecoverable error, such as a parity error, or to a program error. Halt can also be used to indicate that the processor has failed the built-in self test that is invoked on reset.

Externally, a halt differs from a shutdown only in the resulting address bus outputs and in the processor's ability to acknowledge a bus hold while in the halt condition. The processor will remain in the halt condition until INTR, NMI, or RESET is asserted.

Bus lock and pseudo-lock

When it is critical that two cycles follow each other immediately, with no disruption between them, the 80486 can "lock" the bus. The 80486 has two locking features, called bus lock and bus pseudo-lock.

Bus lock Locked cycles are used when it is critical that two or more bus cycles follow one another immediately, back-to-back, in a system where several devices (bus masters) can control the local bus. Without the lock, cycles can be separated by a cycle from another bus master.

When the LOCK# output is asserted, the processor will not acknowledge a bus hold (HOLD) request. The LOCK# signal is asserted automatically during interrupt acknowledge cycles. The processor also asserts LOCK# when you do any of the following:

- Execute a TEST or SET instruction (semaphore updates).
- Execute an XCHG instruction with a memory operand.
- Apply the LOCK prefix on certain instructions, such as XADD and CMPXCHG.
- Update the Accessed bit in segment descriptors.
- Update the Accessed and Dirty bits in page table entries.
- Set the Busy bit in a task state segment (TSS) descriptor.
- Set the Access bit in a segment descriptor.

Locked read cycles are not cacheable. In systems that have an external cache between the processor bus and a system bus, locked cycles should always trigger a system bus cycle. This ensures consistent synchronization between multiple agents on the system bus. During locked cycles, the processor ignores a HOLD request, but it recognizes BOFF# (Bus Backoff) and AHOLD (Address Hold) requests.

The duration of LOCK# depends on the instruction being executed and the number of wait states per cycle. In real mode, the longest period is two bus cycles plus about two clocks. This occurs during the XCHG instruction and during locked read-modify-write operations. In protected mode, the longest period of LOCK# is five bus cycles plus about 15 clocks. This occurs when a hardware or software interrupt happens and the 80486 performs a locked read of the gate in the interrupt descriptor table (8 bytes), a read of the target descriptor (8 bytes), and a write of the Accessed bit in the target descriptor.

Bus pseudo-lock   The PLOCK# output offers a protection that is new with the 80486. This signal performs the same function as LOCK#—locking out bus hold request signals—but PLOCK# is asserted under circumstances that differ from those of LOCK#.

Pseudo-locking protects transfers of data transfers that are longer than 32 bits. PLOCK# is asserted only for cycles in a single direction; that is, for read cycles or write cycles, but not for read-modify-write cycles. During pseudo-locked cycles, the processor does not recognize a HOLD request, although it will recognize a BOFF# or AHOLD request.

The PLOCK# output is generated by

- Any data transfer longer than 32 bits in which the data is aligned to boundaries equal to the data structure size (that is, any multi-cycle sequence with aligned data).

    Specifically, 32-bit data must be aligned to 4-byte boundaries, 64-bit data to 8-byte boundaries, and 128-bit cache line fills to 16-byte boundaries.
- Whenever BLAST# is asserted. (This case overlaps with the preceding case.)
- During the first cycle of 64-bit floating-point writes.

Pseudo-locked cycles include 128-bit cache line fills, 64-bit floating-point operand reads or writes, and doubleword transfers on an 8- or 16-bit bus. In 80-bit floating-point operands, only the first 64 bits are pseudo-locked.

In systems that have an external cache between the processor bus and a system bus, pseudo-locked cycles (unlike locked cycles) would not usually trigger a system bus cycle between external cache hits. The pseudo-locked cycle should be confined to the processor bus, and the external cache controller should not let system bus activity interfere with pseudo-locked cycles on the processor bus.

Sometimes both PLOCK# and LOCK# may be asserted simultaneously. For example, the 80486 asserts both signals during 64-bit segment descriptor loads. Because these operands are longer than 64 bits, they are protected by PLOCK#. However, they are also specifically protected by LOCK#.

Bus hold

Bus masters other than the processor take control of the bus by asserting the HOLD input. When HOLD is asserted, the processor completes the current bus operation or sequence of locked or pseudo-locked cycles, floats most of its outputs to high impedance, and asserts the HLDA acknowledgement. Specifically, the processor completes the following operations before acknowledging the bus hold:

- The bus cycle in progress (burst or non-burst) or the current sequence of bus cycles for which BLAST# is de-asserted for all but the last data transfer.
- Pseudo-locked cycles; that is, multi-cycle sequences during which PLOCK# is asserted.
- Locked cycles.

The processor stays in the hold state until HOLD is de-asserted. During bus hold, the processor continues to execute from its Instruction Prefetch Unit and internal cache. When it needs to access the bus again, it issues a bus request by asserting BREQ.

On the 80486, bus hold uses the same hold-acknowledge protocol as earlier Intel processors. The HLDA, BREQ, PCHK#, and FERR# outputs are not floated and can be asserted during bus hold. The processor will respond to HOLD during reset; none of the outputs that are floated in response to HOLD have internal pullup resistors. The processor also recognizes the AHOLD, EADS# and BOFF# inputs during bus hold. AHOLD (Address Hold) is not associated with the bus hold operation but is used for cache invalidation.

Multiple processors can be in the bus hold state. An external arbitration unit can then use their BREQ signals to see which processors are ready to perform bus cycles.

Bus backoff (BOFF#)

To complete, some bus cycles initiated by the processor may require an external bus master to complete its own cycles. For example, to access data in another bus master's cache may require the processor to write-back the cached data to memory. Bus backoff is used to avoid this deadlock, where neither the processor or the other bus master can complete its operation because each is waiting for something from the other.

The BOFF# input indicates that another bus master needs to complete a bus cycle before the processor's current cycle can finish. The processor's response to bus backoff is similar to the bus hold operation, but more immediate: the processor releases the bus in the next clock without giving an acknowledge. When BOFF# is de-asserted, the processor restarts (reliably) the bus cycle that was aborted.

The restarted cycle begins with a new assertion of ADS#, but the transfer continues from the state at the clock in which BOFF# was asserted. Any transfer that completed before BOFF# was asserted is assumed correct and is not repeated.

Cache control

When caching is enabled for systems that contain multiple bus masters, cache control involves maintaining consistency between the processor's internal cache, main memory, and external (second-level) caches when any of them are updated. The 80468 has cache control signals to perform three functions:

- Page-level cache control.
- Internal cache line validation.
- Internal cache flush.

The 80486 also has special bus cycles to implement cache flush and cache flush/write-back.

Page-level cache controls

Caching and memory updating are page-based. That is, each 4K page of contiguous memory can have its cacheability and write-through or write-back policy controlled on a cycle-by-cycle basis. This involves two software-controlled outputs:

- The PCD (Page Cache Disable) output controls cacheability for the current page. When the corresponding bit is cleared in software, PCD is de-asserted and caching is enabled for the internal cache. PCD can be used to enable external caching. When it is asserted, internal caching is disabled even if the KEN# (Cache Enable) input is asserted; the PCD control bit is internally ANDed with KEN#.

- The PWT (Page Write-Through) output is only useful for external cache. (Internal cache is always write-through.) When asserted, PWT applies a write-through caching policy for the current page; updates to cache will be written through to memory.

Internal cache line invalidation

Unlike previous Intel 8086-family processors, the address bus of the 80486 is bidirectional. An address can be driven into the 80486 processor to invalidate any cache line at that address. The system should provide address bus latches; this will prevent loss of the address information when the address bus is turned around to provide a cache line invalidation address.

Cache invalidations can be performed at any time. Because the address is not used during a burst transfer, cache invalidations can be done simultaneous with burst transfers. During non-burst single-transfer cycles with wait states, invalidation can also be performed during wait states if the address of the invalidation is latched externally.

The cache line invalidation sequence is as follows:

1. Cache line invalidation starts when external logic asserts AHOLD (Address Hold).

2. In the next clock, the processor floats $A_2 - A_{31}$, allowing the external bus master to drive the address of a 16-byte cache line into the processor. (No address hold acknowledgement is given.)

    The A_2, A_3, and BE0#–BE3# signals should not be driven because the smallest unit of storage in the cache is four double-words.

3. External logic then asserts EADS# (Internal Cache Line Invalidation) to request the cache line invalidation.

    Multiple addresses can be invalidated by asserting EADS# multiple times while asserting AHOLD. The processor sample EADS# every clock cycle and can accept a cache line invalidation at every clock, except in the last clock of a cache line fill.

4. Normal operation of the bus resumes when the external logic de-asserts AHOLD.

Internal cache flush

When the address of modified data is not available, a partial invalidation cannot be performed; a cache flush is the only alternative. Changes to address mapping information also require a cache flush. Asserting the FLUSH# input for one clock invalidates (clears) the entire internal cache. It can begin storing new data in the next clock.

The cache can also be disabled; set the PCD and PWT bits in CR3 and then flush the cache.

Cache flush cycle

This special bus cycle is invoked by executing the INVD (Invalidate Data Cache) instruction. This causes BE1# to be asserted and BE0#, BE2#, and BE3# to be de-asserted, forcing the internal cache to invalidate its entire contents.

External logic should decode this cycle and cause external cache to invalidate its contents, too. (The external cache should not write its contents back to memory before the flush.) Moreover, if a system has multiple processors on the bus, hardware should propagate the external cache flush indications to all processors.

Cache write-back and flush cycle

This special bus cycle is like the cache flush cycle, except it adds a write-back function for external caches. The cycle is invoked by executing the WBINVD (Write-Back and Invalidate Cache) instruction. This causes BE3# to be asserted and BE0#–BE2# to be de-asserted, forcing the internal cache to invalidate its entire contents. External logic should decode this cycle and cause external cache to write its entire contents back to memory, then invalidate its contents.

Unlike the 80486's internal write-through cache, a write-back cache does not immediately update memory with data received during a write cycle. Instead, each block of the cache has a bit set in the Tag field if the cache contains data that is more recent than the corresponding memory area. The data contained in this block is written out to memory only if it is about to be overwritten. This reduces bus activity.

Floating-Point Error control

Two signals are used to maintain compatibility with DOS floating-point error reporting procedures:

- The FERR# (Floating-Point Error) output indicates that an unmasked floating-point error has occurred.
- The IGNNE# (Ignore Floating-Point Errors) tells the processor to ignore floating-point errors and continue execution.

For each floating-point instruction except the no-wait control instructions, the 80486 checks whether the preceding floating-point instruction generated an unmasked numeric exception (overflow, underflow, zero-divide, and so on). If so, the processor reports the error by asserting FERR#. In this respect, FERR# is analogous to the ERROR# output of the 80287 and 80387 math coprocessors.

If IGNNE# is de-asserted when a floating-point error is detected, one of two things happens:

- If the NE bit in the Machine Status Register (CR0) is clear, the processor stops and waits for an external interrupt. (Because NE is cleared at reset, this is the default.)
- IF the NE bit in CR0 is set, the processor raises interrupt 16 and jumps to the floating-point interrupt location.

When IGNNE# is asserted and NE is clear, the processor executes floating-point instructions regardless of pre-existing error conditions. The IGNNE# input can be asynchronous to the processor's clock.

Input/Output and I/O interfacing

The 80486 processor supports 8-, 16-, and 32-bit Input/Output (I/O) devices where I/O can be mapped either (1) onto the 4 gigabyte physical memory address space using general-purpose operand manipulation instructions or (2) onto the 64K I/O address space using specific I/O instructions. I/O mapping and memory mapping differ in three major ways.

- Memory mapping offers more flexibility in protection than I/O mapping does because memory-mapped devices are protected by protection and memory management features. Depending on where the device is mapped in memory space, a device can be inaccessible to a task, can be visible but protected, or can be fully accessible. Paging gives the same protection levels to each 4K page and shows whether that page has been written to or not.

- The address decoding necessary to generate chip selects for I/O mapped devices is generally simpler than for memory-mapped devices. In addition, I/O-mapped devices reside in the 64K I/O space of the 80486, while memory-mapped devices reside in much larger memory space that makes use of more address lines, the 4 gigabytes.

- Memory-mapped devices can be accessed using any 80486 instruction. This allows efficient coding of I/O-to-memory, memory-to-I/O, and I/O-to-I/O transfers. I/O-mapped devices can be accessed through four instructions: IN, INS, OUT, OUTS. All I/O transfers are done via the AL (8-bit), AX (16 bit), or EAX (32 bit) registers. The first 256 bytes of I/O space are directly addressable, and the entire 64K I/O space is indirectly addressable through the DX register.

Interfaces to peripheral devices depend not only upon data width, but also on the signal requirements of the device and its location within the memory or I/O space. Address decoding to generate the correct chip selects must be done whether I/O devices are memory-mapped or I/O-mapped. Addresses can be assigned to I/O devices arbitrarily within the I/O or memory space. These addresses should be selected to minimize the number of address lines needed.

The 80486 has a separate I/O address space that is distinct from physical memory and that can be used to address the input/output ports used for external 16-bit devices. This I/O address space is made up of 2^{16} (65K) individually addressable 8-bit ports. Any even-numbered consecutive 8-bit port can be treated as a 16-bit port, and any doubleword-addressed consecutive 8-bit port can be treated as a 32-bit port. Thus, the total I/O address space accommodates up to 64K of 8-bit ports (numbered 0 through 65535), up to 32K 16-bit ports (numbered 0, 2, 4, up to 65534), or up to 16K 32-bit ports (numbered 0, 4, 8, up to 65532).

Memory-mapped I/O allows programming flexibility. Any instruction that references memory can be used to access an I/O port located in the memory space. Memory-mapped I/O is performed using the full instruction set and maintains the full complement of addressing modes for selecting the desired I/O device. However, memory-mapped I/O, like any of the other memory references, is still subject to access protection and control when executing in protected mode.

I/O instructions

The 80486 I/O instructions give access to the processor's I/O ports for transfer of data to and from peripheral devices. These instructions have as one operand the address of a port in the I/O space. There are two classes of I/O instructions: those that transfer strings of items located in memory (known either as "string I/O instructions" or "block I/O instructions") and those that transfer a single byte, word, or doubleword located in a register.

The block I/O instructions INS and OUTS move blocks of data between I/O ports and memory space. These instructions use the DX register to specify the address of a port in the I/O address space. The 8-bit ports are numbered 0 through 65535. The 16-bit ports are numbered 0, 2, 4, and up to 65534. The 32-bit ports are numbered 0, 4, 8, and up to 65532.

The IN and OUT instructions move data between I/O ports and the AL (for 8-bit I/O), AX (for 16-bit I/O) and EAX (for 32-bit I/O). IN and OUT address I/O ports either directly (with the addresses of one of up to 256 port addresses coded in the instruction) or indirectly (using the DX register to one of up to 64K port addresses).

Protection, privilege, and I/O

The I/O privilege level offers protection by allowing a task to access all I/O devices or by preventing a task from accessing any I/O device. In virtual-8086 mode, the I/O permission bit map can be used to select the privilege level for any combination of I/O bytes.

I/O protection is provided in two ways: the I/O permission bit map of an 80486 TSS segment defines the right to use ports in the I/O address space, and the IOPL (I/O Privilege Level) in the EFLAGS register defines the right to use I/O related instructions. These mechanisms work only in protected mode, which includes the virtual 8086 (V86) mode. They do *not* work in real mode. In real mode, any procedure executes I/O instructions and any I/O port can be addressed by any of those instructions.

I/O permission bit map Instructions that directly use addresses in the 80486's I/O space are IN, INS, OUT, and OUTS. The 80486 can selectively trap references to specific I/O addresses. The mechanism that allows this trapping is the I/O Permission Bit Map in the TSS segment. Figure 5-3 shows where the I/O Map appears in the TSS.

The Map is a bit vector and its size and location in the TSS segment are variable. The 80486 locates the Map by means of the 16-bit *I/O Map*

I/O Permission Bitmap Base	0 0 0 0 0 0 0 0 0 0 0 0 0 0 0 0 T	64
0 0 0 0 0 0 0 0 0 0 0 0 0 0 0 0	Local Descriptor Table (LDT)	60
0 0 0 0 0 0 0 0 0 0 0 0 0 0 0 0	GS	5C
0 0 0 0 0 0 0 0 0 0 0 0 0 0 0 0	FS	58
0 0 0 0 0 0 0 0 0 0 0 0 0 0 0 0	DS	54
0 0 0 0 0 0 0 0 0 0 0 0 0 0 0 0	SS	50
0 0 0 0 0 0 0 0 0 0 0 0 0 0 0 0	CS	4C
0 0 0 0 0 0 0 0 0 0 0 0 0 0 0 0	ES	48
EDI		44
ESI		40
EBP		3C
ESP		38
EBX		34
EDX		30
ECX		2C
EAX		28
EFLAGS		24
EIP		20
Reserved		1C
0 0 0 0 0 0 0 0 0 0 0 0 0 0 0 0	SS2	18
ESP2		14
0 0 0 0 0 0 0 0 0 0 0 0 0 0 0 0	SS1	10
ESP1		0C
0 0 0 0 0 0 0 0 0 0 0 0 0 0 0 0	SS0	08
ESP0		04
0 0 0 0 0 0 0 0 0 0 0 0 0 0 0 0	Back link to Previous TSS	00

Note: Zeros indicate Intel reserved bits. Do not define.

5-3 TSS with I/O map.

Base field in the fixed portion of the TSS that contains the offset of the beginning of the Map. The upper limit of the I/O Permission Map is the same as the limit of the TSS segment. Because the I/O Permission Map is in the TSS, different tasks can have different Maps. Thus, the operating system can allocate ports to a task by changing the I/O Permission Map in the task's TSS.

Each bit in the Map corresponds to an I/O port byte address. That is, the bit for port 41 is found at I/O Map Base + 5, bit offset 1. The 80486 tests all bits that correspond to the I/O addresses spanned by an I/O operation. In other words, a doubleword operation will test four bits that correspond to four adjacent byte addresses. If any tested bit is set, the 80486 signals a general protection exception. If all tested bits are zero, the I/O operation proceeds.

When the 80486 encounters an I/O instruction in protected mode, it first checks whether CPL (Current Privilege Level) is less than or equal to IOPL. If true, the I/O operation proceeds. If not true, the 80486 checks the I/O Permission Map. (Note that in virtual 8086 mode, the 80486 checks the Map without regard for IOPL.) If the I/O Map Base is greater than or equal to TSS limit, the TSS segment has no I/O Permission Map and *all* I/O instructions cause exceptions when CPL is greater than IOPL.

Instructions that deal with I/O not only need to be restricted; they need to be executed by procedures that execute at privilege levels other than zero. To allow this, the 80486 uses two bits of the flags register to store the IOPL. The IOPL defines the privilege level needed to execute I/O related instructions. The following six instructions can be executed only if CPL is less than or equal to IOPL. The instructions are called "sensitive" because they are sensitive to the value stored in IOPL.

IN	Input
INS	Input string
OUT	Output
OUTS	Output string
CLI	Clear interrupt-enable flag
STI	Set interrupt-enable flag

To use sensitive instructions, a procedure executes at a privilege level at least as privileged as that stored in the IOPL. Any attempt by a less privileged procedure to use one of the six instructions produces a general protection exception.

Each task in the system has its own unique copy of the flags register. Therefore each task can have a different IOPL. A task can change the IOPL *only* with a POPF instruction. Such changes are privileged. No procedure may alter IOPL in the flag register unless the procedure is executing at privilege level zero. Any less privileged instruction or procedure attempting to alter IOPL does not result in an exception; IOPL remains unchanged.

Basic I/O interface

In a typical 80486 system design, a number of slave I/O devices are controlled through the same local bus interface. Other I/O devices, especially those who can control the local bus, require more complex interfaces.

The performance and flexibility of the 80486 local bus interface plus the increased availability of programmable and semi-custom logic make it feasible to design custom bus control logic that meets the requirements of any particular system. The basic I/O interface is shown in the FIG. 5-4.

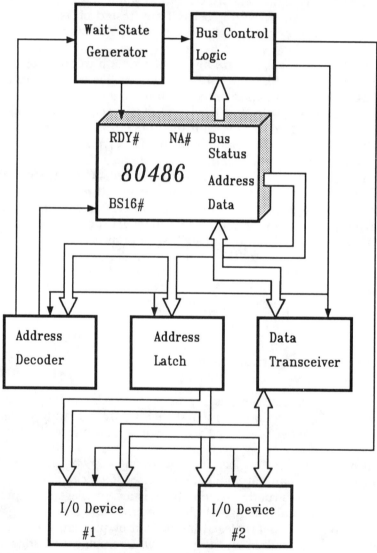

5-4 Basic I/O interface block diagram.

8-, 16-, and 32-bit I/O   Dynamic data bus sizing allows the 80486 processor to be connected directly to 8-, 16-, or 32-bit buses. Data transfers to and from 8-, 16-, or 32-bit devices are performed by determining the bus width during each bus cycle. For each bus cycle, the decoding circuitry may assert BS8# for 8-bit devices or BS16# for 16-bit devices. When BS8# is asserted, a 32-bit transfer is converted into four 8-bit transfers. Similarly, when BS16# is asserted, a 32-bit transfer is converted into two 16-bit transfers.

To address 32-bit devices, both signals are negated. If both signals are asserted, the 80486 assumes that the bus is 8 bits wide.

The 80486 drives the appropriate byte enables (BE0#–BE3#) during the independent cycles initiated by BS8# and BS16#. Addresses A_2–A_{31} do not change if accesses are to a 32-bit aligned area.

The dynamic bus sizing feature of the 80486 is significantly different from that of the 80386. The 80486 requires the data bytes to be driven on the addressed lines only; the 80386 expects both high- and low-order bytes on D_0–D_{15}. In a 32-bit BS16# read, for example, the 80486 expects the two higher-order bytes on data lines D_{16}–D_{31}, and it expects the two low-order bytes on D_0–D_{15}.

The external system design must provide buffers to allow the 80486 to read or write data on the appropriate data bus pins. TABLE 5-3 (shown earlier in this chapter) lists the bus lines where the 80486 expects valid data to be returned for each valid combination of byte enable and bus sizing options. Valid data is driven only on data bus pins that correspond to byte enable signals that are active during write cycles. Other data pins will also be driven, but they will not contain valid data. Unlike the 80386, the 80486 does not duplicate write data on the data bus when corresponding byte enables are negated.

Dynamic bus sizing allows external 8- and 16-bit buses to be supported using fewer components. It also allows the power-up and boot-up program to be stored in 8-bit EPROM, while high-speed program execution uses 32-bit memory.

Bus control logic   The bus control logic for the basic I/O interface is the same as for the memory interface. The bus controller decodes the 80486 status outputs (W/R#, M/IO#, and D/C#) and activates command signals for the type of bus cycle requested. The bus controller also controls the RDY# input to the 80486 that ends each bus cycle. In addition, RDY# indicates that the I/O device has returned valid data to the 80486's data pins following an I/O write cycle.

Wait-state generator logic   When the memory subsystem or the I/O device cannot respond to the microprocessor in the optimum time, wait states are added to the bus cycles. During wait states, the microprocessor freezes the state of the bus. On the 80486, wait states are activated by the RDY# (when asserted) signal. Additional wait states are generated as long as RDY# stays de-asserted, and the microprocessor resumes its operations when RDY# is asserted.

Address decoding for I/O devices Decoding addresses for I/O devices is similar to decoding them for memory devices. The primary difference is that the block size (range of addresses) for each address signal is much smaller. The minimum block size depends on how many addresses the I/O device uses. In most processors, where I/O instructions are separate, I/O addresses are shorter than memory addresses. Typically, a microprocessor with a 16-bit address bus uses 8-bit addresses for I/O.

One way to decode memory-mapped I/O address is to map the entire address space of the 80486 into a 64K region of the memory space. The address decoding logic can be configured so that each I/O device responds to a memory address and an I/O address. This configuration is compatible with software that uses either I/O instructions memory-mapped or I/O techniques.

Addresses can be assigned arbitrarily within the I/O or memory space. Addresses for either I/O-mapped or memory-mapped devices should be selected to minimize the number of address lines needed.

Figure 5-5 shows the 80486 microprocessor address interface to 8-, 16-, and 32-bit devices. To access 32-bit memory-mapped devices, $A_2 - A_{31}$ can

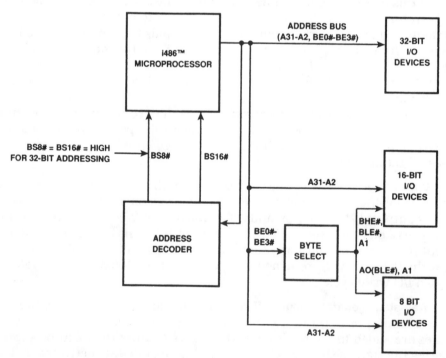

5-5 Address Interface to 32/16/8-bit I/O devices. Reprinted by permission of Intel Corporation, © Intel Corporation 1990.

be used in conjunction with BE0#–BE3#. To address 16-bit devices, the byte enables must be decoded to produce the A_1, BHE#, and BLE# (A_0) signals. To address 8-bit devices, the byte enable signals must be decoded to generate A_0 and A_1. Because A_0 and BLE# are the same, the same generation logic can be used.

Address decoder   The address decoder decodes the most significant address bits and generates address-select signals for each system device. The address space is divided into blocks, and the address-select signals indicate whether the address on the address bus is within the predetermined range. The block size usually represents the amount of address space that can be accessed within a particular device, and the address-select signal is asserted for any address within that range.

Data transceivers   Standard data transceivers (as shown in FIG. 5-4) provide isolation and additional drive capability for the 80486 data bus. Transceivers prevent the contention on the data bus that occurs if some devices are slow to remove read data from the bus after a read cycle. If a write cycle follows a read cycle, the 80486 might drive the data bus before a slow device has totally removed its outputs, possibly causing bus contention problems.

A bus interface should have enough transceivers to accommodate the device with the most inputs and outputs on the data bus. Only eight transceivers are needed if the widest device has 16 data bits and if the I/O device addresses are connected only to the lower byte of the data bus. The 74×245 transceiver is controlled through two input signals:

- **DT/R# (Data Transmit/Receive)**—A write cycle is enabled when this signal is high; a read cycle is enabled when it is low. This is simply a latched version of the 80486's W/R# output.
- **DEN# (Data Enable)**—When low, this input enables the transceiver output. It is generated by the byte-swapping logic and by the BE0# –BE3# signals.

6

Privilege and protection, pipelining, multitasking, and multiprocessing

This chapter discusses how the 80486 works with pipelining, multitasking with its associated Task State Segments (TSSs) and descriptors, and multiprocessing. First, here are some additional terms that appear in the discussion.

PRIVILEGE—A privilege is a property (generally established during system design) that determines which computer operations are allowed at any point in time and which accesses to memory are legal. Privilege is used to provide security in a computer system.

PL—PRIVILEGE LEVEL. One of four 80486 hierarchical privilege levels. Level 0 is the *most* privileged level and level 3 is the *least.*

RPL—REQUESTER PRIVILEGE LEVEL. A requester is a program or device that desires to use system resources. RPL is the privilege level requested by the original supplier of the selector. RPL is determined by the *least two* significant bits of a selector.

CPL—CURRENT PRIVILEGE LEVEL. The privilege level at which a task is currently executing. CPL normally equals the privilege level of the code segment being executed. (It can be different if the code segment is a conforming segment.) CPL also can be determined by examining the lowest 2 bits of the CS (Code Segment) register, except for conforming code segments.

DPL—DESCRIPTOR PRIVILEGE LEVEL. The DPL is the least privileged level at which a task may access that descriptor and the segment associated with that descriptor. DPL is determined by bits 6:5 in the Access Right Byte of a descriptor.

EPL—EFFECTIVE PRIVILEGE LEVEL. The EPL is the least privileged of the RPL and DPL. Note that smaller privilege level values indicate greater privilege. The EPL is the numerical maximum of RPL and DPL.

Privilege and protection

Privilege and protection are a means of controlling access to operating system code and to data. The security of the system is maintained, as is the integrity of the information. Privilege and protection became a necessity of programming life when the concept of multiple users or multiple uses became a reality.

Privilege

The concept of privilege is central to several facets of protection. Applied to procedures, privilege is the degree to which the procedure can be *trusted* not to make a mistake that might affect other procedures or data. Applied to data, privilege is the *degree of protection* that a data structure should have from less trusted procedures.

Privilege levels and rules

The 80486 uses four levels of protection to optimize support of multitasking. Privilege is implemented by assigning a value from zero to three to key objects which are recognized by the processor. This value is called the *privilege level.* The value zero is the greatest privilege, while the value three is the least privileged. The key items that the processor recognizes are as follows:

DESCRIPTOR PRIVILEGE LEVEL—DPL. Descriptors contain a field called the DPL. This is the least privilege that a task must have to access the descriptor.

REQUESTER'S PRIVILEGE LEVEL—RPL. The RPL represents the privilege level requested by the procedure that originates a selector.

CURRENT PRIVILEGE LEVEL—CPL. Generally, the CPL is equal to the segment DPL of the code segment that the processor is currently executing. CPL changes when control transfers to segments with differing DPLs.

Figure 6-1 shows how the four privilege levels are interpreted as rings of protection. The center, level 0, is for segments containing the most critical software, usually the kernel of the operating system. The outer rings are for segments of less critical software and data. It is not necessary to use all four privilege levels. Existing software that was designed with fewer levels can simply ignore the other levels offered. It is advised that a one-level system use privilege level zero. A two- level system should use privilege levels zero and three. If you have second thoughts, you can move from kernel up and application down, expanding your design to use three or four levels.

The 80486 automatically verifies a procedure's right to access another segment by comparing the procedure's CPL to one or more other privilege levels. This verification occurs at the time a descriptor selector is loaded into a segment register.

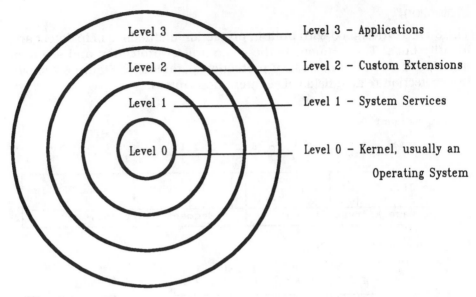

6-1 Privilege levels.

Privileged instructions

Privileged instructions that affect system data structures can only be executed when the CPL is zero. If the processor finds one of these instructions when CPL is greater than zero, it signals a general protection exception. These instructions, described more fully in Chapter 10, are

CLTS	Clear Task-Switched Flag
HLT	Halt Processor
LGDT	Load Global Descriptor Table
LIDT	Load Interrupt Descriptor Table
LLDT	Load Local Descriptor Table
LMSW	Load Machine Status Word
LTR	Load Task Register
MOV to/from CR0	Move to Control Register 0
MOV to/from DRn	Move to Debug Register
MOV to/from TRn	Move to Test Register

Sensitive instructions

Instructions that deal with I/O need to be restricted to protect system operating code and various levels of data. However, they also may need to be executed by procedures that execute at privilege levels other than zero. This can reduce the need for state switches.

Protection

The 80486 is designed with built-in protection methods to help detect and identify bugs. The segment is the basic unit of protection and segment descriptors store the necessary protection parameters. Figure 6-2 shows the protection-related fields of segment descriptors.

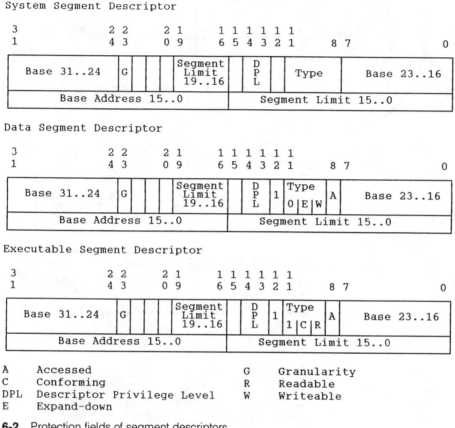

A   Accessed   G   Granularity
C   Conforming   R   Readable
DPL Descriptor Privilege Level   W   Writeable
E   Expand-down

6-2 Protection fields of segment descriptors.

The type fields of data and executable code segments include bits that further define the purpose of the segment. Bit 9 is interpreted differently in executable and data segments.

- **Readable bit**—In an executable-segment, Bit 9 indicates if instructions are allowed to read data from the segment. Reading from an executable segment can be attempted either via the CS register by using a "CS:" override prefix or by loading a selector in the descriptor into a data segment register (DS, ES, FS, or GS).
- **Writeable bit**—In a data segment, Bit 9 specifies whether instructions can write into the segment.

In addition to the descriptors for data and executable code segments, the 80486 has descriptors for system segments and gates. These data structures manage tasks as well as exceptions and interrupts. TABLE 6-1 lists all the types defined for system segments and gates. Note that not all descriptors define segments; gate descriptors hold pointers to procedure entry points.

Table 6-1   System segment and gate types.

Type	Name
0	Reserved
1	Available 80286 TSS
2	Load Descriptor Table
3	Busy 80286 TSS
4	80286 call gate
5	80286/386/486 task gate
6	80286 interrupt gate
7	80286 trap gate
8	Reserved
9	Available 80386/486 TSS
A	Reserved
B	Busy 80386/486 TSS
C	80386/486 call gate
D	Reserved
E	80386/486 interrupt gate
F	80386/486 trap gate

Before a memory cycle starts, the hardware checks each reference to memory to verify that the reference satisfies the protection criteria. Any violation prevents that cycle from starting and results in an exception. Because the checks are performed concurrently with address translation, there is little or no performance penalty.

Protection parameters are stored in the segment descriptors by systems software at the time a descriptor is created. When a program loads the selector into a segment register, the 80486 loads not only the base address of the segment but also protection information. Each segment register has bits in the programmer-invisible portion for storing base, limit, type and privilege level. Any subsequent protection checks on the same segment do not consume additional memory access cycles.

Protection has eight aspects: type checking, limit checking, restriction of access to data, restriction of procedure entry points, restriction of instruction set, pointer validation, descriptor validation, and page and segment protection.

TYPE checking

The TYPE field of a descriptor distinguishes between differing descriptor formats and it specifies the intended usage of a segment. Type checking can be used to detect programmer errors that would attempt to use a segment in ways not intended by the programmer. The processor checks type information on two occasions.

- When an instruction implicitly or explicitly refers to a segment register. Some segments can be used by instructions only in predefined ways. For example,
  - ~ If the writeable bit is not set, no instruction may write into a data segment.
  - ~ Unless the readable bit is set, no instruction can read an executable segment.
  - ~ No instruction may write into an executable segment.

- When a descriptor selector is loaded into a segment register. Some segment registers can contain only certain descriptor types. For example,
  - ~ Only selectors of writeable data segments can be loaded into the SS register.
  - ~ The CS register can be loaded only with the selector of an executable segment.
  - ~ Selectors of executable read-protected segments cannot be loaded into data-segment registers.

Limit checking   Limit checking catches programming errors such as invalid pointer calculations or runaway subscripts. These errors are detected when they occur, which makes it much easier to determine the cause. Without limit checking, such errors could corrupt other modules. This corruption would only be discovered later when the corrupted module runs incorrectly. At that point, error identification is much more difficult.

In a segment descriptor, the processor uses the LIMIT field to prevent programs from addressing outside the segment. The processor uses the G (granularity) bit to interpret the LIMIT. For data segments, the processor also uses the E (Expansion-direction) bit.

When $G = 0$, LIMIT is the value of the 20-bit LIMIT field as it appears in the descriptor. LIMIT can range from 0 to 0FFFFFH ($2^{20} - 1$, or 1 megabyte). When G = 1, the 80486 appends 12 low-order one-bits to the value of the LIMIT field. In this case, the actual limit can range from 0FFFH (2^{12} − 1, or 4 kilobytes) to 0FFFFFFFFH (2^{32} − 1, or 4 gigabytes).

The processor uses the LIMIT field of descriptors for descriptor tables to prevent programs from selecting a table entry outside the descriptor table. The descriptor table LIMIT identifies the last valid byte of the last descriptor in that table. Because the descriptor is eight bytes long, the limit value is (N * 8 − 1) for a table that contains N descriptors.

The expand-down feature allows a stack to expand by copying it to a larger segment without needing also to update intra-stack pointers.

For all types of segments except expand-down data segments, the value of LIMIT is one less than the segment size, expressed in bytes. The 80486 causes a general protection exception in any of the following cases:

- Attempt to access a memory doubleword (DWord) at an address > = (LIMIT − 2).
- Attempt to access a memory word at an address > = LIMIT.
- Attempt to access a memory byte at an address > LIMIT.

For expand-down data segments, LIMIT has the same function but is interpreted differently. For these data segments, the range of valid addresses is (LIMIT + 1) to 2^{32} − 1. An expand-down segment reaches maximum size when LIMIT is zero.

Restriction of access to data   Before the processor can address operands in memory, an 80486 program loads the data segment selector into a data-segment register (DS, ES, FS, GS, or SS). Then the 80486 compares the privilege levels to evaluate access to that data. As FIG. 6-3 shows, three different privilege levels enter into this check: the current privilege level (CPL), the requester's privilege level (RPL) of the selector used to specify the target segment, and the descriptor privilege level (DPL) of the target segment.

Instructions are allowed to load a data-segment register and its target segment only if the DPL of the target segment is numerically greater than (lesser privilege level) or equal to the maximum of the CPL and the selector's RPL. This can prevent applications from changing or reading operating system tables.

Less common is the use of code segments to store data. Code segments can hold constants but cannot be written to. Three methods of reading data in code segments are as follows:

- Use a "CS:" override prefix to read a readable, executable segment whose selector is already loaded in the CS register.
- Load a data-segment register with a selector for a non-conforming, readable, executable segment.
- Load a data-segment register with a selector of a conforming, readable, executable segment.

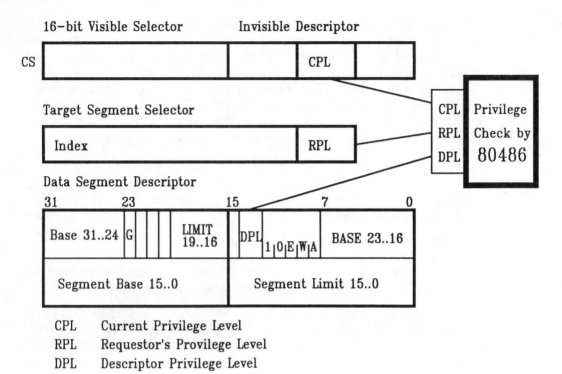

16-bit Visible Selector   Invisible Descriptor

CS

CPL

Target Segment Selector

Index   RPL

Data Segment Descriptor

31	23		15	7	0
Base 31..24	G	LIMIT 19..16	DPL 1 0 E W A	BASE 23..16	
Segment Base 15..0			Segment Limit 15..0		

CPL   Current Privilege Level
RPL   Requestor's Provilege Level
DPL   Descriptor Privilege Level

6-3 Data access privilege check.

Case 1 is always valid because the DPL of the code segment in CS is, by definition, equal to CPL. Case 2 uses the same rules as for access to data segments. Case 3 is always valid because the privilege level of a segment whose conforming bit is set is effectively the same as CPL, regardless of its DPL.

Control transfers The 80486 transfers control by use of exceptions, interrupts, and by the instructions CALL, JMP, INT, IRET, and RET. Exceptions and interrupts are special cases and are covered in Chapter 3. This section discusses forms of the instructions; the CALL, JMP, and RET instructions have both ''near'' and ''far'' forms.

The *near* form transfers within the current code segment and therefore is subject only to limit checking. The 80486 simply ensures that the destination of the instruction is within the current executable segment. Because this limit is cached in the CS register, protection checks for near transfers require no extra clock cycles.

Far CALLs and JMPs transfer to other segments. Because of this, the 80486 checks the privilege levels. Two ways exist for a CALL or JMP to refer to another segment: the operand can select a call gate descriptor, or the operand can select the descriptor of another executable segment.

Two different privilege levels enter into the privilege check for a control transfer that does not use a call gate: the current privilege level (CPL), and the descriptor privilege level (DPL) of the target segment's descriptor. Generally, the CPL is equal to the DPL of the segment currently being executed. The CPL, however, may be greater than the DPL if the conforming bit is set in the descriptor of the current executable segment.

An executable segment whose descriptor has the conforming bit (bit 10) set is called a *conforming segment.* The conforming segment allows sharing of procedures that may be called from differing privilege levels but should execute at the privilege level of the calling procedure. When control is transferred to a conforming segment, the CPL does not change. This is the only case when CPL may be unequal to the DPL of the currently executable segment.

The 80486 allows a CALL or JMP directly to another segment only if the conforming bit of the target code-segment descriptor is set *and* the DPL of the target is less than or equal to the CPL, or if the DPL of the target is equal to the CPL.

Most code segments are *not* conforming. For these segments, control can be transferred without a gate only to executable segments at the same privilege level. To transfer control to numerically smaller privilege levels, the CALL instruction is used with call-gate descriptors. The JMP instruction may never transfer control to a nonconforming segment whose DPL does not equal CPL.

Through the use of gate descriptors, the 80486 provides protection for control transfers among executable segments at differing privilege levels. There are four types of gate descriptors: Task gates, Trap gates, Interrupt gates, and Call gates. Task gates are used for task switching and are discussed in another section which discusses Tasks. Trap gates and interrupt gates are used by exceptions and interrupts and are described in those sections. This section is concerned with CALL gates only.

A CALL gate specifies the privilege level and defines an entry point of a procedure. Call gate descriptors are used by CALL and JMP instructions in the same way as code segment descriptors. When the hardware recognizes that the destination selector refers to a gate descriptor, the instruction operation is executed depending on the contents of the call gate.

Where protection comes in is that the selector and offset fields are ''guaranteed'' to be a pointer to the entry point of a procedure. All transitions from another segment go to a valid entry point, rather than possibly into the middle of a procedure or into the middle of an instruction. The point is that the operating system controls the building and can ensure that trusted code is going to be executed, which allows the proper granting of increased privilege.

The processor checks four different privilege levels to validate the control transfer via a call gate: the current privilege level (CPL), the descriptor privilege level (DPL) of the gate descriptor, the requester's privilege level

(RPL) of the selector specifying the call gate, and the DPL of the target executable segment's descriptor.

Only CALL instructions can use gates to transfer to smaller privilege levels. A gate may be used by a JMP instruction only to transfer to an executable segment with the same privilege level or to a conforming segment.

An interlevel transfer is being requested if the destination code segment of the call gate is at a different privilege level than the CPL. To keep system integrity, each privilege level has a separate stack. These stacks ensure that sufficient stack space is allocated to process calls from less privileged levels. Without the stack, a trusted procedure would work incorrectly if the calling procedure provided insufficient space on the caller's stack.

The 80486 locates these stacks via the Task State Segment (TSS). Because each task has a separate TSS, it follows that each task has a separate stack. Systems software creates the TSSs and places correct stack pointers in them; the initial pointers are read-only values. The 80486 *never* changes them during the course of execution. The systems software also ensures that each stack contains enough space to hold the old SS:ESP (Stack Segment, Extended Stack Pointer), the return address, and all parameters and local variables that may be needed to process a call.

When a call gate is used to change privilege levels, a new stack is selected by loading a pointer value from the TSS. The 80486 uses the DPL of the target code segment (which is the new CPL) to index the initial stack pointer for PL 0, 1, or 2. The TSS does not have a stack pointer for a PL 3 stack because privilege level 3 cannot be called by any procedure at any other privilege level. If the DPL of the new stack data segment does not equal the CPL, a stack exception occurs.

To ease privilege transitions, the 80486 copies the parameters to the new stack. It uses the count field of the call gate as to how many doublewords (the maximum is 31) it is to copy from the caller's stack to the new stack. If the count is zero, it copies no parameters. Procedures that are called from another privilege level and that require more than the 31 doublewords must use the saved SS:ESP link to access all parameters beyond the last doubleword copied.

The *near* forms of the RET instruction transfer control within the current code segment. They are, therefore, subject only to limit checking. To do this, the offset of the instruction following the corresponding CALL is popped from the stack. The 80486 checks that this offset does not exceed the limit of the current executable segment.

On the other hand, the *far* form of RET pops the return pointer that was pushed onto the stack by a prior far CALL. Normally, the return pointer will be valid because of its relation to the prior CALL or INT. The processor still performs privilege checking because of the possibility that the current procedure failed to correctly maintain the stack or altered the pointer. The RPL of the CS selector popped off the stack by the return instruction identifies the privilege level of the calling procedure. An inter-segment return instruction *can* change privilege levels, but only toward procedures of lesser privilege.

Restriction of instruction set   Certain instructions can affect the protection mechanism or influence general system performance. These instructions can only be executed by trusted procedures. The 80486 has two classes of restricted instructions: privileged instructions and sensitive instructions. They are described more fully under the preceding section on Privilege.

Pointer validation   Validity checking refers to finding the limits that data can have. Pointer validation is an important part of finding programming errors and is necessary for maintaining isolation between privilege levels. It consists of the following three steps:

1. Check if the segment type is appropriate to its intended use.
2. Check if the pointer violates the segment limit.
3. Check if the supplier of the pointer is entitled to access the segment.

The 80486 automatically checks steps 1 and 2 during instruction execution, but software must assist in performing step 3. The unprivileged instruction ARPL (Adjust RPL Field of Selector) does this. Software can also do steps 1 and 2, rather than waiting for an exception. The unprivileged instructions LAR (Load Access Rights Byte), LSL (Load Segment Limit), VERR (Verify a Segment for Reading), and VERW (Verify a Segment for Writing) help do this. LAR verifies that a pointer refers to a segment of the proper privilege level and type. LSL allows software to test the limit of a descriptor. VERR and VERW determines whether a selector points to a segment that can be read or written at the current privilege level. Neither VERR or VERW causes a protection fault if the result is negative.

The Requester's Privilege Level (RPL) can aid prevention of the faulty use of pointers that could corrupt the operation of more privileged code or data from a less privileged level. The RPL field allows a privilege attribute to be assigned to a selector, which normally shows the privilege level of the code that generated the selector. The 80486 automatically checks the RPL of any selector loaded into a segment register to verify that the RPL allows access.

Page and directory protection   Each page table entry has two bits associated with type protection: the U/S bit and the R/W bit. The Present bit can be used to restrict the addressable domain. At the level of page addressing, two types are defined: Read-only access (where R/W = 0) and Read/write access (where R/W = 1).

When the processor executes at a supervisor level (CPL − 3), the setting of U/S and R/W are ignored. All pages are both readable and writeable. At user level (CPL = 3), only pages that belong to the user level (U/S

= 1) *and* are marked for write access (R/W = 1) are writeable. Pages that belong to the supervisor level are neither readable nor writeable from the user level. The "ownership" of pages is established through page restriction.

Page restriction is implemented by assigning each page to one of two levels:

- **User level** (Bit 2 of the Page Table Entry U/S = 1). This is for applications procedures and data.
- **Supervisor level** (Bit 2 of the Page Table Entry, U/S = 0). This is for operating system and other systems software and related data.

The current level (U or S) is related to CPL. If CPL is 0, 1, or 2, the processor is executing at supervisor level. If CPL is 3, the processor is executing at user level. When the processor executes at supervisor level, all pages are addressable. At the user level, only pages that belong to the user level can be addressed.

The 80486 computes the effective protection attributes for a page by examining the protection attributes in *both* the directory and the page table. For any one page, the protection attributes of its page directory entry may be different from those of its page table entry.

There are overrides to page protection. Certain accesses are checked as if they are privilege level 0 references, even if CPL = 3. Those are any LDT, GDT, TSS, and IDT references or access to inner stack during ring crossing CALL/INT.

When paging is enabled, the processor first checks segment protection and then evaluates page protection. If the 80486 detects a protection violation at either the segment or the page level, the requested operation is not allowed to proceed. Instead, a protection exception is generated.

Pipelining for performance

System performance measures how fast a microprocessor system performs a given task or set of instructions. Through increased processing speed and data throughput, an 80486 operating at the heart of a system can improve overall performance. One of the greatest benefits of instruction pipelining is that it is transparent to the user. When implemented properly, the performance of instructions can be increased significantly without affecting the code already written. See Chapter 14 for additional, background information on pipelining.

Because a system will include devices whose response is slow relative to the 80486 bus cycle, the overall system performance is often less than the potential the 80486 offers. Two techniques for accommodating slow devices are address pipelining and slowing the system clock.

Address pipelining

The actual execution of an instruction is divided into four distinct parts. First, the instruction is fetched from memory. Second, it is interpreted or decoded. Third, the operand or operands are fetched from memory. Finally, the instruction is executed. If all these operations are performed serially for successive instructions (as on an assembly line), the next instruction is fetched while the first one is decoded, and so on. The pipe can be kept full so the incremental time to complete an instruction can be reduced to just the execution time.

Address pipelining increases the time that a memory has to respond by one CLK cycle without lengthening the bus cycle. This extra CLK cycle eliminates the output delay of the 80486 address and status outputs. Address pipelining overlaps the address and status outputs of the next bus cycle from the point of view of the accessed memory device. An access that requires two wait states without address pipelining would require one wait state with pipelining.

Address pipelining is advantageous for most bus cycles, but if the next address is not available before the current cycle ends, the 80486 cannot pipeline the next address. In this case, the bus timing is identical to a non-pipelined bus cycle. Also, the first bus cycle after an idle bus must always be non-pipelined because there is no previous cycle in which to generate the address early. If the next cycle is to be pipelined, the first cycle must be lengthened by at least one wait state so that the new address can be output before the end of the cycle.

Address pipelining is less effective for I/O devices requiring several wait states. The larger the number of wait states required, the less significant the elimination of one wait state through pipelining becomes. This fact coupled with the relative infrequency of I/O accesses means that address pipelining for I/O devices usually makes little difference to system performance.

The 80486 offers both pipelined and nonpipelined bus cycles. When pipelining is selected, the 80486 overlaps bus cycles, which allows longer access times. Because cache memory can be accessed without wait states, non-pipelined cycles are often preferred. Using non-pipelined cycles minimizes latency between the processor requesting information from the outside world and data becoming available at the 80486 pins. Because performance benefits of a cache result from its ability to provide a 32-bit doubleword in 2 clock cycles, address pipelining is recommended only for systems with slower memory devices that would otherwise require one or more wait states.

Slowing the 80486

While pipelining instructions is one way of allowing slower devices to "feed" the fast 80486, a less-common way to accommodate memory speed is to reduce the 80486 operating frequency. In other words, slow it down. Clock frequency is the periodic pulses that are used to schedule computer operations. Clock generators produce clock and processor time-phasing signals. The rate at which these signals pulse determines the rate at which logical gating and movement is performed within the computer system.

Because a slower clock frequency increases the bus cycle time, fewer wait states may be required for particular memory devices. On the other hand, system performance depends directly on the clock frequency. Execution time increases in direct proportion to the increase in clock period. A 25 MHz 80486 requires almost 30 percent more time to execute a program than a 33 MHz 80486 operating with the same number of wait states.

Multitasking

Multitasking is a technique that manages a computer system's work when that work consists of multiple activities such as editing a file, compiling a program, or performing inter-system transfers. Individual tasks execute as if they run on dedicated processors and share a common memory. It appears that, except for pauses to communicate or synchronize with other tasks, each task runs in parallel with all other tasks. The 80486 contains hardware to support efficient multitasking.

The 80486 uses no special instructions to control multitasking. Instead, it interprets ordinary control-transfer instructions differently when they refer to the special data structures. The registers and data structures that support multitasking are Task State Segment, task state segment descriptor, task register, and task gate descriptor.

In addition to the simple task switch, the 80486 offers two other task-management features:

- With each task switch, the processor can also switch to another LDT and to another page directory. Thus each task can have a different logical-to-linear mapping and a different linear-to-physical mapping. Using this feature, tasks can be isolated and prevented from interfering with one another.

- Interrupts and exceptions can cause task switches if needed in the system design. The 80486 not only switches to the task that handles the interrupt or exception, but it automatically switches back to the interrupted task when the interrupt or exception has been serviced.

In reality, the multitasking simulates multiple processors by providing each task with a virtual processor. That is, at any one instant, the operating system assigns the real processor to any one of the virtual processors, which then runs that virtual processor's task. To do this, the 80486 uses Task State Segments (TSS) and instructions that switch tasks.

Task State Segment (TSS)

A TSS is a data structure that holds the state of a task's virtual processor. The TSS is divided into two parts. The first class of information is the dynamic set that the processor updates with each switch from the task. This set includes fields that store the following:

SEGMENT REGISTERS—GS, FS, DS, SS, CS, and ES
GENERAL REGISTERS—EDI, ESI, EBP, ESP, EBX, EDX, ECX, and EAX
FLAGS REGISTER—EFLAGS
INSTRUCTION POINTER—EIP

The selector of the TSS of the previously executing task. This is updated only when a return is expected.

The second class of information in the TSS is a static set that the processor reads but does not change. This set includes fields that store the following:

- The I/O map base.
- The debug trap bit, T-bit, which causes the 80486 to raise a debug exception when a task switch occurs.
- The selector of the task's LDT.
- The stack definitions for level 0, 1, or 2 interrupt handlers that are to execute in the task's environment.

A TSS may reside anywhere in the linear space. The single caution is when the TSS spans a page boundary and the higher-addressed page is not present. In this case, the 80486 raises an exception if it encounters the not-present page while reading the TSS during a task switch. To avoid this, either allocate the TSS so that it does not cross a page boundary or ensure that both pages are either both present or both not-present at the time of a task switch. In this latter case, if both pages are not-present, the page-fault handler makes both pages present before restarting the instruction that caused the page fault. Figure 6-4 shows the 80486 32-bit Task State Segment.

When creating a new task, the operating system creates the TSS and initializes it to the values the task should have when it begins execution. The information is updated when any of the values change.

Task State Segment descriptor

Like all segments, the TSS is defined by a descriptor. This descriptor resides only in the Global Descriptor Table (GDT). An attempt to identify a TSS with a selector that has TI = 1 (Table Indicator flag to indicate the current LDT) generates an exception. Also, even if it has access to a TSS descriptor, a procedure does not have the right to read or modify the TSS. Reading and changing can be done only with another descriptor that redefines the TSS as a data segment. An attempt to load a TSS descriptor into

31 ... 16	15 ... 0	
I/O Permission Bitmap Base	0 0 0 0 0 0 0 0 0 0 0 0 0 0 0 T	64
0 0 0 0 0 0 0 0 0 0 0 0 0 0 0 0	Local Descriptor Table (LDT)	60
0 0 0 0 0 0 0 0 0 0 0 0 0 0 0 0	GS	5C
0 0 0 0 0 0 0 0 0 0 0 0 0 0 0 0	FS	58
0 0 0 0 0 0 0 0 0 0 0 0 0 0 0 0	DS	54
0 0 0 0 0 0 0 0 0 0 0 0 0 0 0 0	SS	50
0 0 0 0 0 0 0 0 0 0 0 0 0 0 0 0	CS	4C
0 0 0 0 0 0 0 0 0 0 0 0 0 0 0 0	ES	48
EDI		44
ESI		40
EBP		3C
ESP		38
EBX		34
EDX		30
ECX		2C
EAX		28
EFLAGS		24
Instruction Pointer EIP		20
Reserved		1C
0 0 0 0 0 0 0 0 0 0 0 0 0 0 0 0	SS2	18
ESP2		14
0 0 0 0 0 0 0 0 0 0 0 0 0 0 0 0	SS1	10
ESP1		0C
0 0 0 0 0 0 0 0 0 0 0 0 0 0 0 0	SS0	08
ESP0		04
0 0 0 0 0 0 0 0 0 0 0 0 0 0 0 0	Back link to Previous TSS	00

Note: Zeros indicate Intel reserved bits. Do not define.

6-4 Task state segment (TSS) for 80486.

any of the segment registers (CS, DS, ES, FS, GS, or SS) causes an exception. Figure 6-5 shows the format of a TSS descriptor.

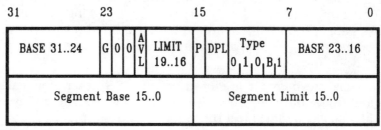

6-5 TSS descriptor.

Tasks are *not* re-entrant because both the LDT selector and CR3 (Control Register 3) for the task are stored in the TSS. The B-bit (busy) of the TYPE field allows the processor to detect an attempt to switch to a task that is already busy. A TYPE code of 9 shows the task is not-busy. A TYPE code of 11 indicates it is busy.

The BASE, LIMIT, and DPL (Descriptor Privilege Level) fields and the G-bit (Granularity) and P-bit (Present) have functions similar to their counterparts in data-segment descriptors. The BASE defines the location of the segment within the linear address space. The LIMIT defines the size of the segment. With the TSS descriptor, the LIMIT must contain a value of 103 or higher because the TSS itself requires 104 bytes. An attempt to switch to a task whose LIMIT has less than 103 causes an exception.

Task switching

The 80486 schedules and executes tasks based on a priority set by the operating system. To do this, the 80386 uses a *Task Register* (TR) in which it keeps a selector and a descriptor for the running task's TSS. The TR has both a visible and an invisible portion. The visible and changeable portion can be read and modified by instructions. The invisible portion is maintained by the processor to correspond to the changeable portion and cannot be read by any instruction.

Two instructions (Load Task Register, LTR; and Store Task Register, STR) read and modify the changeable portion of the TR. Both instructions take one operand, which is a 16-bit selector located in memory or in a general register.

The LTR instruction loads the changeable portion of the task register with the selector operand that must select a TSS descriptor in the GDT. The execution of LTR also loads the invisible portion with information from the TSS descriptor selected by the operand. LTR is a privileged instruction; in essence, it may be executed only if CPL (Current Privilege Level) is zero. Generally, LTR gives an initial value to the task register during system initialization. After that, the contents of TR are changed by task switch operations.

The STR instruction stores the changeable portion of the TR in a general register or memory word. STR is not a privileged instruction.

A task gate descriptor gives an indirect, protected reference to a TSS. The 80486 uses task gates, in addition to TSS descriptors, to satisfy three needs.

- Because the busy-bit is stored in the TSS descriptor, each task should have only one such descriptor. However, there may be several task gates that select the single TSS descriptor.
- With task gates, systems software can limit the right to cause task switches to specific tasks.
- Task gates may also reside in the IDT, so it is possible for interrupts and exceptions to cause task switching.

To switch tasks, the operating system issues a Jump (JMP) or Call (CALL) instruction whose operand is a selector for the TSS or the task gate of the new task.

The 80486 first checks that the current task is allowed to switch to the designated task. Data access privilege rules apply in the cases of JMP or CALL instructions. The DPL (Descriptor Privilege Level) of the TSS descriptor or task gate must be less than or equal to the maximum of CPL (Current Privilege Level) or the RPL (Requesters Privilege Level) of the gate selector.

Next, the TSS descriptor is checked to see if it is marked present and has a valid limit. A detected error up to this point occurs in the context of the *outgoing* task. Errors are restartable and can be handled in a way that makes its applications transparent.

The processor next executes the JMP TSS instruction by first storing its current registers in the current TSS. The EIP (instruction pointer) is loaded with the address of the instruction after the one that caused the task switch.

The processor then loads the TR with the selector specified in the JMP instruction. It marks the incoming task's TSS descriptor as busy and sets the TS (task switched) bit of the MSW (Machine Status Word). Because it now has the new TSS, the 80486 loads its registers with the values in this new TSS. Execution continues at the instruction pointed to by the new task's Instruction Pointer. Any errors detected in this step occur in the context of the incoming task.

To an exception handler, it appears as if the first instruction of the new task has not yet executed. Exception handlers that field task-switch exceptions in the incoming task should be cautious about taking action that might load the selector causing the exception. Unless the handler first examines the selector and fixes any potential problems, such an action may well cause another exception.

Every task switch sets the TS (Task Switch) bit in the MSW. The TS flag is helpful when using a coprocessor such as the numeric coprocessor. The TS bit signals that the context of the coprocessor *may not* correspond to the current 80486 task.

To resume execution of the old task, the operating system issues a JMP instruction to the old task's TSS. The process repeats with the storing of current registers, loading of new registers, and continuing execution. The task switch takes about 17 microseconds.

The privilege level at which execution restarts in the incoming task is not restricted by the privilege level of the outgoing task. The tasks are isolated by their separate address spaces, and TSSs and privilege access rules are used to prevent improper access to a TSS. Thus, no special privilege rules are needed to constrain the relations between the CPLs of the individual tasks. The new task simply begins executing at the privilege level indicated by the RPL of the CS selector value that is loaded from the TSS.

JMP, CALL, IRET, interrupts and exceptions are all ordinary mechanisms that can be used when a task switch is not required. Either the type of descriptor reference or the NT (Nested Task) bit in the flag word distinguishes between the standard mechanism and the variant that causes a task switch.

Multiprocessing

Multiprocessing is the execution of several programs or program segments concurrently with a processor per program. Execution and I/O may occur in parallel using shared resources such as memory and I/O devices.

The 80486 supports multiprocessing on the system bus. Processors on this bus can have different bus widths.

Locked and pseudo-locked bus cycles

While the system architecture of multiprocessor systems varies greatly, they generally have a need for reliable communication with memory. A processor that is updating the Accessed bit of a system descriptor, for example, should reject other attempts to change the descriptor until the operation is finished.

It is also necessary to have reliable communication with other processors that can serve as bus masters. For example, several bus masters might share a bit in memory for use as an indicator that a particular resource, such as a peripheral device, is idle. A bus master that wants to use this resource might test the bit, find out that the resource is free, and reverse the state of the bit. The new state would signal other potential bus masters that the resource is in use.

However, a problem could arise if another bus master reads the bit between the time the first bus master reads the bit and the time the state of the bit is changed. Both bus masters would then think the resource is available, and interfere with each other as they both attempt to use the resource. The processor prevents this problem by supporting locked bus cycles, during which requests for control of the bus are ignored.

The 80486 protects the integrity of certain memory operations by asserting an output signal called LOCK#. It also protects reads and writes of aligned 64-bit operands and (128-bit) instruction prefetches with an output called PLOCK#. An instruction prefix called LOCK asserts the LOCK# signal from within a program.

LOCK prefix and the LOCK# signal   The LOCK prefix and its output signal, LOCK#, are used to prevent other bus masters from interrupting a data movement operation. The LOCK prefix can only be used with the following instructions:

BTS, BTR, BTC	*mem, reg/imm*
XCHG	*reg, mem* or *mem, reg*
ADD, ADC, AND, OR, SBB, SUB, XOR	*mem, reg/imm*
NOT, NEG, INC, DEC	*mem*
CMPXCHG, XADD	*reg, reg* or *mem, reg*

Using the LOCK prefix with any other instruction generates an Invalid Opcode exception.

On an 80386 or 80486 system, a LOCKed instruction will always lock the area of memory (starting address and length) defined by the destination operand. In typical 8086 and 80286 configurations, LOCK locks the entire physical address space.

Automatic locking   For the following critical memory operations, the processor asserts the LOCK# signal automatically:

- **Acknowledging interrupts**.
  After an interrupt request, the interrupt controller uses the data bus to send the interrupt vector of the interrupt source to the 80486. The processor issues a LOCK# to keep all other data off the bus during this time.

- **Executing an XCHG instruction that references memory**.
  The 80486 always asserts LOCK# during an XCHG (Exchange Register/Memory With Register) instruction that involves a memory operand, even if the LOCK prefix is not used.

- **Setting the Busy bit of a TSS descriptor**.
  When switching to a task, the 80486 tests and sets the Busy bit of the TSS descriptor's Type field. To keep two different processors from switching to the same task, the 80486 asserts LOCK# during its test-and-set operation.

- **Updating segment descriptors**.
  When loading a segment descriptor, the 80486 will set the Accessed bit if it is clear. During this test-and-set operation, the 80486 issues a LOCK# so that another processor does not modify the descriptor while it's being updated.

- **Updating Page Directory and Page Table entries**.
  When updating these entries, the 80486 uses locked cycles to set the Accessed and Dirty bits.

Pseudo-locking   The PLOCK# pin indicates that the current bus cycle and the following one should be treated as a single transfer. By implementing the pseudo-lock mechanism, system hardware can guarantee that reads and writes of 64-bit operands will not be disrupted. The operand must be aligned on a doubleword boundary so that the read or write can be completed in no more than two bus cycles.

The pseudo-lock mechanism can also be used to protect instruction prefetches and other transfers of more than 32 bits.

7

Hardware and hardware subsystems

Hardware interfacing is important in designing the best possible system. Often, programmers' knowledge of hardware, and of its internal functioning, allows them to choose the best software design or set of instructions to promote system efficiency. Once aware of what hardware is *supposed* to do, a programmer can quickly determine whether a bug lies in hardware or in the software use of that hardware. This chapter overviews the remaining hardware requirements and concepts not handled earlier.

The 80486 processor is packaged in a high density package, the *pin grid array* (PGA). The PGA looks like a square bed of nails extending from a ceramic base. It uses a ceramic substrate, has 0.100 inch pin spacings, excellent thermal characteristics, and provides for very high density. The 80486 is built on a 32-bit internal and external bus architecture. All instruction prefetch operations are made on a 32-bit basis that takes advantage of the bandwidth of the memory bus. See FIG. 7-1 for the pin grid array; and see TABLE 7-1 and TABLE 7-2 for pin assignments by function and number.

Intel X86-family peripherals

The 80486 can interface to earlier peripheral devices from the Intel X86 family. Here, we discuss just two of them: the 8041/42 Universal Peripheral Interface and the 8259A Interrupt Controller.

Universal Peripheral Interface (UPI)

The 8041 and 8042 Universal Peripheral Interface (UPI) devices allow customized solutions for peripheral device control. These microcontrollers

	1	2	3	4	5	6	7	8	9	10	11	12	13	14	15	16	17	
S	A27	A26	A23	NC	A14	VSS	A12	VSS	VSS	VSS	VSS	VSS	A10	VSS	A6	A4	ADS#	S
R	A28	A25	VCC	VSS	A18	VCC	A15	VCC	VCC	VCC	VCC	A11	A8	VCC	A3	BLAST#	NC	R
Q	A31	VSS	A17	A19	A21	A24	A22	A20	A16	A13	A9	A5	A7	A2	BREQ	PLOCK#	PCHK#	Q
P	D0	A29	A30												HLDA	VCC	VSS	P
N	D2	D1	DP0												LOCK#	M/IO#	W/R#	N
M	VSS	VCC	D4												D/C#	VCC	VSS	M
L	VSS	D6	D7												PWT	VCC	VSS	L
K	VSS	VCC	D14				i486™ Microprocessor PIN SIDE VIEW								BE0#	VCC	VSS	K
J	VCC	D5	D16												BE2#	BE1#	PCD	J
H	VSS	D3	DP2												BRDY#	VCC	VSS	H
G	VSS	VCC	D12												NC	VCC	VSS	G
F	DP1	D8	D15												KEN#	RDY#	BE3#	F
E	VSS	VCC	DIO												HOLD	VCC	VSS	E
D	D9	D13	D17												A20M#	BS8#	BOFF#	D
C	D11	D18	CLK	VCC	VCC	D27	D26	D28	D30	NC	NC	NC	NC	FERR#	FLUSH#	RESET	BS16#	C
B	D19	D21	VSS	VSS	VSS	D25	VCC	D31	VCC	NC	VCC	NC	NC	NC	NMI	NC	EADS#	B
A	D20	D22	NC	D23	DP3	D24	VSS	D29	VSS	NC	VSS	NC	NC	NC	IGNNE#	INTR	AHOLD	A
	1	2	3	4	5	6	7	8	9	10	11	12	13	14	15	16	17	

7-1 Pin assignment of 80486. Reprinted by permission of Intel Corporation, © Intel Corporation 1990.

have a slave interface on board and include an 8-bit CPU, ROM, RAM, an I/O timer/counter, and a clock.

Intel also supplies an EPROM implementation, comprised of the 8741 and 8742. The 8742 has a 2K×8 ROM and 256K×8 RAM, an 8-bit timer-/counter, and 18 programmable I/O pins. It also has an 8-bit status register and two data registers for asynchronous slave-to-master interfacing. The 8742 supports DMA, interrupt and polled operations.

8259A interrupt controller

The 8259A Programmable Interrupt Controller manages the interrupts for an 80486 system. One 8259A can accept interrupts from as many as eight external sources, although as many as 64 requests can be handled by cascading several 8259A chips. The 8259A arbitrates the priority of simultaneous interrupts, then interrupts the processor and passes a code to the 80386 to identify the interrupting source.

Table 7-1   Pin assignments by function.

Address Signal	Pin	Data Signal	Pin	Control Signal	Pin	N/C	V_{cc}	V_{ss}
A_2	Q14	D_0	P1	A20M#	D15	A3	B7	A7
A_3	R15	D_1	N2	ADS#	S17	A10	B9	A9
A_4	S16	D_2	N1	AHOLD	A15	A12	B11	A11
A_5	Q12	D_3	H2	BE0#	K15	A13	C4	B3
A_6	S15	D_4	M3	BE1#	J16	A14	C5	B4
A_7	Q13	D_5	J2	BE2#	J15	B10	E2	B5
A_8	R13	D_6	L2	BE3#	F17	B12	E16	E1
A_9	Q11	D_7	L3	BLAST#	R16	B13	G2	E17
A_{10}	S13	D_8	F2	BOFF#	D17	B14	G16	G1
A_{11}	R12	D_9	D1	BRDY#	H15	B16	H16	G17
A_{12}	S7	D_{10}	E3	BREQ#	Q15	C10	J1	H1
A_{13}	Q10	D_{11}	C1	BS8#	D16	C11	K2	H17
A_{14}	S5	D_{12}	G3	BS16#	C17	C12	K16	K1
A_{15}	R7	D_{13}	D2	CLK	C3	C13	L16	K17
A_{16}	Q9	D_{14}	K3	D/C#	M15	G15	M2	L1
A_{17}	Q3	D_{15}	F3	DP0	N3	R17	M16	L17
A_{18}	R5	D_{16}	J3	DP1	F1	S4	P16	M1
A_{19}	Q4	D_{17}	D3	DP2	H3		R3	M17
A_{20}	Q8	D_{18}	C2	DP3	A5		R6	P17
A_{21}	Q5	D_{19}	B1	EADS#	B17		R8	Q2
A_{22}	Q7	D_{20}	A1	FERR#	C14		R9	R4
A_{23}	S3	D_{21}	B2	FLUSH#	C15		R10	S6
A_{24}	Q6	D_{22}	A2	HLDA	P15		R11	S8
A_{25}	R2	D_{23}	A4	HOLD	E15		R14	S9
A_{26}	S2	D_{24}	A6	IGNNE#	A15			S10
A_{27}	S1	D_{25}	B6	INTR	A16			S11
A_{28}	R1	D_{26}	C7	KEN#	F15			S12
A_{29}	P2	D_{27}	C6	LOCK#	N15			S14
A_{30}	P3	D_{28}	C8	M/IO#	N16			
A_{31}	Q1	D_{29}	A8	NMI	B15			
		D_{30}	C9	PCD	J17			
		D_{31}	B8	PCHK#	Q17			
				PWT	L15			
				PLOCK#	Q16			
				RDY#	F16			
				RESET	C16			
				W/R#	N17			

Single and cascaded interrupt controller   When an interrupt occurs, the 8259A Programmable Interrupt Controller activates its own Interrupt (INT) output. This output is connected to the 80486 Interrupt Request (INTR). The 80486 automatically executes two back-to-back interrupt acknowledge cycles. The 8259A timing requirements are as follows:

- Four idle bus cycles must be inserted between the two interrupt-acknowledge cycles. The 80486 automatically inserts these idle cycles.
- Each interrupt-acknowledge cycle must be extended by at least one wait state. Wait-state generator logic must provide for this extension.

Table 7-2 Pin assignments by pin number.

Pin	Signal	Pin	Signal	Pin	Signal	Pin	Signal
A1	D_{20}	C9	D_{30}	J15	BE2#	Q10	A_{13}
A2	D_{22}	C10	N/C	J16	BE1#	Q11	A_9
A3	N/C	C11	N/C	J17	PCD	Q12	A_5
A4	D_{23}	C12	N/C	K1	V_{ss}	Q13	A_7
A5	DP3	C13	N/C	K2	V_{cc}	Q14	A_2
A6	D_{24}	C14	FERR#	K3	D_{14}	Q15	BREQ#
A7	V_{ss}	C15	FLUSH#	K15	BE0#	Q16	PLOCK#
A8	D_{29}	C16	RESET	K16	V_{cc}	Q17	PCHK#
A9	V_{ss}	C17	BS16#	K17	V_{ss}	R1	A_{28}
A10	N/C	D1	D_9	L1	V_{ss}	R2	A_{25}
A11	V_{ss}	D2	D_{13}	L2	D_6	R3	V_{cc}
A12	N/C	D3	D_{17}	L3	D_7	R4	V_{ss}
A13	N/C	D15	A20M#	L15	PWT	R5	A_{18}
A14	N/C	D16	BS8#	L16	V_{cc}	R6	V_{cc}
A15	IGNNE#	D17	BOFF#	L17	V_{ss}	R7	A_{15}
A16	INTR	E1	V_{ss}	M1	V_{ss}	R8	V_{cc}
A17	AHOLD	E2	V_{cc}	M2	V_{cc}	R9	V_{cc}
B1	D_{19}	E3	D_{10}	M3	D_4	R10	V_{cc}
B2	D_{21}	E15	HOLD	M15	D/C#	R11	V_{cc}
B3	V_{ss}	E16	V_{cc}	M16	V_{cc}	R12	A_{11}
B4	V_{ss}	E17	V_{ss}	M17	V_{ss}	R13	A_8
B5	V_{ss}	F1	DP1	N1	D_2	R14	V_{cc}
B6	D_{25}	F2	D_8	N2	D_1	R15	A_3
B7	V_{cc}	F3	D_{15}	N3	DP0	R16	BLAST#
B8	D_{31}	F15	KEN#	N15	LOCK#	R17	N/C
B9	V_{cc}	F16	RDY#	N16	M/IO#	S1	A_{27}
B10	N/C	F17	BE3#	N17	W/R#	S2	A_{26}
B11	V_{cc}	G1	V_{ss}	P1	D_0	S3	A_{23}
B12	N/C	G2	V_{cc}	P2	A_{29}	S4	N/C
B13	N/C	G3	D_{12}	P3	A_{30}	S5	A_{14}
B14	N/C	G15	N/C	P15	HLDA	S6	V_{ss}
B15	NMI	G16	V_{cc}	P16	V_{cc}	S7	A_{12}
B16	N/C	G17	V_{ss}	P17	V_{ss}	S8	V_{ss}
B17	EADS#	H1	V_{ss}	Q1	A_{31}	S9	V_{ss}
C1	D_{11}	H2	D_3	Q2	V_{ss}	S10	V_{ss}
C2	D_{18}	H3	DP2	Q3	A_{17}	S11	V_{ss}
C3	CLK	H15	BRDY#	Q4	A_{19}	S12	V_{ss}
C4	V_{cc}	H16	V_{cc}	Q5	A_{21}	S13	A_{10}
C5	V_{cc}	H17	V_{ss}	Q6	A_{24}	S14	V_{ss}
C6	D_{27}	J1	V_{cc}	Q7	A_{22}	S15	A_6
C7	D_{26}	J2	D_5	Q8	A_{20}	S16	A_4
C8	D_{28}	J3	D_{16}	Q9	A_{16}	S17	ADS#

Several 8259As can be cascaded to handle up to 64 interrupt requests. In this type of cascaded system, one 8259A is designated the master controller and receives input from the other 8259As, known as slave controllers. Each slave controller resolves priority between up to eight interrupt requests and transmits a single interrupt request to the master controller.

The master, in turn, resolves interrupt priority between the slaves and transmits a single interrupt request to the 80486.

The timing of the interface is essentially the same as that of a single 8259A. During the first interrupt-acknowledge cycle, all the 8259As freeze the states of their interrupt request inputs. When the master outputs the cascade address to select the slave controller with the highest priority request, the selected slave outputs an interrupt vector to the 80486. This occurs during the second 80486 interrupt-acknowledge cycle.

If the 80486 system needs more than 64 interrupt request lines, a third level of 8259As can be added. When one of the third level slave controllers receives an interrupt request, it drives active one of the interrupt request inputs of a second level. After the priorities have been determined, the second level slave sends the service-routine vector to the 80486. The service routine must contain commands to poll the third level of interrupt controllers to determine the source of the interrupt request. The extra 8259A and their chip-select logic are the only additional hardware required to handle more than 64 interrupts. For maximum performance, it's recommended that third-level interrupt controllers should be used only for noncritical and infrequently used interrupts.

80486 system peripheral devices

Intel offers several new peripheral devices and chip sets for higher-performance 80486-based system design.

Local Area Network (LAN) coprocessor

The 82596 Local Area Network (LAN) coprocessor is a 32-bit multitasking LAN coprocessor. The 82596 supports a wide variety of networks, including the IEEE 802.3, the IBM PC, and the Carrier-Sense, Multiple-Access and Collision-Detect (CSMA/CD) networks. It executes high-level commands and performs command chaining and inter-processor communication via memory shared with the 80486. This relieves the processor of all time-critical local-network control functions.

The 82596 chip has two subsystems:

- A serial subsystem interfaces to the physical-layer device for the network. This subsystem performs CSMA/CD media access control and channel-interface functions. It supports the full set of IEEE 802.3 and other industry-standard and proprietary network functions.

- A parallel subsystem interfaces to the 80486 processor. It contains a data interface unit, bus interface unit, 4-channel DMA unit, and a micro-machine command processor.

The serial and parallel run independently. (See FIG. 7-2.)

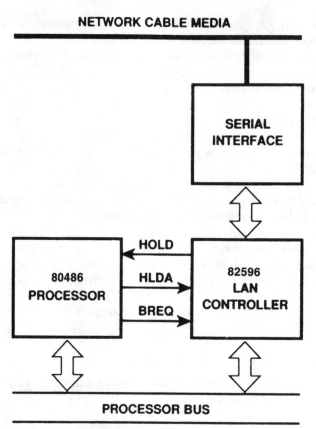

NETWORK CABLE MEDIA

SERIAL
INTERFACE

80486
PROCESSOR

HOLD

HLDA

BREQ

82596
LAN
CONTROLLER

PROCESSOR BUS

7-2 82596 serial and parallel interfaces. Reprinted by permission of Intel Corporation, ©
Intel Corporation 1990.

The 82596 interacts with the processor bus as either a bus master or a
slave. In normal operation, it is a master that moves data between the system memory and the coprocessor's control registers or internal FIFO
stacks. The processor and coprocessor communicate directly through the
Interrupt (INT/INT#) and Channel Attention (CA) signals using a system
control block of memory to store command and status information.

With a 25-MHz clock, the 82596 can transfer data at up to 80 Mb/sec-
ond in burst cycles or 50 Mb/second in non-burst cycles.

The 82596 coprocessor is an extension of the earlier 82586 LAN
Coprocessor, which interfaces an Ethernet network to a 16-bit Intel bus.
The 82596 can be configured to run software drivers written for the 82586
device without modification.

EISA chip set

The Extended Industry-Standard Architecture (EISA) is a superset of the
functionality and performance provided by ISA (PC/AT-compatible) sys-

tems. Intel's 82350 set of peripheral chips interfaces the 80486 to an EISA bus.

The chip set includes three motherboard devices: 82358 EISA Bus Controller (EBC), 82357 Integrated System Peripheral (ISP), and 82352 EISA Bus Buffer (EBB). Three EBBs are required. The chip set also includes one device for EISA-bus expansion boards: 82355 Bus Master Interface Controller (BMIC). Figure 7-3 shows a general system diagram.

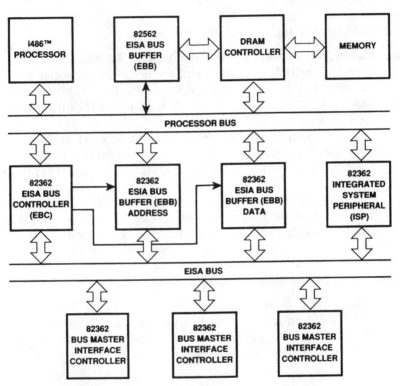

7-3 EISA system diagram. Reprinted by permission of Intel Corporation, © Intel Corporation 1990.

EISA Bus Controller (EBC) The 82358 EISA Bus Controller (EBC) is located between the processor bus and the 8-MHz EISA bus. It performs functions common to all peripherals, including translating cycles (among processor, EISA, and ISA buses), data buffer control and byte-swap logic, processor-bus arbitration, and data assembly for mismatched cycles.

The EBC is tightly coupled with the Integrated System Peripheral (ISP). The EBC handles address and data buffers between buses and inserts delays between back-to-back I/O cycles from the processor bus to the EISA bus. The controller also subdivides bus cycles so that transfers between different-size buses or transfers with misaligned addresses can be performed correctly.

EISA Integrated System Peripheral (ISP) The 82357 EISA Integrated System Peripheral (ISP) contains most of the EISA-specific peripheral functions, including

- 32-bit, seven-channel programmable DMA controller.
- EISA bus arbiter.
- Two 8-channel, 15-level programmable interrupt controllers.
- Nonmaskable interrupt logic for multiple NMI control and generation.
- Five counter/timers.
- DRAM refresh address generation and control.

Bus Master Interface Controller (BMIC) The 82355 EISA Bus Master Interface Controller (BMIC) is the primary interface between local functions on the EISA expansion board and the EISA bus on the 80486 system motherboard. Examine FIG. 7-3 to see how the BMIC connects to other parts of the system.

The primary function of the controller is to support burst data transfers between the expansion board and main memory. It supports data transfer rates of up to 33 Mb/second—the fastest rate available on an EISA bus.

With the help of external buffer devices, the BMIC provides all EISA control, address, and data signals. This greatly simplifies the design of EISA expansion boards because a board can be implemented with simple logic similar to that used in traditional ISA DMA designs. However, the EISA standard also allows designs with 32-bit data and address buses, burst transfers, and automatic configuration.

Bus buffers The system uses three 82352 EISA Bus Buffer chips (each strapped differently) to buffer EISA addresses, EISA data, and local DRAM data. As a group, these three chips support some EISA timing requirements that are difficult to implement with discrete components.

Clock and reset circuits

Microprocessor systems require some kind of clock pulse to perform and time their various functions. The clock is the very heart of the system because it generates accurately-timed pulses to which the logic subsystems are gated or enabled.

The 80486 processor uses a 1X clock that must satisfy TTL levels. Because the clock goes to most logic areas, it must be distributed to minimize skew and distortion yet maintain drive requirements.

An external, TTL-compatible 25/33-MHz clock synchronizes both the internal functional blocks of the microprocessor and the external signals. Most of the 80486 processor's board logic circuitry also uses this signal. The 80486 clock circuit that Intel recommends (shown in FIG. 7-4) consists of a 25/33-MHz oscillator and a fast buffer.

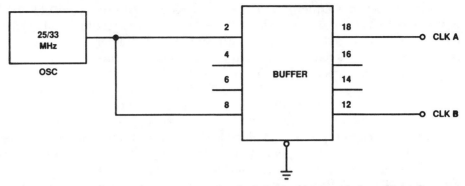

7-4 Typical 80486 microprocessor clock circuit. Reprinted by permission of Intel Corporation, © Intel Corporation 1990.

The clock input requirements for 80486 microprocessor systems are more stringent than those for commonly-used TTL devices, however. The specifications are 0.3 volts to 0.8 volts for a logic low and 2.0 volts to VCC + 0.3 volts for a logic high. The minimum high and low times are specified as 11 ns at 25 MHz and 5 ns at 33 MHz.

The reset signal to the 80486 processor must meet the setup and hold time requirements referenced to the clock signal. The system requires RESET to be asserted about 1 msec. to boot up from a cold start and at least 15 clock cycles to reboot from a warm start.

Power and ground requirements

Because power dissipation depends mostly on frequency, there is almost no DC power dissipation for the CHMOS IV 80486. The 80486's power is primarily capacitive. Internal power varies with operating frequency and, to some extent, with wait states and software.

Accounting for about 10 to 25 percent of the total power dissipation, I/O power varies with frequency and the supply voltage. It also depends on capacitive bus load, and performance will be reduced if loading exceeds maximums listed in Intel's i486 Processor Data Sheet. The addressing pattern of the software can affect I/O buffer power dissipation by changing the effective frequency of the address pins. The frequency variations at the data pins tend to be smaller; thus, a varying data pattern should not cause a significant change in the total power dissipation.

Power and ground planes (as opposed to lines) must be used in 80486 systems to minimize noise. Because power and ground lines have inherent inductance and capacitance, an impedance $Z = (L/C)^{1/2}$ must be considered in the design if they're used. The 80486 has 24 power (VCC) pins and 27 ground (VSS) pins. All power and ground pins must be connected to their respective planes. Ideally, the 80486 should be located at the center of the board to take full advantage of these planes.

At high signal frequencies, the transmission line properties of signal paths in a circuit must be considered. Reflections, interference, and noise can cause false signal transitions, input voltage level violations, and data errors. These errors can be transient and difficult to debug.

Input voltage level violations are usually due to voltage spikes that raise input levels over the maximum (called *overshoot*) or under the minimum (called *undershoot*). These voltage levels cause excess current on input gates that could damage the device permanently.

Interference is the result of electrical activity in one conductor causing transient voltages to appear in another conductor. There are two types of interference: electromagnetic interference (EMI) and electrostatic interference (ESI). EMI (also called crosstalk) is caused by the magnetic field that exists around any current-carrying conductor. ESI is caused by the capacitive coupling of two adjacent conductors. The conductors act as the plates of a capacitor; a charge built on one induces the opposite charge on the other.

Thermal characteristics

Acceptable thermal (heat) levels are critical for correct performance of any electronic component, especially a processor. The heat at the surface of a chip is called the *junction temperature*. This temperature can be determined from external measurements using the known heat characteristics of the electronic package. To calculate the junction temperature, use the following equations (which are courtesy of Intel Corporation):

$$T_j = T_a + (O_{ja} * PD)$$
$$T_j = T_c + (O_{jc} * PD)$$

Where

T_j = Junction temperature
T_a = Ambient temperature
T_c = Case temperature
O_{ja} = Junction-to-ambient temperature coefficient
O_{jc} = Junction-to-case temperature coefficient
PD = Power dissipation

Using case equations to compute ambient temperatures had its advantages. Because the measurement is localized to a single point—the top center of the package, case temperature is easier to calculate and measure than ambient temperature. In addition, the worst-case junction temperature (shown as T_j in the equations) is lower when figured with case temperature because the junction-to-case thermal coefficient (O_{jc}) is lower than the junction-to-ambient thermal coefficient (O_{ja}). This means that computed junction temperature varies less with power dissipation (PD).

Ambient temperature is the still air surrounding a power supply or component. The temperature of circulating air, such as a chamber with a fan, is not a correct ambient-temperature measurement because the components are being cooled by the circulating air. When using case-temperature specifications, the system designer can either set the ambient temperature or use fans to control case temperature. Conductive cooling or finned heat sinks also may be used where fans are precluded.

Consult the current data sheet to determine the values of O_{ja} for the system's air flow and ambient temperature; this should give the desired case temperature.

Hardware building and debugging

A designer first considers the entire system, while knowing that the core portions must be tested prior to actually building that system. Designing and building an 80486 system incrementally is a short-cut to coming live in the shortest amount of time. Once the basic system is designed, built, and finally debugged, more software and enhancements can be added.

Incremental system design guidelines

Intel design engineers suggest the following guidelines to use in conjunction with the latest hardware data sheets.

1. First, install the clock circuitry. Check that the CLK signal is clean, then connect it to the 80486.
2. Connect the RESET line to the 80486 RESET input. With CLK running, check that the 80486 reset state is correct.
3. Tie the INT and HOLD pins to low (negated from the active state). So that the first bus cycle will not end, tie the READY# pin high.
4. Reset the 80486. Check that the processor emits the correct signals to perform its first code fetch from physical address FFFF-FF00H. Then connect the address latch and verify that the address is driven at its outputs.
5. Connect the PAL that implements the address decoder to the 80486. After reset, check that the processor attempts to select the EPROM device that holds the initial code to be executed.

When the 80486, address decoder, address latch, clock circuit, and RDY# generation logic are functioning correctly, the 80486 can run the software stored in the EPROM. A simple debug program (suggested by Intel) shown in FIG. 7-5 can be run to verify that the parts of the system work together. If the program does not run, use a logic analyzer to determine where the problem is.

The sample program loops back on itself and runs continuously. When the RDY# input is connected to the RDY# generation logic, run the program and check the results.

Check that the address latches have latched the first latch and that the address decoder is applying a chip-select signal to the EPROM. The

```
                                        ASSUME CS:SIMPLEST_CODE

       0000                SIMPLEST_CODE          SEGMENT
       FFF0                START:                 ORG 0FFF0h
       FFF0    90                                 NOP
       FFF1    90                                 NOP
       FFF2    EB FC                              JMP START
       FFF4                SIMPLEST_CODE          ENDS
                                                  END
```

7-5 A sample 4-byte diagnostic program.

EPROM should emit the first four opcode bytes of the first code to be executed: 90H, 90H, EBH, and FCH for the four-byte program in FIG. 7-5. The
opcode should propagate to the 80486 data pins.

Debugging guides

The 80486 can stop running for any of three reasons:

- It encounters a predefined shutdown condition. In real mode, a
  shutdown generally indicates that the 80486 has detected garbage
  on the data bus.
- The 80486 enters a HALT state due to a HALT instruction.
- The RDY# signal is never asserted to end the bus cycle.

The 80486 emits codes on its W/R#, D/C#, and M/IO# pins and address
outputs to indicate the halt or shutdown. If the shutdown occurs and the
80486 stops running, check the EPROM contents, the wiring of the
address and data paths, and the data transceivers. Use the 4-byte diagnostic program to investigate the system. Make this program work before
attempting more complex software.

If the 80486 stops, check the RDY# generation circuit. It probably
hasn't activated the RDY# to complete the bus cycle. The processor is adding wait states to the cycle, waiting for that RDY# signal to go active. Check
the circuit with a logic analyzer.

Performance considerations

At its most basic level, system performance measures how fast a microprocessor system performs a task or set of instructions. Often because the
system includes devices whose response time is slow relative to the processor, overall system performance is less than its potential. When evaluating
which device to give the most consideration for performance improvements, realize that the impact of memory speed on performance is much

greater than that of I/O device speeds because most programs access memory more than I/O.

The first method generally used to interface slower devices to fast processors is the wait state. Wait states are extra clock cycles added to the bus cycle. On the 80486, some external logic generates the wait by delaying the RDY# input. That means, for an 80486 running at 25 MHz, one wait state adds 4 nanoseconds to the time available for memory to respond.

A second method is to pipeline addresses. Unlike the wait state, address pipelining increases the time memory has to respond by one clock cycle *without* lengthening the bus cycle. These extra clock cycles virtually eliminate the output delay of the 80486 status and address outputs. Address pipelining is advantageous for most bus cycles. However, if the next address is not available before the current cycle ends, the 80486 obviously cannot pipeline the next address because it has not yet arrived. In this case, the bus timing is identical to a non-pipelined bus cycle. Note also that the first bus cycle after an idle bus always is non-pipelined because there was no previous cycle in which to output the address. And, if the next cycle is to be pipelined, the first cycle must be lengthened by at least one wait state so that the address can be output before the end of the cycle.

Address pipelining is less effective for I/O devices that require several wait states. In fact, the larger the number of waits required, the lesser the significance of eliminating a single wait through pipelining. Couple this fact with the *relative* infrequency of I/O accesses and you should see why address pipelining for I/O devices usually makes little difference to system performance.

A third (and interesting) approach to accommodating slower memory speed is to reduce the 80486's clock frequency. This approach requires very fine tuning because a somewhat slower clock increases the bus cycle time, which means fewer wait states may be required for particular memory devices. Note that, at the same time, overall system performance depends directly on the clock frequency. Execution time increases in direct proportion to the reduction in clock frequency. A 25 MHz 80486 takes almost 32 percent more time to execute a program than a 33 MHz 80486 operating with the same number of WAITs.

8
Programming the 80486

This chapter discusses software development strategy in general, virtual-8086 (V86) environment, the 80286 protected-mode, and 80486 real-address mode. Chapter 9 reviews general programming guidelines and lists programming notes of special cases for the 80486 programmers. Chapter 10 discusses the complete 80486 instruction set, which is a superset of all the instructions for the previous generations: 8086/88 through 80486.

Software system design

Software design is the application of principles, skills, and a subtle art to the design and construction of programs and systems. The environment for these programs consists of the computer system on which the program runs.

A software system has these properties:

- The program(s) are implemented under one authority, generally the operating system that runs on the main, central processor.
- The hierarchy of other software is subservient to this major authority, generally running at different priority and/or privilege levels.
- Inner levels of the operating system are hidden from computer system end-users. These inner levels are held to be "sacred" and unchangeable by end-users.

The design of a software system is the creation of a complete and precise description of the system, where that description is a collection of sub-descriptions of the software and hardware components and their interactions. The complete description of a software component is a program written in a well-defined programming language. The semantics of the programming language must be known prior to actual start of programming in order to ensure that all the software components can be implemented correctly in that language.

A software designer strives to achieve four goals: required function, correctness, performance, and reliability.

Required function is achieving the desired and correct output, given known inputs. Input is comprised of all the information taken in by the software system. Output is the information delivered.

Correctness is the definition of how closely the software system meets the objectives as specified by the design.

Performance is the speed and effectiveness of a software system as it uses resources toward meeting the objectives of the original design.

Finally, *reliability* is the ability of a software system to perform its function correctly in spite of failures of computer system components. Failure, here, means a temporary or permanent change in the component's characteristics that alters its function. Most programmers do not feel, for instance, that software *fails*; it is merely *incorrect*.

Modular means "constructed with standardized units or dimensions for flexibility and variety in use." Applied to software engineering, modularity refers to the building of software systems by putting together parts called *program modules*. A large system is a precise representation of a system that is composed of many interacting parts or modules.

Language elements

Very simply, a language or an instruction set is made up of those elements (mnemonics) that a set of designers found necessary to do a set of predefined tasks. For instance, if doing floating-point arithmetic is unnecessary, then instructions for doing it will not be written.

The limits and rules within the language or instruction set were defined during design. One major requirement for the 80486 was the support of previous generations' instruction set. Another important fact that influenced the design of the 80386 instruction set was the requirement for implementing privilege levels; as software systems become more powerful, security becomes an increasingly important issue. Third, a powerful operating system needs to be protected from applications programs; a protected system is a controlled environment in which some well-defined boundaries and ground rules exist to restrict communication and movement.

Addressing modes

Some instructions access memory to obtain or store data involved in the operation of the instruction. Other instructions refer to memory to indicate the location to which a program jump is to be made. In either case, the instruction must specify the address of the memory location being referenced. The part of the instruction that provides the memory location is called the *address field*. The contents of the address field is the *stated address*, and the address of the referenced memory location is the *effective address*.

In *direct addressing*, the effective address is given in the instruction. If all the locations in the computer memory are to be addressed directly, then the instruction must consist of several words. The operand for the instruction is part of the instruction itself in *immediate addressing*. The location of the operand immediately follows the memory location that contains the operation portion of the instruction.

A useful and important addressing mode is *indirect addressing*, where the stated address in the address field of the instruction is a pointer to the location that contains the effective address. Some microprocessors allow the stated address in an instruction to be added to the contents of a specified register. This is called *indexed* addressing, and the specified register is an *index register*. Closely related to indexed addressing is *relative addressing*, where the stated address in the instruction is added to the content of the instruction pointer to form the effective address. The stated address is regarded as a signed quantity so that relative addressing in a jump instruction allows a jump forward or backward (from the location indicated by the instruction pointer) by the amount shown in the address field of the instruction.

The 80486 has 11 instruction types: arithmetic, bit manipulation, data transfer, high-level language support, logical and shift/rotate, processor control, program control, protection, string manipulation, floating-point, and miscellaneous. The instructions in each type are listed in the next section. In addition, to provide software compatibility with the 8086, the 80486 can execute 16-bit instructions in real and protected mode.

The processor itself determines the default operand size of the instructions it is executing by examining the "D-bit" in the CS Segment Descriptor. If D = 0, all operand lengths and effective addresses are assumed to be 16 bits long. If D = 1, the operands and addresses are 32 bits long. However, in real mode, the default operand and address size is 16 bits (no 80486 descriptors in real mode).

Regardless of default size, two prefixes (The Operand Size Prefix and the Address Length Prefix) override the D-bit value on an individual instruction basis. These prefixes are automatically added by Intel assemblers.

Instruction set overview

Instructions in a set can be considered as tools of a trade. Each tool was designed to perform a specific task that satisfied some requirement. Useful, high-quality tools are closely associated with quality end-products.

The 80486 instruction set is a superset of the set developed for the 8086/8088, 80286, and 80386 processors. Major highlights of the 80486's extensions to the previous processors are as follows:

- An on-chip cache memory allows frequently-used data and code to be stored on the chip, reducing accesses to the external bus.
- RISC (Reduced Instruction Set Computer) design techniques have been used to reduce instruction cycle times.
- A burst bus feature enables fast cache fills.

These features combined lead to performance *twice* that of the 80386 microprocessor.

The 80486 instruction set offers 8-, 16-, and 32-bit data types. As stated earlier, the 80486 instructions are divided into 11 functional categories. The instructions are listed in summary form below. In Chapter 10, each instruction is defined and described in detail.

Arithmetic

Addition

ADD	Add operands
ADC	Add with carry
INC	Increment operand by 1
AAA	ASCII adjust for addition
DAA	Decimal adjust for addition

Subtraction

SUB	Subtract operands
SBB	Subtract with borrow
DEC	Decrement operand by 1
NEG	Negate operand
CMP	Compare operands
DAS	Decimal adjust for subtraction
AAS	ASCII adjustment for subtraction

Multiplication

MUL	Multiply Double/Single precision
IMUL	Integer multiply
AAM	ASCII adjust after multiply

Division

DIV	Divide unsigned
IDIV	Integer divide
AAD	ASCII adjust before division

Bit manipulation

Single bit instructions

BT	Bit Test

BTS	Bit Test and Set
BTR	Bit Test and Reset
BTC	Bit Test and Complement
BSF	Bit Scan Forward
BSR	Bit Scan Reverse

Data transfer

General purpose

MOV	Move Operand
PUSH	Push operand onto stack
POP	Pop operand off stack
PUSHA	Push all registers on stack
POPA	Pop all registers off stack
XCHG	Exchange Operand, Register

Conversion

MOVZX	Move byte or Word, Dword, w/zero extension
MOVSX	Move byte, Word, Dword, sign extended
CBW	Convert byte to Word in AX
CWDE	Convert Word to DWord in EAX
CWD	Convert Word to DWord in DX, AX
CDQ	Convert DWord to QWord in EDX, EAX

Input/Output

| IN | Input operand from I/O space |
| OUT | Output operand to I/O space |

Address object

LEA	Load Effective Address
LDS	Load pointer into D segment register
LES	Load pointer into E segment register
LFS	Load pointer into F segment register
LGS	Load pointer into G segment register
LSS	Load pointer into S segment register

Flag manipulation

LAHF	Load A register from Flags
SAHF	Store A register in Flags
PUSHF	Push flags onto stack
POPF	Pop flags off stack
PUSHFD	Push EFLAGS onto stack
POPFD	Pop EFLAGS off stack
CLC	Clear Carry Flag
CLD	Clear Direction Flag
CMC	Complement Carry Flag
STC	Set Carry Flag
STD	Set Direction Flag

High level language support

BOUND	Check Array Bounds
ENTER	Set up Parameter Block to enter procedure
LEAVE	Leave procedure
SETcc	Byte set on condition

Logical instructions and shift/rotate

Logical

NOT	"NOT" operands
AND	"AND" operands
OR	"Inclusive OR" operands
XOR	"Exclusive OR" operands
TEST	"Test" operands

Shifts

SHL/SHR	Shift logical left or right
SAL/SAR	Shift arithmetic left or right
SHLD/SHRD	Double shift left or right

Rotates

ROL/ROR	Rotate left/right
RCL/RCR	Rotate through carry left/right

Processor control

ESC	Processor Extension Escape
HLT	Halt
LOCK	Lock bus—Instruction Prefix
MOV	Move To/From Control Registers
NOP	No operation
WAIT	Wait until BUSY # negated

Program control

Conditional transfers

JA/JNBE	Jump if above/not below nor equal
JAE/JNB	Jump if above or equal/not below
JB/JNAE	Jump if below/not above nor equal
JBE/JNA	Jump if below or equal/not above
JC/JNC	Jump if carry/Not carry
JE/JZ	Jump if equal/zero
JG/JNLE	Jump if greater/not less nor equal
JGE/JNL	Jump if greater or equal/not less
JL/JNGE	Jump if less/not greater nor equal
JLE/JNG	Jump if less or equal/not greater
JNE/JNZ	Jump if not equal/not zero
JNO	Jump if not overflow
JNP/JPO	Jump if not parity/parity odd

JNS	Jump if not sign
JO	Jump if overflow
JP/JPE	Jump if parity/parity even
JS	Jump if sign

Unconditional transfers

CALL	Call a procedure or task
RET	Return from a procedure
JMP	Jump

Iteration controls

LOOP	Loop
LOOPE/LOOPZ	Loop if equal/zero
LOOPNE/LOOPNZ	Loop if not equal/not zero
JCXZ	Jump if register CX = 0
JECXZ	Jump short if ECX = 0

Interrupts

INT	Interrupt
INTO	Interrupt if overflow
IRET	Return from Interrupt/Task
CLI	Clear interrupt enable
STI	Set interrupt enable

Protection

CLTS	Clear Task Switched Flag
SGDT	Store Global Descriptor Table
SIDT	Store Interrupt Descriptor Table
STR	Store Task Register
SLDT	Store Local Descriptor Table
LGDT	Load Global Descriptor Table
LIDT	Load Interrupt Descriptor Table
LTR	Load Task Register
LLDT	Load Local Descriptor Table
ARPL	Adjust Requested Privilege Level
LAR	Load Access Rights
LSL	Load Segment Limit
VERR/VERW	Verify segment for reading or writing
LMSW	Load Machine Status Word
SMSW	Store Machine Status Word

String manipulation

MOVS	Move byte or Word, DWord string
INS	Input string from I/O space
OUTS	Output string to I/O space
CMPS	Compare byte or Word, DWord string
SCAS	Scan byte or word, DWord string

LODS	Load byte or Word, DWord string
STOS	Store byte or Word, DWord string
REP	Repeat Prefix
REPE/REPZ	Repeat while equal/zero
RENE/REPNZ	Repeat while not equal/not zero
XLAT	Translate String

Floating-point

F2XM1	Computer $2^x - 1$
FABS	Absolute Value
FADD/FADDP	Add Real
FBLD	Load Binary-Coded Decimal
FBSTP	Store Binary-Coded Decimal and Pop
FCHS	Change Sign
FCLEX/FNCLEX	Clear Floating-Point Exceptions
FCOM/FCOMP/FCOMPP	Compare Real
FCOS	Cosine
FDECSTP	Decrement Stack-Top Pointer
FDIV/FDIVP	Divide Real
FDIVR/FDIVPR	Reverse Divide Real
FIDIVR	Reverse Divide Integer
FFREE	Free Floating-Point Register
FIADD	Add Integer
FICOM/FICOMP	Compare Integer
FIDIV	Divide Integer
FILD	Load Integer
FIMUL	Multiply Integer
FINCSTP	Increment Stack-Top Pointer
FINIT/FNINIT	Initialize Floating-Point Unit
FIST/FISTP	Store Integer
FISUB	Subtract Integer
FISUBR	Reverse Subtract Integer
FLD	Load Real
FLD1	Push + 1.0 onto the FPU Stack
FLDL2T	Push $\log_2 10$ onto the FPU Stack
FLDL2E	Push $\log_e 10$ onto the FPU Stack
FLDPI	Push pi onto the FPU Stack
FLDLG2	Push $\log_{10} 2$ onto the FPU Stack
FLDLN2	Push $\log_e 2$ onto the FPU Stack
FLDZ	Push +0.0 onto the FPU Stack
FLDCW	Load Control Word
FLDENV	Load FPU Environment
FMUL	Multiply Real
FNOP	No Operation
FPATAN	Partial Arctangent

FPREM/FPREM1	Partial Remainder
FPTAN	Partial Tangent
FRNDINT	Round to Integer
FRSTOR	Restore FPU State
FSAVE/FNSAVE	Store FPU State
FSCALE	Scale by a Power of 2
FSIN	Sine
FSINCOS	Sine and Cosine
FSQRT	Square Root
FST/FSTP	Store Real
FSTCW/FNSTCW	Store Control Word
FSTENV/FNSTENV	Store FPU State
FSTSW/FNSTSW	Store Status Word
FSUB/FSUBP	Subtract Real
FSUBR/FSUBPR	Reverse Subtract Real
FTST	Test
FUCOM/FUCOMP/FUCOMPP	Unordered Compare Real
FWAIT	Wait
FXAM	Examine
FXCH	Exchange Register Contents
FXTRACT	Extract Exponent and Significand
FYL2X	Compute y times $\log_2 x$
FYL2XP1	Compute y times $\log_2(x + 1)$

Miscellaneous

BSWAP	Byte Swap
CMPXCHG	Compare and Exchange
INVD	Invalidate Cache
INVLPG	Invalidate TLB Entry
WBINVD	Write-Back and Invalidate Cache
XADD	Exchange and Add

All instructions operate on either 0, 1, 2, or 3 operands. The operands reside in a register, in the instruction itself, or in memory. Most zero-operand instructions take only one byte, while two-operand instructions are generally two bytes long. However, prefixes can be added to all instructions to override the default length of the operand.

Operands can be 8-, 16-, or 32-bits long. Normally, when executing 32-bit code written for the 80486, they are 8 or 32 bits. When executing existing 80286 or 8086 code, operands are 8 or 16 bits. Prefixes can be added to operands to override the operand default lengths; in essence, use 32-bit operands for 16-bit code and vice versa.

Memory is addressed with either 16- or 32-bit addresses. Each instruction that accesses memory has an address-size attribute of 16 or 32 bits. A 16-bit address both indicates the use of a 16-bit displacement in the instruction and an effective address calculation; in other words, it means the generation of a 16-bit address offset, a segment relative address. The 32-bit addresses use a 32-bit displacement and the creation of a 32-bit address offset. Any instruction that reads or writes a 16-bit word or a 32-bit doubleword has an operand-size attribute of either 16 or 32 bits.

Instructions that implicitly use a stack—such as POP EAX—also have a stack address-size attribute of either 16 or 32 bits. To form the address of the top of the stack, the 16-bit addresses use the 16-bit SP (stack pointer register). Instructions with a stack address-size attribute of 32 bits use the 32-bit ESP (Extended Stack Pointer register). The stack address-size attribute is shown by the B-bit of the data-segment descriptor in the SS (Stack Segment) register. A zero B-bit selects a stack address-size attribute of 16. A one selects an attribute of 32.

Programs executed in real mode or virtual-8086 mode have 16-bit addresses and operands by default. On the other hand, in the protected mode, the D-bit (in executable-segment descriptors) determines the default size attribute for both operands and addresses. These default attributes apply to the execution of all instructions in the segment. If the D-bit is zero, the default address and operand sizes are 16 bits. If it's a one, the default is 32 bits.

There is an override for the default segment attribute. The internal encoding of an instruction can include two byte-long prefixes: the address-size prefix (67H) and the operand-size prefix (66H). TABLE 8-1 shows how each prefix affects the combinations of defaults and overrides.

To help you program, the 80486 has testability and debug features. They include a self-test and direct address to the page translation cache.

Table 8-1   Size attributes.

Segment Default D =	0	0	0	0	1	1	1	1
Operand–size Prefix (66H)	N	N	Y	Y	N	N	Y	Y
Address–size Prefix (67H)	N	Y	N	Y	N	Y	N	Y
Operand Size	16	16	32	32	32	32	16	16
Address Size	16	32	16	32	32	16	32	16

N = No, this instruction prefix is not present

Y = Yes, this instruction prefix is present

In addition, the 80486 has four breakpoint registers that provide break-point traps on code execution or data access.

Virtual 8086 environment

The 80486 allows 8086/88 and 80186/188 application programs to execute unchanged in real mode. A protected mode operating system also can run their programs unchanged. 8086 applications and operating systems run in protected mode as part of a virtual (V86) task that takes advantage of the hardware support of multitasking offered by protected mode.

The V86 task forms a "virtual machine" that consists of the 80486 hardware and systems software. The software controls the V86 external interfacing, the interrupts and I/O. The hardware provides the TSS containing the *virtual registers* (a virtual memory space that is the task's first megabyte of the linear address space) and executes the instructions that deal with the registers and address space.

Entering and leaving Virtual 8086 Mode

The 80486 systems software does not manipulate the VM (*Virtual Mode*) flag in EFLAGS directly. It changes the EFLAGS image stored in the TSS or on the stack. A V86 monitor would set the VM bit in the EFLAGS image when first creating a V86 task. The exception and interrupt handlers examine the VM bit as stored on the stack. If VM is set, the interrupted procedure was executing in V86 mode and the handler may need to invoke the V86 monitor.

The 80486 can enter virtual 8086 mode in one of two ways:

- As an IRET from a procedure of an 80486 task that loads EFLAGS from the stack. If the VM flag is 1, the 80486 returns control to an 8086 procedure. The Current Privilege Level (CPL) must be zero when IRET is executed, or the 80486 does not change VM.

- As a switch to an 80486 task that loads the EFLAGS from the new Task State Segment. The new TSS must be an 80486 TSS, not an 80286 TSS, because the 80286 TSS does not store the high-order word of EFLAGS (which contains VM). If VM is 1, the new task is executing 8086 instructions and the 80486 forms base addresses as if it were an 8086 processor.

The 80486 leaves virtual mode when it handles an interrupt or an exception. Again, two possibilities exist:

- If the interrupt or exception vectors to a privilege level zero procedure, the 80486 stores the current EFLAGS on the stack and clears the VM flag. That causes the interrupt or exception handler to execute as native 80486 protected mode code. If the interrupt or exception vectors to a conforming segment or to a privilege level other than 3, the 80486 signals a general protection exception. The exception error code is the selector of the executable segment to which transfer was attempted.

- The interrupt or exception causes a task switch. A task switch from a V86 task to any other loads EFLAGS from the new task's TSS. If the new TSS is an 80486 TSS and the VM flag is zero, or the new TSS is an 80286 TSS, the processor resets the VM flag, loads the segment registers from the new TSS using 80486 address formation, and then begins to execute the new task instructions according to 80486 protected mode.

Figure 8-1 shows how the 80486 enters and leaves an 8086 program.

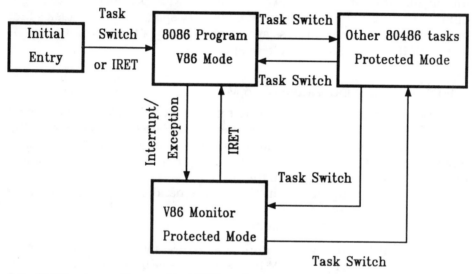

8-1   80486 enters and leaves virtual 8086 mode.

A switch to or from the V86 task may be due to several things. It can be an interrupt that vectors to a task gate, an IRET when the NT (Nested Task) flag is set, or an action of the scheduler of the 80486 operating system. Regardless of which occurred, the 80486 changes the VM flag in EFLAGS in the new TSS. If the new TSS is an 80286 TSS, the processor clears VM because the high-order word is not in the TSS. The 80286 updates VM before loading the segment registers from the images in the new TSS. The new setting of VM determines whether the 80486 interprets the new segment register images as 80286/386/486 or 8086 selectors.

Interrupt and trap gates   If the 80486 leaves V86 mode as the result of an exception or interrupt that vectors via a trap or interrupt gate to a privilege level zero procedure, the exception or interrupt handler returns to the 8086 code by executing an IRET. Because it was designed for execution by an 8086, the 8086 program has an 8086-style interrupt table that starts at linear address zero. The 80486 does not use this table; it vectors through the IDT for all exceptions and interrupts that occur in V86 mode. The IDT entry for interrupts or exceptions that occur in V86 mode must contain a trap gate, an 80486 trap gate (type 14), or an 80486 interrupt gate (type 15). The type 14 and 15 gates must point to a nonconforming, privilege level zero code segment.

If the interrupt is to be reflected to the virtual 8086 task's interrupt handler, the 80486 interrupt handler emulates an 8086-style interrupt for the task.

Interrupts and exceptions, with 80486 trap or interrupt gates in the IDT, vector to the appropriate handler procedure at privilege level zero. The 80486 stores the contents of the 8086 segment registers on the PL0 stack. Then it loads all the segment registers with zeros before beginning to execute the handler procedure. Interrupt procedures that expect values in the segment registers or that return values via segment registers must use the register images stored on the PL0 stack. Interrupt handlers that need to know if the interrupt occurred in V86 mode examine the VM flag in the stored EFLAGS.

After processing the interrupt or exception, the 80486 returns to the 8086 code in the following steps:

1. Locates the appropriate handler procedure by referring to the 8086 interrupt vector.
2. Stores the 8086 program state on PL3 (Privilege Level three) stack.
3. Modifies the return link on the PL0 stack to point to the PL3 handler procedure.
4. Executes IRET to pass control to the handler.
5. When the PL3 handler's IRET traps to the V86 monitor, restores the return line on PL0 to point to the original interrupt, privilege level three procedure.
6. Executes an IRET to pass control back to the original, interrupted procedure.

Virtual 8086 Mode addressing

The 80486 executes V86 mode when the VM (Virtual Mode) flag is set in the EFLAGS register. The processor tests the VM flag when decoding instructions to determine which instructions are sensitive to IOPL (I/O Privilege Level), and when loading segment registers to determine if it is to use 8086-style address formation.

All 80486 registers are accessible to V86, including the segment registers FS and GS, Control and Test Registers, and the Debug registers. V86 code also may use the new 80486 instructions that explicitly operate on FS and GS, along with the segment-override prefixes that cause instructions to use FS and GS for address calculations. The new instructions are

LSS, LFS, and LGS, bit scan, double-shift, byte set on condition, long-displacement conditional jumps, move with sign/zero extension, and a generalized multiply.

Address formation

When in the V86 mode, the 80486 does not interpret 8086 selectors by referring to descriptors; it forms linear addresses as if it were an 8086. The selector is shifted left by four bits to form the 20-bit base address. The effective address is extended with four high-order zeros and added to the base address. There is a possibility of a carry, so the resulting linear address can contain up to 21 significant bits. The 8086 program running in V86 can generate linear addresses in the range of 0 to 10FFEFH, one megabyte plus approximately 64K.

V86 tasks actually generate 32-bit linear addresses. While the 8086 program only uses the low-order 21 bits (of that 32-bit address), the linear address can be mapped via page tables to a 32-bit physical address. Using the address-size prefix, 32 bit effective addresses can be generated, unlike the 8086 and 80286 processors. However, if the value of the 32-bit addresses exceeds 65535, it creates an exception (interrupt 12 or 13 with no error code).

Virtual 86 task

A virtual 8086 task must be represented by an 80486 TSS, which the 80486 uses to execute the 8086 program before it returns to protected mode to execute the 80486 tasks. The V86 task consists of two parts: the 8086 program to be executed, and 80486 code that serves as the virtual machine monitor.

The V86 monitor is actually 80486 protected mode code that executes at privilege level zero and consists mainly of initialization and exception handling procedures. The monitor, as with any other 80486 program, uses executable segment descriptors that must exist in the GDT or in the task's LDT. The monitor may also need data segment descriptors to allow it to examine the interrupt vector table or other parts of the 8086 program that are in the first megabyte of address space.

Operating system services can be left as part of the 8086 code or emulated in the V86 monitor. The major reasons for choosing to leave them are that the application code modifies the operating system, and the development group may not have sufficient development time to reimplement the 8086 operating system in 80486 code.

Some reasons to implement or emulate in the V86 monitor are that the functions of the 8086 operating system often can be easily emulated by CALLs to the 80486 operating system and that operating system functions (and system resources such as hard disks and printers) can be more easily coordinated among several V86 tasks. Regardless how V86 is implemented, note that different V86 tasks can use different 8086 operating systems, which opens choices available to systems programmers.

Paging is not required for a single V86 task but is useful in order to do the following:

- Redirect or trap references to memory-mapped I/O devices.
- Share 8086 operating system code or ROM code common to several 8086 programs that may be executing simultaneously.
- Create a virtual address space larger than the physical address space.
- Create multiple V86 tasks, in which each task must map the lower megabyte of linear addresses to different physical locations.
- Emulate the megabyte wrap of the 8086.

The 80486 does not refer to descriptors while executing 8086 programs, so it does not use the protection mechanisms offered by descriptors. A couple of approaches can be used to protect the systems software in a V86 task from the 8086 program. The software designer may choose to use the U/S bit of the page table entries to protect the virtual machine monitor and other systems software that is in each V86's task space. When the 80486 is in V86 mode, the Current Privilege Level (CPL) is 3, which means that the 8086 program has only user privileges. If the virtual machine monitor's pages have supervisor privileges, they cannot be accessed by the 8086 program.

Another way to protect the V86 system from a V86 application is to reserve the first megabyte and 64K of each task's linear address space for the 8086 program. The 8086 tasks cannot generate addresses outside that range.

Sensitive instructions in Virtual 8086 Mode

When the 80486 executes in V86 mode, the instructions IN, INS, OUT and OUTS are *not* sensitive to the IOPL bits in EFLAGS, although they are normally sensitive in protected mode. Several instructions are sensitive to the IOPL bits that are not normally sensitive; they are CLI (Clear Interrupt Enable Flag), INTn (Software Interrupt), IRET (Interrupt Return), LOCK (Assert Bus Lock Signal), POPF (Pop Flags), PUSHF (Push Flags), and STI (Set Interrupt Enable Flag). These instructions are made sensitive to IOPL so that their function can be simulated by the V86 monitor.

In virtual 8086 mode, the Current Privilege Level is always three. If IOPL is less than three, these seven instructions trigger a general protection exception.

Many 8086 operating systems are called by pushing parameters onto the stack and then executing an INTn instruction. INTn is sensitive so that the V86 monitor can intercept calls to the 8086 operating system if IOPL is less than three. The V86 monitor can then emulate the required function of the 8086 operating system or direct the interrupt back to the 8086 operating system.

The instructions POPF, PUSHF and IRET are sensitive to IOPL so that the V86 monitor can control any changes to the Interrupt Enable Flag (IF). CLI and STI are sensitive to IOPL in both 8086 code and 80486 code.

Virtual Mode Input/Output

Some 8086 programs were designed to operate on a single-task system and use I/O devices directly. These programs are disruptive when running in a multitasking environment. Instead of direct control, system designers may take other approaches. The method chosen to control the I/O depends on whether the I/O ports are memory mapped or I/O mapped. Some options for control are to

- selectively trap and then emulate references that a task makes to specific I/O ports.
- trap or redirect references to memory-mapped I/O addresses.
- emulate the 8086 operating system as an 80486 program and require it to do I/O via software interrupts to the operating system. Trap all attempts to do I/O directly.

I/O-mapped input/output in the V86 differs from protected mode in one way. The protection mechanism does not consult IOPL when it executes the IN, INS, OUT and OUTS instructions; only the I/O permission Bit Map controls whether the V86 tasks execute these I/O instructions. The I/O Permission Bit Map traps I/O instruction selectively, depending on the I/O address to which they refer. Because each task has its own I/O Permission Bit Map, the addresses trapped for one task may be different for those trapped for others.

Each task that executes memory-mapped I/O must have a page (or several pages) for the memory-mapped address space. The V86 monitor can control the memory-mapped I/O by either

- causing a monitor trap, which forces a page fault on the memory-mapped page (read-only pages will trap writes and not-present pages will trap both reads and writes).
- assigning the memory-mapped page to appropriate physical addresses.

Intervening for each I/O may be excessive for some kinds of I/O devices. In this case, a page fault can intervene on the first I/O operation. Then the monitor can make sure that the task has exclusive access to the device and can change the page status to present and read/write, which allows subsequent I/O to proceed at full speed.

Differences between Virtual—8086 and 8086

In general, most software operates the same on an 8086 processor and on the 80486 in virtual mode. You should keep some differences in mind.

- Opcodes that were not defined for the 8086 and 8088 processors cause an Exception 6. However, if the undefined 8086/88 opcode translates to a defined 80486 opcode, it will execute in the 80486 manner.

- Because the 80486 takes fewer clocks for most instructions than does the 8086 or 8088, two affected areas can be assumed delays with the 8086/88 operating in parallel with an 8087 numerics coprocessor and delays required by I/O devices between I/O operations.

- The 80486 generates the largest negative number as a quotient for the IDIV instruction. The 8086/88 causes an exception zero.

- On both the 8086 and 8088, divide exceptions leave the instruction pointer (CS:IP) pointing to the instruction *after* the failing one. The 80486 CS:IP points directly at the failing instruction.

- The 8086/88 has no instruction length limit. The 80486 sets a 15 byte limit on instruction length and exception 13 occurs if this limit is violated. The only way to exceed the 80486 limit is to put redundant prefixes before the instruction.

- Flags bit positions 12 through 15 differ, depending on whether they were stored in real or virtual-8086. The 8086 stores them as ones. V86 stores bit 15 *always* as zero anD-bits 14 through 12 as whatever the last value loaded into them.

- An 8086/88 processor PUSHes the value of SP *after* it is decremented. The 80486 PUSHes the value of SP *before* it is decremented as part of the PUSH operation.

- The 80486 masks all shift and rotate counts to the low-order five bits. This MOD 32 operation limits the count to a maximum of 31 bits; it also limits the time that interrupt response is delayed while the instruction executes.

- On the 8086, an offset 0 (for example, to PUSH a word when SP = 1) or an attempt to access a memory operand that crosses offset 65535 (e.g., a MOV of a word to offset 65535) causes the offset to wrap around, modulo 65536. The 80486 raises an exception in these cases—exception 12 if the segment is a stack segment, or 13 if the segment is a data segment.

- On the 8086, if sequential access goes past offset 65535, the 8086 fetches the next instruction byte from offset 0 of the same segment. The 80486 raises Exception 13 in this case.

- The 80486 single-step exception (1) has a different priority than the 8086. This change prevents an external interrupt handler from being single-stepped if the interrupt occurs while a program is being single-stepped. The 80486 single-step exception has higher priority than any external interrupt. The 80486 will still single-step through an interrupt handler called by an INT instruction or by an exception.

- After the 80486 accepts an NMI interrupt, the NMI interrupt is masked until an IRET instruction is executed.

- On the 80486, floating-point exceptions call the floating-point error exception handler. If an 8086/88 system uses a vector other than 16 for the 8087 interrupt, both vectors should point to the floating-point error exception handler. The 80486 has signals that, with the addition of external logic, support user-defined error reporting for emulation of the interrupt mechanism used in many personal computers.

- On the 80486, the value of CS:IP saved for floating-point exceptions points at any prefixes that precede the ESC instruction. On the 8086/88, the saved CS:IP points to the ESC instruction itself.

- The 8087 INT signal passes through an interrupt controller; the floating-point error signal to the 80486 does not. Instructions in a coprocessor-error exception handler that use the interrupt controller might need to be deleted. The 80486 has signals that, with the addition of external logic, support user-defined error reporting for emulation of the interrupt mechanism used in many personal computers.

- Unlike the 8086 and 80286, the 80486 responds to requests for control of the bus from other potential bus masters (such as DMA controllers) between transfers of parts of an unaligned operand (for example, between two words that form a doubleword).

- Because the 8086/88 does not support protection, it has no CPL (Current Privilege Level). Virtual-8086 mode uses CPL=3, which prevents the execution of privileged instructions. The privileged instructions are LIDT, LGDT, LMSW, CLTS, HLT, INVD, WBINVD, INVLPG, and special forms of MOV that load and store the control registers.

These instructions may be executed while the processor is in real-address mode following reset initialization. This allows system data structures such as descriptor tables to be set up before entering protected mode. Virtual-8086 mode is entered from protected mode, so it has no need for these instructions.

The 80286 processor implements the bus lock function differently than the 80486. Depending on how the V86 monitor handles LOCK, this difference may or may not be apparent to 8086 programs. If 8086 programs execute LOCK directly, programs that use forms of memory locking specific to the 8086 may not execute properly on the 80486 system.

Executing 80286 protected-mode code

Programs designed for execution in protected mode on an 80286 execute without change on the 80486 because of the design requirement that the 80486 be a superset of the 8086, 80286, and 80386.

Descriptors used in the 80286, executable segments, task gates, and local descriptor tables are used in both the 80286 and 80486. The 80486 has new versions of TSS descriptors, but both the 80286 and 80486 descriptors can be used simultaneously in the same system. For the common descriptors, the 80486 looks for zeros in the final word to determine if it should interpret the descriptor as an 80286 descriptor.

When moving 80286 software to the 80486, consider the following two cases:

CASE 1: Porting selected 80286 applications to the 80486 environment with an 80486 system builder, loader, and operating system.

The TSSs used to represent the 80286 should be changed to 80486 TSSs. It is not necessary to change the 80286 object modules. TSSs are usually constructed by the operating system, loader or the system builder.

CASE 2: Porting an entire 80286 system, complete with 80286 operating system, loader and system builder.

All tasks have 80286 TSSs. The 80486 acts as a fast 80286.

Restricted LOCK

LOCK and its corresponding output signal should be used to prevent other bus masters from interrupting a data movement operation. In typical 8086 and 80286 configurations, LOCK locked the entire physical memory space. With the 80486, memory is guaranteed to be locked against access by a processor executing a locked instruction on *exactly* the same memory (i.e., an operand with identical starting address and identical length).

LOCK can be used only with the following instructions when they modify memory: BT, BTS, BTR, BTC, XCHG, XADD, INC, DEC, NOT, NEG, ADD, ADC, SUB, SBB, AND, OR, and XOR. Using LOCK before any other instruction generates an undefined opcode.

The bus lock function is implemented differently in the 80286 and the 80486. Software that uses forms of memory locking that are specific to the 80286 *may* not run correctly when transported to a specific application of the 80486.

80286 address wraparound

With the 80286, base and offset combinations that address beyond 16Mb wrap around to the first megabyte of the 80286 address space. The

80486's greater physical address space has these addresses fall into the 17th megabyte. If software depends on the 80286 wraparound, the same effect can be simulated by using paging to map the first 64K of the 17th megabyte of the logical addresses to physical addresses in the first megabyte.

80486 real-address mode

The 80486 real-address mode executes object code designed for the 8086, 8088, 80186, 80188, 80286, and 80386 real-address mode. The 80486 architecture is nearly identical to that of the 8086/88 and 80186/188. From a programmer's view, the 80486 in real-address mode is a high-speed 8086 with some extensions to the registers and the instruction set.

Entering and leaving real-address mode

Real-address mode is automatically in effect after the RESET signal. Even when the system is intended to be used in protected mode, the start-up program (system initialization or boot) executes in real-address mode temporarily initializing for protected mode.

Switching to protected mode is the only way to leave real-address mode. The 80486 enters protected mode when a MOV to CR0 instruction sets the PE (Protection Enable) bit in CR0. If maintaining 80286 compatibility, the LMSW instruction can be used to set the PE bit.

If software clears the PE bit in CR0 with a MOV to CR0 instruction, the 80486 re-enters real-address mode. Be sure to take the necessary steps. For instance,

- if paging is enabled,
    - ~ transfer control to linear addresses that have their linear addresses equal to physical addresses.
    - ~ clear the PG (Paging) bit in CR0.
    - ~ move zeros to CR3 to flush the TLB.
- transfer control to a segment with a 64K limit. This loads the CS register with the limit it needs for real mode.
- load segment registers (SS, DS, ES, FS, and GS) with a selector that points to a descriptor that contains the appropriate values for real mode:
    - ~ Base = any value
    - ~ Limit = 64K
    - ~ Byte granular, G = 0
    - ~ Expand up, E = 0
    - ~ Writeable, W = 1
    - ~ Present, P = 1
- disable interrupts, perhaps with a CLI instruction that disables INTR interrupts. NMIs can be disabled with external circuitry.

- clear the PE bit in CR0.
- jump to real mode code to be executed. Use a far JMP that flushes the instruction queue and puts the correct values in the access rights of CS.
- ensure that the 8086 interrupt vectors are set in locations 0 through 4*(Highest interrupt possible) − 4.
- enable interrupts.
- load the segment registers as needed by the real-mode code.

Real-address physical address formation

For an 8086 program, the 80486 provides byte memory space of one megabyte plus 64K. Segment relocation is done as in the 8086: the 16-bit value stored in a segment selector is shifted left by four bits (with zeros added) to form the segment base address. The effective address is extended with four high-order zeros and added to the base to form a linear address. The linear address is equivalent to the physical address because paging is not used in real-address mode. There can be a carry when the linear address is formed. On the 8086, this carry is truncated. On the 80486, the carrieD-bit is stored in the linear address bit position 20.

The 80486 can generate a 32-bit effective address via the address-size prefix, unlike the 8086 and 80286. The value of that address must be in the range of 0 to 65536, or it causes an exception: Interrupt 12 or 13 with no error code. This is for compatibility with the 80286.

New 80486 exceptions

For a detailed description of all the exceptions and interrupts recognized by the 80486, see Chapter 3. There are eight *new* exceptions:

EXCEPTION 5—A BOUND instruction was executed with a register value outside the limit values.

EXCEPTION 6—An undefined opcode was found, or LOCK was used improperly before an instruction to which it does not apply.

EXCEPTION 7—The EM (Emulation) in the MSW (Machine Status Word) is set when an ESC instruction is found. This exception also occurs when a WAIT instruction is encountered if TS (Task Switch) is set.

EXCEPTION 8—An interrupt or exception vectored to an interrupt table entry beyond the interrupt table limit in IDTR. This occurs only if the LIDT instruction changed the limit from the default value of 3FFH, which can hold all 256 interrupt IDs.

EXCEPTION 12—The operand crosses extremes of stack segment. For example, MOV operation at 0FFFFH; or PUSH, CALL, or INT with SP = 1.

EXCEPTION 13—An operand crosses extremes of a segment other than a stack segment; or sequential instruction execution attempts to proceed beyond offset 0FFFFH; or an instruction is longer than 15 bytes, including the prefixes.

EXCEPTION 14—Paging is enabled and an attempt to translate encounters a page directory or page table entry marked non-present or would violate access privilege.

EXCEPTION 17—Alignment check. This cannot occur without setting previously-reserveD-bits.

Differences between real-mode and 8086

In real-address mode, the 80486 generally correctly executes ROM-based software designed for 8086/8088 and 80186/80188. The following is an overview of the differences programmers find.

- Opcodes that were not defined for the 8086 and 8088 processors cause an Exception 6. If the undefined 8086/88 opcode translates to a defined 80486 opcode, it will execute in the 80486 manner.

- The 80486 generally takes fewer clock counts for most instructions than did the 8086 or 8088. Two affected areas can be assumed delays with 8086/88 operating in parallel with an 8087 numeric coprocessor, and delays required by I/O devices between I/O operations.

- The 80486 generates the largest negative number as a quotient for the IDIV instruction. The 8086/88 causes exception zero.

- On both the 8086 and 8088, Divide (DIV) exceptions left the instruction pointer (CS:IP) pointing to the *next* instruction *after* the failing one. The 80486 CS:IP points directly at the failing instruction.

- The 8086/88 have no instruction limit. The 80486 sets a 15 byte limit on instructions, and Exception 13 occurs if this limit is violated. The only way to exceed the 80486 limit is to put redundant prefixes before the instruction.

- Flags bit positions 12 through 15 differ, depending on whether they were stored in 8086 or virtual-8086. The 8086 stores them as ones. V86 stores bit 15 *always* as zero anD-bits 14 through 12 as whatever the last value loaded into them.

- The additional eight exceptions arise only if the 8086 program has a hidden bug. Exception handlers should be added that treat these exceptions as invalid operations. Because these interrupts do not normally occur, this additional software does not significantly affect existing 8086 code. *Note:* these interrupt handlers should not already have been used by the 8086 software because they are in a range that was reserved by Intel.

- An 8086/88 processor PUSHes the value of SP *after* it is decremented. The 80486 PUSHes the value of SP *before* it is decremented as part of the PUSH operation.

- The 80486 masks all shift and rotate counts to the low-order five bits. This MOD 32 operation limits the count to a maximum of 31 bits; it also limits the time that interrupt response is delayed while the instruction executes.

- On the 8086, an offset 0 (for example, to PUSH a word when SP = 1) or an attempt to access a memory operand that crosses offset 65535 (e.g., a MOV of a word to offset 65535) causes the offset to wrap around modulo 65535. The 80486 raises an exception in these cases: Exception 12 if the segment is a stack segment, or 13 if the segment is a data segment.

- On the 8086, if sequential access goes past offset 65535, the 8086 fetches the next instruction byte from offset 0 of the same segment. The 80486 raises exception 13 in this case.

- After the 80486 recognizes an NMI interruption, the NMI is masked until an IRET is executed.

- The 80486 always asserts LOCK during an XCHG with memory, even if the LOCK prefix is not used. An undefined-opcode exception (Interrupt 6) results if LOCK is used before any instruction other than ADD, ADC, AND, BTS, BTR, BTC, DEC, INC, NEG, NOT, OR, SBB, SUB, XCHG, XADD, or XOR.

- On the 8086 family of processors, it is possible to specify addresses greater than one megabyte. The 8086 can form addresses only up to 20 bits long. It truncates the high-order bit, which "wraps" the overflowing address to the range 00000H to 0FFEFH.

- The 80486 single-step exception (1) has a different priority than the 8086. This change prevents an external interrupt handler from being single-stepped if the interrupt occurs while a program is being single-stepped. The 80486 single-step exception has higher priority than any external interrupt. The 80486 will still single-step through an interrupt handler called by an INT instruction or by an exception.

- On the 80486, floating-point exceptions call the floating-point error exception handler. If an 8086/88 system uses a vector other than 16 for the 8087 interrupt, both vectors should point to the floating-point error exception handler. The 80486 has signals that, with the addition of external logic, support user-defined error reporting for emulation of the interrupt mechanism used in many personal computers.

- On the 80486, the value of CS:IP saved for floating-point exceptions points at any prefixes that precede the ESC instruction. On the 8086/88, the saved CS:IP points to the ESC instruction itself.

- The 8087 INT signal passes through an interrupt controller; the floating-point error signal to the 80486 does not. Instructions in a coprocessor-error exception handler that use the interrupt controller might need to be deleted. The 80486 has signals that, with the addition of external logic, support user-defined error reporting for emulation of the interrupt mechanism used in many personal computers.

- Unlike the 8086 and 80286, the 80486 responds to requests for control of the bus from other potential bus masters (such as DMA controllers) between transfers of parts of an unaligned operand (for example, between two words that form a doubleword).

- The LIDT instruction can be used to set a limit on the size of the interrupt vector table. Shutdown occurs if an interrupt or exception attempts to read a vector beyond the limit. Shutdown also occurs if a stack operation wraps around the address limit. The 8086 has no shutdown mode.

Differences between real-mode and 80286

The differences between real-address mode on the 80486 and 80286 are not likely to affect existing 80286 programs, with the possible exception of system initialization. The four differences are as follows:

- Certain general registers may contain different values after RESET on the 80486 than on the 80286. The compatibility problems should be minimized because these registers are undefined in the 8086.

- The 80286 initializes the MSW register (in CR0 in the 80386) to FFF0H. The 80486 initializes this register to 0000H. Programs that read the MSW value may have problems, but these bits are undefined on the 80286 and should not have been used.

- The 80286 implements bus lock differently than the 80486. 80286 programs that use forms of memory locking specific to the 80286 may not execute properly on the 80486. Typical 8086 and 80286 configurations lock the entire physical memory space. With the 80486, the defined area of memory is guaranteed to be locked against access by a processor executing a locked instruction on exactly the same memory (i.e., memory with an identical starting address and length).

- The 80286 uses a starting location of 0FFFFF0H, sixteen bytes from the end of 24-bit address space. The 80386 uses the starting location of 0FFFFFFF0H, sixteen bytes from the end of 32-bit address space. Many 80286 ROM initialization programs work correctly. Others will by redefining external hardware signals on A_{31-20}.

Identifying the processor Figure 8-2 shows a code sequence that can be used in real-address mode to distinguish between 8086/88, 80286, and 80386 processors.

```
is_386   proc   near
;
;   This procedure returns the processor type in the AX register.
;   Code courtesy of Intel Corp.
;.

        pushf                    ; Save FLAG register
        pop bx                   ; Store FLAGs in BX
        and bx,0fffh             ; Clear bits 12-15
        push bx                  ; Store new value on stack
        popf                     ;  and pop it into FLAG register
        pushf                    ; Put another copy on stack
        pop ax                   ;  and pop it into AX

        and ax,0f000h            ; If bits 12-15 are set, then
        cmp ax,0f000h            ;  then the processor is an 8086
        jz is_8086               ;

        or bx, 0f000h            ; Try to set FLAG bits 12-15
        push bx                  ; Store new value on stack
        popf                     ;  and pop it into FLAG register
        pushf                    ; Put another copy on stack
        pop ax                   ;  and pop it into AX

        and ax,0f000h            ; If bits 12-15 are cleared, then
        jz is_80286              ;  then the processor is an 80286

is_80386:                        ; Otherwise, processor is an 80386
        mov ax,386h              ; Load the 80386 indicator
        jmp done
is_80286:
        mov ax,286h              ; Load the 80286 indicator
        jmp done
is_8086:
        mov ax,86h               ; Load the 8086 indicator

done:
        popf                     ; Recover FLAG register
        ret

is_386   endp
```

8-2 Real-address processor detection code.

RESET and initialization

An input pin called RESET can be used to start or restart the 80486.
When the processor detects a low-to-high transition on RESET, it terminates all activities. When RESET goes low again, the 80486 initializes to a
known internal state and fetches instructions starting at the reset address.

A self-test may also be requested at reset by asserting the AHOLD
input during the falling edge of the RESET signal. The self-test takes
about 2^{20} CLK cycles, or approximately 42 milliseconds on an 80486 running at 25 MHz.

Hardware asserts the RESET signal. The RESET input to the 80486
must remain high for at least 20 CLK cycles to ensure proper initializa-

tion. RESET should kept high for at least one millisecond after V_{CC} and CLK have reached their DC and AC specifications. Prior to its first instruction fetch, the 80486 makes no internal bus requests and, therefore, relinquishes bus control if it receives a HOLD request.

About 217 CLK cycles (or 2^{20} CLK cycles, with self-test) after RESET has gone low, the 80486 fetches its first instruction from linear address FFFFFFF0H. Generally, this location contains a JMP instruction that points to the beginning of a bootstrap program.

RESET causes the following pins to enter high, low, or three-state:

BREQ, A_{31} – A_4, M/IO#, BLAST, PCHK#, LOCK#	High
BE0 – BE3#, PWT, PCD, A_3, A_2, PLOCK#, D/C#, W/R#, ADS#	Low
D_{31} – D_0, DP0-3	3-State

Registers after reset

The contents of EAX depend on the result of the power-up self-test. EAX holds zero if the 80486 passed the test. A nonzero value in EAX after self-test indicates that this particular 80486 chip may be faulty.

Figure 8-3 shows how DX (the low half of EDX) holds a component identifier and revision number after reset. DH contains 4, which indicates an 80486 processor; DL contains a unique revision level identifier.

Figure 8-3 also shows the contents of Control Register Zero (CR0). These settings put the processor into real-address mode with paging disabled. The state of EBX, ECX, ESI, EDI, EBP, ESP, GDTR, LDTR, TR, debug registers (other than DR7), and the floating-point operand stack is undefined following power-up. The remaining registers and flags are set as listed in TABLE 8-2.

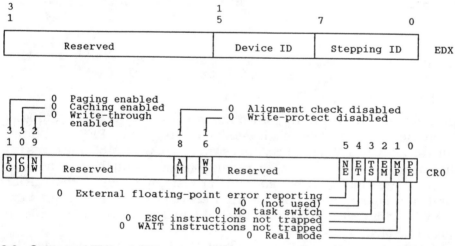

8-3 Contents of EDX and CR0 after reset.

Table 8-2   Processor state following power-up.

Register	State (hexadecimal)
EFLAGS	00000002H[1]
EIP	0000FFF0H
CS	F000H[2]
DS	0000H[3]
SS	0000H[3]
ES	0000H[3]
FS	0000H
GS	0000H
IDTR (base)	00000000H
IDTR (limit)	03FFH
DR7	00000000H
Floating-Point Unit Registers[4]	
Control Word	037FH
Status Word	0000H
Tag Word	FFFFH
IP offset	00000000H
Data Operand offset	00000000H
CS Selector	0000H
Operand Selector	0000H

1. Following power-up, the high 14 bits of EFLAGS are undefined. All of the flags are clear.
2. The invisible part of the CS register holds a base address of FFFF0000H and a limit of FFFFH.
3. The invisible parts of the DS and ES registers hold a base address of 0 and a limit of FFFFH.
4. The registers of the Floating-Point Unit are not initialized unless the built-in self-test is invoked.

Software initialization for real-address mode

Before programs can take advantage of real-address mode, a few structures must be initialized in real-address mode. The stack-segment register (SS) must be loaded before any instructions that reference the stack can be used. SS must point to an area in RAM.

Address lines A_{31-20} are automatically asserted for instruction fetches after RESET. This allows system designers to use a ROM at the high end of address space to initialize the system. Together with the initial values of CS:IP, this address line assertion causes instruction execution to begin at physical address FFFFFFF0H. Intrasegment (near) forms of control transfer instruction can be used to pass control to other addresses in the upper 64K of the address space. The first inter-segment (far) JMP or CALL causes A_{31-20} to drop low. The 80486 continues executing instructions in the lower one megabyte of physical memory.

Interrupts are disabled during the initial state of the 80486. The processor still tries to access the interrupt table if an exception or nonmaskable interrupt occurs. Initialization software should choose one of the following actions:

- Put pointers to valid interrupt handlers in all positions of the IDT that might be used by exceptions or interrupts.
- Change the IDTR to point to a valid interrupt table.
- Change the IDTR limit value to zero that causes a shutdown if an exception or nonmaskable interrupt occurs.

Switching to protected mode

Before switching to protected mode, you must create some data structures and initialize some registers.

System Tables. To let protected mode software access programs and data, you must create the Global Descriptor Table (GDT) and descriptors for a code and data segment. (The stack can be placed in a regular read/write data segment, so you need not create a separate descriptor for it.) Before the GDT can be used, you must load its base address and limit into the GDTR register; do this with an LGDT (Load Global Descriptor Table Register) instruction.

NMI Interrupt. If hardware allows NMI interrupts to be generated, you must create the Interrupt Descriptor Table (IDT) and a gate for the NMI interrupt handler. Before the IDT can be used, you must load its base address and limit into the IDTR register; do this with an LIDT (Load Interrupt Descriptor Table Register) instruction.

PE Bit. To enter protected mode, you must set the PE (Protection Enable) bit in the CR0 register. To do this, use either a MOV CR0 or LMSW instruction (the MSW register is part of CR0). Because the processor overlaps the interpretation of several instructions, it is necessary to discard the instructions that have already been read into the processor. Following the LMSW with a JMP instruction changes the flow of execution and, in essence, flushes out instructions that the processor has fetched or decoded.

Software initialization for protected mode

Generally, most initialization needed for protected mode is done either before or immediately after switching to protected mode. If the initialization is done after switching, the procedures used afterward must not use protected-mode features that are not yet initialized.

The initialization procedure can run in protected mode before initializing the Task Register. Before the first task switch, however, you must ensure the following:

- The task register must point to an area in which to save the current task state. After the first switch, the information dumped in this area is not needed, and the area can be used for other things.
- There must be a valid TSS for the new task. The stack pointer in TSS (for privilege levels numerically less than or equal to the initial CPL) must point to valid stack segments.

The Stack Segment register (SS) may be loaded in either protected or real-address mode. If loaded in real-address mode, SS continues to point to the same linear base-address after the switch to protected mode.

The format of the interrupt table for protected mode is different than that for real-address mode. Because it is not possible to do both the change to protected mode and to change the interrupt table formats at the same time, the IDTR, when selecting an interrupt table, inevitably will have the wrong format at some time. An interrupt or exception during this change-over will have unpredictable results. To avoid this, interrupts should be disabled until interrupt handlers are in place and a valid IDT has been created in protected mode.

Page tables and the PDBR in CR3 can be initialized in either protected or real-address mode. The PG bit (Paging Enabled) of CR0 cannot be set until the 80386 is in protected mode. Before PG is set, initialize PDBR in CR3 with a physical address that points to a valid page directory. Adopt one of the following to ensure consistent addressing before and after paging is enabled:

- A JMP instruction should immediately follow the setting of PG.
- The page currently being executed should map to the same physical addresses both before and after PG is set.

The Global Descriptor Table Register (GDTR) must point to a valid GDT before any segment register is changed in protected mode. The GDT and LDTs should reside in RAM because the 80486 modifies the accessed-bit of descriptors. Initialization of both the GDT and the GDTR can be done in real-address mode.

9

80486 programming notes

In general, software developed for one generation of the Intel microprocessor family works without modification on the next higher level system. This chapter lists various facts you need to remember when you program or design around the 80486 chip.

The chapter first addresses the current software/hardware environment with a list of guidelines for software developers. Then the chapter reviews certain aspects of programming for the 80486.

Software guidelines

Applications that are designed for the 8086/8088 execute transparently in virtual-8086 mode. Virtual environments are used as bridges to provide upward compatibility with existing applications while offering a new environment with enhanced functions and performance. You must remember that performance of applications executed in virtual-8086 mode tends to be lower than in real mode in the same processor. This occurs because an operating system is intervening to handle interrupts and emulate certain instructions. To this intervention time is added the execution time of the code that saves and restores machine state and emulates the instruction. The primary impact is in interrupt-intensive programs because straight code tends to execute unimpeded in virtual-8086 mode.

Certain guidelines should be kept in mind when developing a software product that is intended to run on 80486 systems. Suggested guidelines are as follows:

- If the software is intended to run on various levels of processors (8086/8088, 80286, 80386, or 80486), write to the least common denominator: the 8086/8088.

- Avoid any implicit or explicit use of register bits, flags, or data structures that are declared undefined or reserved for future Intel development.
- Routines written to run specifically on an 80486 system should be insensitive to the state of the PE (Protection Enable) bit in the Machine Status Word of CR0. Setting PE causes the processor to begin executing in protected mode. The visibility of the PE bit via the Store Machine Status Word (SMSW) may cause problems for code that attempts to act differently based on whether the 80486 is executing in real or protected mode.
- The value of various registers and flags after reset is different on the various processors. Do not depend on the power-on state of a particular processor. A program should explicitly load the required values.
- Do not use instruction opcodes not explicitly documented in Intel literature. An opcode that is not part of the supported instruction set may be defined differently in a later generation, even if it seemed to have a function in the earlier processor.
- The 80486 tends to execute specific code sequences significantly faster than earlier processors. Any code that interacts with real-time events or that depends on its execution time to perform its function should use a timing source independent of the 80486 clock speed.

Programming for the 80486

The 80486 provides compatibility with applications developed for earlier Intel processors while providing a full 32-bit, large linear address programming environment. You should keep several issues in mind that may not be clear from the documentation when programming specifically for the 80486 environment. These issues are seperated into paragrpahs and follow start with memory.

Memory

Physical address formation in real-address mode: When calculating the effective address, unlike the 8086, the 80486's resulting linear address may have up to 21 significant bits. A carry may be possible when the base address is added to the effective address. On the 8086, the carry bit is truncated. On the 80486, the carry bit is stored in bit position 20 of the linear address.

Unlike the 8086 and the 80286, 32-bit effective addresses can be generated via the address-size prefix. However, the value of a 32-bit address in real mode may not exceed 65536, or it will cause an exception.

With the 80286, any base and offset combination that addresses beyond 16Mb wraps around to the first megabyte of the 80286 address space. With the 80486, because it has greater physical address space, any such address falls into the 17th megabyte. In the event that any software depends on this anomaly, the same effect can be simulated on the 80486 by using paging to map the first 64K of the 17th megabyte of logical address to physical addresses in the first megabyte.

To allow maximum flexibility in data structures efficient memory utilization, words do *not* need to be aligned at even-numbered addresses. Also, doublewords do *not* need to be aligned at addresses evenly divisible by four. However, when using a system with a 32-bit bus, actual transfers of data between processor and memory take place in units of doublewords that begin at addresses evenly divisible by four. The misaligned words cause an increase in the number of memory cycles to fetch data, thus decreasing performance.

It may be expedient to turn off the 80486 segmentation when the 80486 executes software designed for special architectures not having segments. The processor does not have a specific mode to disable segmentation. However, the same effect is achieved by initially loading the segment registers with selectors for descriptors that encompass the entire 32-bit linear address space. Once the descriptors are loaded, the segment registers are not changed. The 80486 instructions' 32-bit offsets address the entire linear-address space.

In a write cycle (with 8-bit I/O devices), if BE3# and/or BE2# but not BE1# or BE0#, the write data on the top half of the data bus is duplicated on the bottom half. If the addresses of two devices differ only in the values of BE3#–BE0# (that is, the addresses lie within the same doubleword boundaries), BE3#–BE0# must be decoded to provide a chip select signal that prevents a write to one device from erroneously performing a write to the other. This chip select can be generated using an address decoder PAL device or TTL logic.

Descriptors

Because the 80486 uses the contents of the reserved word (the low order word) of every descriptor, 80286 programs that place values in this word may not execute correctly on the 80486.

Code that manages space in descriptor tables often uses an invalid value in the access-rights field of descriptor-table entries to identify unused entries. Access rights values of 80H and 00H remain invalid on the 80486. Other values that may have been invalid for the 80286 may now be valid for the 80486 because of new descriptor types.

To distinguish an 80286-type descriptor from an 80486-type descriptor, the processor checks the upper word. If the word is zero, then the descriptor is an 80286-type.

An executable segment whose descriptor has the conforming bit (bit 10) set is called a *conforming segment.* The conforming-segment allows sharing of procedures that may be called from differing privilege levels but should execute at the privilege level of the calling procedure. When control is transferred to a conforming segment, the CPL does not change. This is the only case when CPL may be unequal to the DPL of the currently executable segment.

Program instructions

The 80286 implements the bus lock function differently than the 80486. Programs that use forms of memory locking specific to the 80286 may not execute correctly when transported to a specific program on the 80486.

LOCK may only be used with the following 80486 instructions when they modify memory. An undefined opcode exception results from using LOCK before any other instruction.

- One-operand arithmetic and logical: INC, DEC, NOT, and NEG.
- Two-operand arithmetic and logical: ADD, ADC, SBB, SUB, AND, OR, and XOR.
- Exchange: XCHG, XADD, and CMPXCHG.
- Bit test and change: BT, BTS, BTR, BTC.

The LOCK prefix and its corresponding output signal should only be used to prevent other bus masters from interrupting a data movement operation.

A locked instruction is guaranteed to lock only the areas of memory specifically defined by the destination operand. Typical 8086 and 80286 configurations lock the entire physical memory space. With the 80486, the defined area of memory is guaranteed to be locked against access by a processor executing a locked instruction on *exactly* the same memory area (i.e., only with an operand with *identical* starting address and identical length).

The 80486 allows a CALL or JMP directly to another segment only if one of the two following conditions is satisfied: the conforming bit of the target code-segment descriptor is set *and* the DPL of the target is less than or equal to the CPL, or the DPL of the target is equal to the CPL. Most code segments are *not* conforming. For these segments, control can be transferred without a gate only to executable segments at the same privilege level. To transfer control to numerically smaller privilege levels, the CALL instruction is used with call-gate descriptors. The JMP instruction may never transfer control to a nonconforming segment whose DPL does not equal CPL.

Only CALL instructions can use gates to transfer to smaller privilege levels. A gate may be used by a JMP instruction only to transfer to an executable segment with the same privilege level or to a conforming segment.

BSF—BIT SCAN FORWARD. This instruction scans a word or double-word for a one bit and stores the index of the first set bit into a register. The bit string being scanned may be either in a register or in memory. ZF is set if the entire word is zero (that is, if no set bits are found). ZF is cleared if a one-bit is found.

Note: If no set bit is found, the value of the destination register is undefined.

DIV—UNSIGNED INTEGER DIVIDE. Non-integer quotients are truncated to integers toward zero. The remainder is always less than the divisor. For unsigned byte division, the largest quotient is 255; for unsigned word division, it is 65535. For unsigned doubleword division, it is $2^{32} - 1$.

SAL—SHIFT INSTRUCTIONS. CF (Carry Flag) always contains the value of the last bit shifted out of the destination operand. In a single-bit shift, OF (Overflow Flag) is set if the value of the high-order (the sign) bit was changed by the operation. If the sign bit was not changed, OF is cleared. After a multi-bit shift, the contents of OF is *always* undefined.

The difference between TEST (Logical Compare) and AND is that TEST does *not* alter the destination operand. TEST differs from BT (Bit Test) in that TEST tests the value of multiple bits in one operation, while BT tests a single bit.

Use the EAX register when possible. Many instructions are one byte shorter when EAX is used. These faster operations include loading from and storing to an absolute address in memory, transfers to other registers using XCHG, and operations using immediate operands.

Emphasize short one-, two-, and three-byte instructions. Because instructions for the 80486 begin and end on byte boundaries, it provides many instruction encodings that are more compact than those for processors with word-aligned instruction sets. An instruction in a word-aligned instruction set must be two or four bytes long, or longer. Byte alignment reduces code size and increases execution speed.

Access 16-bit data with the MOVSX and MOVZX instructions. These instructions sign-extend and zero-extend word operands to doubleword length, which eliminates the need for an extra instruction to initialize the high word.

For faster interrupt response, use the NMI interrupt when possible.

The jump instructions come in two forms. One form has an immediate value that can transfer execution 128 bytes backward or 127 bytes forward from the jump instruction. The other form has a full 32-bit displacement. Some assemblers use the short form where it applies, but many assemblers use the long form exclusively. When you are clear that the short form can be used, specify a short jump in your code.

When you are making several references to a variable addressed with a displacement, load the displacement into a register.

Using a PUSH or POP instruction with an operand in memory takes more clock cycles to execute than an equivalent two-instruction sequence that moves the operand through a register before pushing it onto the stack. For example, PUSH MemOp takes 4 cycles, but

```
MOV    EAX, MemOp
PUSH   EAX
```

takes only 2 cycles. Similarly, POP MemOp takes 6 cycles, but

```
POP    EAX
MOV    MemOp, EAX
```

takes 5 cycles.

The unconditional LOOP instruction takes longer to execute than a two-instruction sequence that decrements the count register, then jumps if the count does not equal zero. For example, while the count is nonzero, each execution of LOOP Start takes 6 clock cycles, but

```
DEC    ECX
JNZ    Start
```

takes only 4 cycles.

The JCXZ and JECXZ instructions take longer to execute than a two-instruction sequence comprised of a compare and a conditional jump. For example, while the count is nonzero, each execution of JECXZ Label takes 8 clock cycles, but

```
CMP    ECX, 0
JZ     Label
```

takes only 4 cycles.

For other hints on efficient programming for the 80486, see the "Code Optimization" appendix in Intel's *i486 Microprocessor Programmer's Reference Manual*.

Registers

Certain bits in various registers are shown as either "reserved" or "undefined." When using registers with these bits, treat the bits as truly undefined. Do not depend on the states of any undefined bits when testing the values of defined register bits. Mask the undefined ones out.

Do not depend on the states of any undefined bits when storing them to memory or to another register or on the ability of these bits to retain information. When loading registers, always load the undefined or reserved bits as zeros or unchanged from their values as stored.

The VM bit of the EFLAGS register can be set only two ways: either in protected mode, by the IRET instruction, and only if the current privilege level is zero; or by task switches at any privilege level.

The low-order 16 bits of the CR0 register is the 80286 Machine Status Word and can be addressed separately as the MSW.

Tasks

The only way to leave real-address mode is to deliberately switch to protected mode. The 80486 enters protected mode when a MOV to CR0 instruction sets the protection enable (PE) bit in CR0.

A Task State Segment (TSS) may reside anywhere in the linear address space. The single caution is when the TSS spans a page boundary. In this case, the 80486 raises an exception if it encounters the not-present page while reading the TSS during a task switch.

To avoid this, either allocate the TSS so that it does not cross a page boundary, or ensure that both pages are either both present or both not-present at the time of a task switch. In this latter case, if both pages are not-present, the page-fault handler makes both pages present before restarting the instruction that caused the page default.

Tasks are *not* re-entrant. The B-bit on the TSS descriptor allows the processor to detect an attempt to switch to a task that is already busy.

In the TSS descriptor, the LIMIT defines the size of the segment. This LIMIT must contain a value of 103 or higher. An attempt to switch to a task whose LIMIT has less than 103 causes an exception.

Every task switch sets the TS bit in the MSW (in CR0). The TS bit signals that the context of a numeric coprocessor *may not* correspond to the current 80486 task.

Privilege and protection

The privilege level at which execution restarts in the incoming task is not restricted in any way by the privilege level of the outgoing task.

When paging is enabled, the processor first checks segment protection, then evaluates page protection. If the 80486 detects a protection violation at either level, it cancels the requested operation and generates a protection exception.

The processor examines type information (in segment descriptors) on two sets of occasions:

- When a selector of a descriptor is loaded into a segment register. Certain segment registers can contain only fixed descriptor types, such as the following:
  - ~ Only selectors of writeable data segments can be loaded into SS.
  - ~ The CS register can be loaded only with a selector of an executable segment.
  - ~ Selectors of executable segments (that are not readable) cannot be loaded into data-segment registers.
- When an instruction implicitly or explicitly refers to a segment register. Some segments can be used by instructions only in certain predefined ways, such as the following:
  - ~ Unless the readable bit is set, no instruction may read an executable segment.
  - ~ Unless the writeable bit is set, no instruction may write into a data segment.
  - ~ No instruction may write into an executable segment.

To combine page and segment protection, you can define a large enough data segment that has some subunits that are read-only and other subunits that are read-write. If you do, the page directory or page table entries for the read-only subunits would have the U/S (User or Supervisor) and the R/W (Read/Write) bits set to x0. This indicates that there are no write rights for all the pages described by that directory entry or for the individual pages.

This technique could be useful in a UNIX-like system to define a large data segment, part of which is read only (for shared data or ROMmed constants). This would enable the system to define a "flat" data space as one large segment, use "flat" pointers to address within this space, and yet be able to protect shared data, supervisor areas, and shared files mapped into virtual space.

Code segments can hold constants, but cannot be written to. There are three methods of reading data in code segments:

- Use a CS override prefix to read a readable, executable segment whose selector is already loaded in the CS register.
- Load a data-segment register with a selector or a non-conforming, readable, executable segment.
- Load a data-segment register with a selector of a conforming, readable, executable segment.

Case 1 is always valid because the DPL of the code segment in CS is, by definition, equal to CPL. Case 2 uses the same rules as for access to data segments. Case 3 is always valid because the privilege level of a segment whose conforming bit is set is effectively the same as CPL, regardless of its DPL.

Test and debug

Because the first entry of the Global Descriptor Table (GDT) is not used by the processor, a selector that has an index of zero and a table indicator of zero can be used as a null selector. This process does *not* cause an exception when a segment register (other than CS or SS) is loaded with a null selector. It *will* cause an exception when the segment register is used to access memory. This feature is useful for initializing unused segment registers so as to trap accidental references.

The Translation Lookaside Buffer (TLB) is a cache used for translating linear addresses to physical addresses. Note that the TLB testing mechanism is unique to the 80486 and may not be continued in the same way in future processors. Software that uses this mechanism as it currently is may be incompatible with future processors.

The complement of the Dirty, User, and Writeable bits in Test Register 6 (TR6) are provided to force a hit or miss for TLB lookups. A lookup operation with a bit and its complement both low is forced to be a miss. If both bits are high, a hit is forced. A write operation is *always* performed when a bit and its complement have opposite values.

It is important to avoid writing the same linear address to more than one Translation Lookaside Buffer (TLB) entry. Otherwise, hit information returned during a TLB lookup operation is undefined.

TLB Test Operations—To lookup or read a TLB entry,

- move a doubleword to TR6 that contains the appropriate linear address and attributes. Be sure C = 1 for lookup.
- store TR7. If the HT bit in TR7 is 1, then other values reveal the TLB contents. If HT = 0, then the other values are undefined.
- For the purposes of testing, the V bit acts as another bit of address. The V bit for a lookup request should be set, so that uninitialized tags do not match. Lookups with V = 0 are unpredictable if any tags are uninitialized.

To write a TLB entry,

- Move a doubleword to TR7 that contains the desired physical address, HT, and REP values. HT must contain a 1. REP must point to the associative block in which to place the entry.
- Move a doubleword to TR6 that contains the appropriate linear address, and values for V, D, U, and W. Be sure C = 0 for write command.
- Be careful not to write duplicate tags. The results are undefined.

```
            PAGE    55,132
            .486
;
; Name: INTHNDLR
;
; Purpose: This program shows an example of intercepting an
;          interrupt and replacing it with one specially written.
;          The intercepted interrupt could just as well be an MS-DOS
;          interrupt.  We replace interrupt 5 (print screen) with
;          a handler for the bound interrupt.
;
; Inputs:  The program itself embodies a simple game of guessing the
;          bounds.  All input is prompted for.
;
; Process: The program preserves the original value of the interrupt
;          vector for the INT 5h handler.  It then sets its interrupt
;          handler vector in DS:DX and asks MS-DOS to replace the
;          vector.  The program then prompts for guesses and using the
;          BOUND instruction checks whether the guesses are in bounds.
;          Messages are produced for high, low and in-bounds.
;          The game is over when both upper and lower bounds are
;          found.
;
; Outputs: All outputs are displayed.
;
; Note:    The program demonstrates techniques for swapping interrupt
;          vectors.
;
; Define a range of values for our bound test
;
            MASM51
lowval      EQU     -13
valid       EQU     2
hival       EQU     23

mystack     SEGMENT para 'STACK' STACK USE32
            dq      256 DUP(?)
mystack     ENDS

data        SEGMENT para USE16

int5save    dw      0,0                 ; Will save it here

okbound     dw      lowval,hival        ; Target for our bound check
fndlow      db      0
```

```
fndhi        db      0
string       db      256 DUP(?)              ; String scratch area
rules        db      10,13,"You get to find the lowest and highest"
             db      " valid array bounds."
             db      10,13," If you get tired, a null entry will exit.$"

itisin       db      10,13,"It is in.$"
query        db      10,10,13,"Enter a number to test: $"
gotlow       db      10,13,"You got the low value!$"
gothigh      db      10,13,"You got the high value!$"
data         ENDS
code         SEGMENT para 'CODE' USE16 PUBLIC
             ASSUME  CS:code, DS:data, SS:mystack
;
; Set up the environment
;
Begin:
             mov     AX,data                ; Get data segment pointer
             mov     DS,AX                  ; into DS.
;
; Get int 5's current handler and save it.
;
             mov     AX,3505h               ; Set both AH and AL
             int     21h
             mov     int5save,ES            ; Save segment
             mov     int5save+2,BX          ; and offset
             lea     DX,ibound              ; Point DX to the routine
             mov     CX,CS                  ; Get the CS value
             mov     BX,DS                  ; Save our DS
             mov     DS,CX                  ; Set segment for move
             mov     AX,2505h               ; Set int code
             int     21h                    ; and put our handler in
             mov     DS,BX                  ; restore DS
             lea     DX,rules               ; Point to our simple rules
             mov     AH,9
             int     21h
getnbr:
             lea     DX,query               ; Get a number
             call    getinp
             jcxz    Exit                   ; Got tired
             mov     SI,BX                  ; Set input pointer
             call    Codeasb                ; Do the convert
             jc      getnbr                 ; Go get a good one
             mov     BX,1                   ; Set the good signal
             bound   AX,DWORD PTR okbound ; Do the bound instruction
```

```
            or      BX,BX               ; Was it valid?
            jz      getnbr              ; No - try again
            push    AX                  ; Save the number
            lea     DX,itisin           ; Point to the ok msg
            mov     AH,9
            int     21h                 ; and display it
            pop     AX
            cmp     AX,lowval           ; Is it the low?
            jz      foundlow            ; Yes
            cmp     AX,hival            ; Is it the high?
            jnz     getnbr              ; No
            inc     fndhi               ; Set non zero
            lea     DX,gothigh
            mov     AH,9
            int     21h                 ; Write message
            mov     AL,fndlow           ; Both found?
            or      AL,AL
            jnz     Exit
            jmp     getnbr              ; No
foundlow:
            inc     fndlow              ; Set non zero
            lea     DX,gotlow
            mov     AH,9
            int     21h                 ; Write message
            mov     AL,fndhi            ; Both found?
            or      AL,AL
            jz      getnbr


Exit:
            lds     DX,DWORD PTR int5save ; Point to original
            mov     AX,2505h            ; Set the code and int no.
            int     21h
            mov     AL,0                ; Set return code
            mov     AH,04ch             ; Set good-bye
            int     21h                 ; Return to the system
;
; Interrupt 5 handler.
;       This is a simplified handler for the bound interrupt.
;       It corrects the value in AX to an in-bound value and
;       clears BX to indicate the error.  It then returns.
;
ibound:
            sub     BX,BX               ; Clear the flag register
            mov     AX,valid            ; Set a valid value
            iret                        ; and return
```

```
;
; Read a string in response to a prompt.
; The prompt must be in DX.  The string will be returned in string.
;
getinp     PROC
           push    AX              ; Save registers
           push    SI
           mov     AH,9            ; and DOS request
           int     21h             ; Display the string
           lea     DX,string       ; Point to input area
           mov     string,254      ; Set max length in
           mov     AH,10           ; Ask for read of string
           int     21h             ; from DOS.
           lea     BX,string+2     ; Point to just-read data
           mov     CL,string+1     ; Get length read
           mov     CH,0            ; as a word.
           mov     SI,CX           ; Set length
           mov     string+2[SI],0  ; and make an ASCIIZ string.
           pop     SI
           pop     AX              ; Restore registers
           ret                     ; and return.
getinp     ENDP
;
; Name:    CODEBAS
;
; Purpose: The following converts a binary doubleword to an ASCII
;          decimal string.
;
; Inputs:  EAX contain the doubleword to be converted.
;          ES:DI contains the pointer to a 12 byte area for the
;                converted data.
;
; Process: The sign is 'captured' and if negative, the absolute
;          value is used.  The conversion divides the number by 100.
;          The 2-digit decimal remainder is converted and stored in
;          the target string from right to left.
;          The preceding is repeated until the quotient is zero.
;          If there is a leading zero, it is removed from the string.
;          (A zero value converts to a single ASCII zero.)
;
; Output:  ES:DI point to the first byte of the ASCIIZ string
;          containing the converted value.
;
; Notes:   The technique of repeated division is essentially a brute
;          force method.  It was chosen because it is easily
```

```
;           expandable to larger binary numbers as well as for its
;           simplicity.
;
Codebas     PROC
            push    EDX                 ; Save entry registers
            push    ECX
            push    EAX
            or      EAX,EAX             ; Check the sign.
            jns     posit               ; If positive, no problem.
            not     EAX                 ; Get the inverted number
            inc     EAX                 ; plus one.
posit:
            std                         ; Create digits from right
            add     DI,11               ; to left.
            mov     BYTE PTR ES:1[DI],0 ; Set ASCIIZ terminator
            mov     ECX,100             ; and the divisor.
            sub     EDX,EDX             ; Prepare to do division
divdh:
            div     ECX                 ; Divide by 100
            xchg    EDX,EAX             ; Swap quotient and remainder.
;
;   The remainder is the next 2 digits of the number.
;
            aam                         ; Expand the two digits,
            or      AX,'00'             ; put zones on them,
            stosb
            mov     AL,AH
            stosb                       ; and store the pair.
            sub     EAX,EAX             ; Clear our working register
            xchg    EAX,EDX             ; Get quotient for division.
            or      EAX,EAX             ; Is there more left?
            jnz     divdh               ; Yes, go do it
            cmp     BYTE PTR ES:1[DI],'0' ; Leading zero?
            jne     nolead0             ; No, don't
            inc     DI                  ; back up over it.
nolead0:
            pop     EAX                 ; Get number back,
            or      EAX,EAX             ; check its sign, and
            jns     posit2              ; skip if positive.
            mov     BYTE PTR ES:[DI],'-' ; Set sign
            dec     DI                  ; and make room for it.
posit2:
            inc     DI                  ; Point to first digit.
            pop     ECX
            pop     EDX
            ret                         ; and return.
```

```
Codebas     ENDP


; Name:     CODEASB
;
; Purpose: The following procedure converts an ASCII numeric string
;          to its doubleword binary equivalent.
;
; Inputs:  SI points to the string that is to be converted.  It is
;              edited to ensure it is valid data.
;          CX has the count of ASCII characters which may exceed the
;              count of digits.
;
; Process: The procedure scans the string to get the count of digits.
;              It fetches decimal digit pairs from left to right.
;              The prior result is multiplied by 100, the new pair
;              is converted to binary and added to to the prior result.
;              Each pair in the source is processed.  (If an odd number of
;              digits are presented, the first digit is processed alone.)
;
; Output:  If the conversion is without overflow, carry is reset and
;              EAX contains the result.
;          If the conversion overflows, carry is set and EAX is
;              undefined.
;          If no digits are valid, the result is zero in EAX.
;          SI points to the digit following the last character
;              converted and
;          CX contains the remaining count.
;
Codeasb     PROC
            push    EBX                 ; Save work registers
            push    EDX
            push    DI
            push    SI                  ; Save first character pointer
            sub     EBX,EBX             ; Clear the result
            sub     EAX,EAX             ; and rest of EAX.
            cld                         ; Force direction to up.
            cmp     BYTE PTR[SI],'-'    ; Negative?
            je      signed              ; Yes
            cmp     BYTE PTR[SI],'+'    ; Positive
            jne     unsigned            ; No - skip
signed:
            inc     SI                  ; Step over of sign.
            dec     CX                  ; and counting it
unsigned:
            push    SI                  ; Save for conversion pass
```

```
            mov      DI,CX              ; Save char count.
            mov      DX,0930h           ; set '0' in DL and 9 in DH.
            jcxz     numdone
numscan:
            lodsb                       ; Get a possible digit
            xor      AL,DL              ;
            cmp      AL,DH              ; Is it a digit?
            ja       numdone            ; If not, get out
            loop     numscan            ; Try another digit.
numdone:
            pop      SI                 ; Restore for conversion pass
            xchg     CX,DI              ; Set original count
            sub      CX,DI              ; and get digit count
            test     CL,1               ; Is the count odd?
            jz       cxeven             ; No, skip
            lodsb                       ; the load of the first byte
            and      AL,15              ; as a binary value.
            mov      BL,AL              ; We have a starting value.
cxeven:
            shr      CX,1               ; Divide the count by 2
            jz       outgood            ; If the result is zero - out.
            push     EBP                ;
            mov      EBP,100            ; Get multiplier in a register
dopair:
            lodsw                       ; Get pair of bytes (reversed)
            xchg     AL,AH              ; back in proper order
            and      AX,0F0fh           ; Clear zones
            aad                         ; Convert pair to binary.
            xchg     EAX,EBX            ; Position accum for multiply
            mul      EBP                ; and make room for digits.
            or       EDX,EDX            ; Overflow?
            jnz      outoflo            ; If so - out
            or       EAX,EAX            ; Overflow into sign?
            js       outoflo            ; If so - out
            add      EAX,EBX            ; Add new pair in.
            jo       outoflo            ; Exit if overflow occurred
            xchg     EAX,EBX            ; Put registers back
            loop     dopair             ; Do each pair
            pop      EBP                ; Restore EBP
outgood:                               ; Go back
            mov      EAX,EBX            ; with number in EAX.
            mov      CX,DI              ; Remaining count in CX
            pop      BX                 ; Restore the sign pointer.
            cmp      BYTE PTR [BX],'-'  ; Was a minus entered?
            jne      positive           ; No
```

```
                neg     EAX             ; Force it minus
positive:
                clc                     ; Clear carry (neg could set)
                pop     DI              ; Restore the entry registers
                pop     EDX
                pop     EBX
                ret                     ; and return.
outoflo:
                pop     EBP             ; Restore work register.
                stc                     ; Set error then
                pop     DI              ; clear sign pointer
                pop     DI              ; Restore the entry registers
                pop     EDX
                pop     EBX
                ret                     ; and return.
Codeasb         ENDP
code            ENDS
                END     Begin
```

10
80486 instruction set

The 80486 instruction set is a superset of previous generations' instructions with additional instructions for specific 80486 uses. We've listed it in this chapter in alphabetic order by mnemonic opcode. Along with each instruction, we've given the forms for each operand combination, including the object code produced, the operands required, and a description of the instruction.

The six new instructions on the 80486 are BSWAP, CMPXCHG, INVD, INVLPG, WBINVD, and XADD. These instructions are described in detail in this chapter, along with the remaining instructions.

Instruction format

80486 instructions consist of various elements and have various formats. Of the elements described below, only one (the opcode) is always present in each individual instruction. The other items are optional: they might not be present depending on the operation involved and on the location and type of the operands. Instructions are made up of the following:

- optional instruction prefixes.
- one or two primary opcode bytes.
- possibly an address specifier that consists of the Mod R/M byte and the Scale Index Base byte.
- a displacement—if required.
- an immediate data field—if required.

All the instruction encodings are subsets of the general instruction format shown in FIG. 10-1.

The elements of an instruction, in their order of occurrence, are as follows:

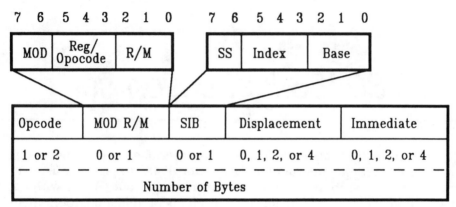

Instruction Prefix	Address Size Prefix	Operand Size Prefix	Segment Override
0 or 1	0 or 1	0 or 1	0 or 1
Number of Bytes			

Opcode	MOD R/M	SIB	Displacement	Immediate
1 or 2	0 or 1	0 or 1	0, 1, 2, or 4	0, 1, 2, or 4
Number of Bytes				

10-1   General instruction format.

- PREFIXES—One or more bytes preceding an instruction that modify the operation of that instruction. There are four types of prefixes:
  - ~ Repeat—Used with a string instruction to cause the instruction to act on each element of the string.
  - ~ Operand Size—Switches between 32-bit and 16-bit operands.
  - ~ Address Size—Switches between 32-bit and 16-bit address generation.
  - ~ Segment Override—Explicitly specifies which segment register an instruction should use. This overrides the default segment-register selection normally used by the 80486 for that instruction.
- OPCODE—This specifies the operation performed by the instruction. Some operations have several different opcodes. Each specifies a different variant of the operation.
- REGISTER SPECIFIER—The instruction might specify one or two register operands. Register specifiers can occur in either the same byte as the opcode or in the same byte as the addressing-mode specifier.
- ADDRESSING-MODE SPECIFIER—When present, this element specifies whether an operand is a register or a memory location. If it's in memory, this specifies whether a displacement, an index register, a base register, or scaling is to be used.

- MOD R/M (REGISTER/MEMORY) AND SIB (SCALE INDEX BASE) BYTES—If present, a MOD R/M operand specifier follows the opcode byte(s). The opcode determines if this specifier is present and whether this field specifies two operands or one operand plus extra opcode bits. See FIG. 10-2 for MOD R/M examples. The bits that indicate registers are shown in the figure.

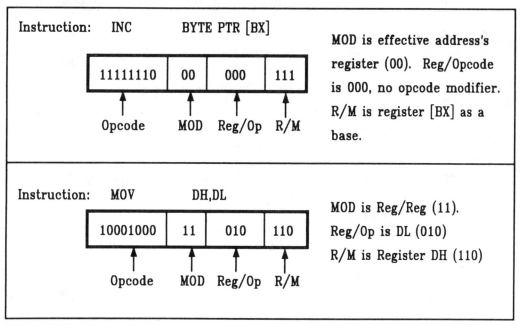

10-2 MOD R/M examples.

Most instructions that can refer to an operand in memory have an addressing form byte following the primary opcode byte(s). This byte specifies the address form to be used. Some encodings of the MOD R/M byte indicate a second addressing byte, the Scale Index Base (SIB) byte.

The MOD R/M and SIB bytes contain the following information:

- The indexing type or register number to be used in the instructions.
- The register to be used, or more information to select the instruction.
- The base, index, and scale information.

The MOD R/M byte contains these three fields:

- MOD—bits 7 and 6, occupies the two most significant bits of the byte. They combine with the R/M field to form 32 possible values: eight registers and 24 indexing modes.
- REG—bits 5, 4, and 3, specify either a register number or three more bits of opcode information. The meaning of REG is specified by the first (opcode) byte of the instruction.

- R/M—bits 2, 1 and 0, can specify a register as the location of an operand, or it can form part of the addressing-mode encoding in combination with the MOD field as described earlier.

The SIB byte includes the three fields:

- SS—bits 7 and 6, specifies the scale factor.
- INDEX—bits 5, 4, and 3, specifies the register number of the index register.
- BASE—bits 2, 1, and 0, specifies the register number of the base register.

Encoding 32-bit address mode

Register modifiers for address computation are all 32-bit registers (EAX for example). Address computations without scale index base (SIB) byte include

- A MOD of 00, which specifies address computation of DS:[R/M]. This specifies a register as follows:

  000   DS:[EAX]
  001   DS:[ECX]
  010   DS:[EDX]
  011   DS:[EBX]
  100   SIB Present
  101   DS:32 bit displacement
  110   DS:[ESI]
  111   DS:[EDI]

Thus, the effective address is DS:32 bit modifier from register or memory.

- A MOD of 01 adds an 8-bit displacement to the above so that R/M:

  000   DS:[EAX + 8 bit displacement]
  100   SIB Present
  101   SS:[EBP + 8 bit displacement]

- A MOD of 10 adds a 32-bit displacement. An R/M of 000 is DS:[EAX + a displacement]

  000   DS:[EAX + 32 bit displacement]
  100   SIB Present
  101   SS:[EBP + 32 bit displacement]

- A MOD of 11 specifies a register in the R/M so that an R/M of

  000   AL or EAX
  001   CL or ECX
  010   DL or EDX
  011   BL or EBX
  100   AH or ESP

    101 CH or EBP
    110 DH or ESI
    111 BH or EDI

The register selected depends on whether an 8-bit operation or a 32-bit operation is specified in the W bit.

The MOD value indicates the length of the displacement field to address:

    00 no displacement, except for base 101
    01 8-bit displacement
    10 32-bit displacement

Therefore, the SIB modifies the computed address (DS:[base + scaled index + displacement]), except for the base where the base is ESP or EBP and the logical substitution of SS: is made for the segment, instead of DS:.

Where an SIB is present, R/M = 100 for MOD=00, 01, or 10. The address computation is done using a combination of the following.

A 32-bit scaled index value is computed as index $* 2^{scale}$ where scale is the first two bits of the SIB byte and specified by its binary value. The index register is specified as an index of the following:

    000 EAX
    001 ECX
    010 EDX
    011 EBX
    100 no index value, scale must be 0
    101 EBP
    110 ESI
    111 EDI

If the byte is laid out, the bits appear as SSIIIBBB, where SS is the scale, III is the index, and BBB is the base. The base is selected as follows:

    000 EAX
    001 ECX
    010 EDX
    011 EBX
    100 ESP
    101 Special (a 32-bit displacement if MOD is 00 and the EBP register otherwise)
    110 ESI
    111 EDI

DISPLACEMENT—An address displacement, if present, follows the MOD R/M field. The mod subfield of the MOD R/M field indicates if the displacement is present and its length. When the addressing-mode specifier indicates that a displacement will be used to compute the address of an operand, the displacement is encoded in the instruction. A displacement is a signed integer of 8, 16, or 32 bits. The 8-bit form is used when the displacement is sufficiently small.

IMMEDIATE OPERAND—This is the simplest type of operand specifier, where the value of the operand is given directly in the instruction. The number of bits in the immediate operand depends on the operand size of the instruction and on the opcode. If present, an immediate operand is always the last field in an instruction, coming after any opcode fields or address mode fields.

When present, this element provides the value of an operand of the instruction. Immediate operands can be 8, 16, or 32 bits wide. In cases where an 8-bit immediate operand is combined in some way with a 16- or 32-bit operand, the processor automatically extends the size of the 8-bit operand, taking into account the sign.

Description notations

The following explains the notational conventions used and abbreviations used when illustrating the instruction set.

+i Used in floating-point instructions when one of the operands is ST(i) from the Floating-Point Unit (FPU) register stack. The digit i, which can range from 0 to 7, is added to the hexadecimal byte that precedes it to form a single opcode byte.

+rb, +rw, +rd A register code, 0 through 7, which is added to the hexadecimal byte given at the left of the plus sign in order to form a single opcode byte. The codes are

rb	rw	rd
AL = 0	AX = 0	EAX = 0
CL = 1	CX = 1	ECX = 1
DL = 2	DX = 2	EDX = 2
BL = 3	BX = 3	EBX = 3
AH = 4	SP = 4	ESP = 4
CH = 5	BP = 5	EBP = 5
DH = 6	SI = 6	ESI = 6
BH = 7	DI = 7	EDI = 7

/digit The digit is generally between 0 and 7. It indicates that the MOD R/M byte of the instruction uses only the register or memory (r/m) operand. The reg field contains the digit that provides an extension to the instruction's opcode.

/r This shows that the instruction's MOD R/M byte contains both a register operand and an r/m operand.

cb, cw, cd, cp A 1-byte (cb), 2-byte (cw), 4-byte (cd), or a 6-byte (cp) value that follows the opcode is used to specify a code offset and possibly a new value for the code segment register.

ib, iw, id A 1-byte (ib), 2-byte (iw), or 4-byte (id) immediate operand to the instruction that follows the opcode, MOD R/M bytes or scale-indexing bytes. The opcode determines if the operand is a signed value. Note that all words and doublewords are given with the low-order byte first.

imm8 An immediate byte value. The number "imm8" is a signed number between -128 and $+127$, inclusive. For those instructions where imm8 combines with a word or doubleword operand, the immediate value is sign-extended to form a word or doubleword. The upper byte of the word/doubleword is filled with the topmost bit of the immediate value.

imm16 An immediate word value used for instructions whose operand-size attribute is 16 bits. Inclusive, this number runs from -32768 to $+32767$.

imm32 An immediate doubleword used for instructions whose operand-size attribute is 32 bits. The range of numbers is, inclusive, from -2147483648 to $+2147483647$.

m8 A memory byte addressed by DS:SI or ES:DI.

m16 A memory word addressed by DS:SI or ES:DI.

m16int, m32int, m64int Word-, short-, and long-integer floating-point operands in memory.

m32real, m64real, m80real Single-, double-, and extended-real floating-point operands in memory.

m32 A memory doubleword addressed by DS:SI or ES:DI.

mNbyte N-byte floating-point operand in memory.

moffs8, moffs16, moffs32 A memory offset. A simple memory variable of type BYTE, WORD, or DWORD used by some variants of the MOV instruction. The actual address is given by a simple offset relative to the segment base. The number shown with the "moffs" indicates its size, which is determined by the address-size attribute of the instruction. No MOD R/M byte is used in the instruction.

ptr16:16, ptr16:32 FAR pointer. Typically, it is in a code segment different from that of the instruction. The notation 16:16 shows that the pointer value has two parts. The value to the left of the colon is the offset within the destination segment. The value to the right of the colon is a 16-bit selector or value destined for the code segment register. When the instruction's operand has a size attribute of 16, use 16:16. For the 32-bit attribute, use 16:32.

r8 One of the byte registers: AL, CL, DL, BL, AH, CH, DH, or BH.

r16 One of the word registers: AX, CS, DX, BX, SP, BP, SI or DI.

r32 One of the doubleword registers: EAX, ECX, EDX, EBX, ESP, EBP, ESI, or EDI.

rel8 A relative address in the range from 128 bytes before the end of the instruction to 127 bytes after the instruction's end.

rel16, rel32 A relative address within the same code segment as the instruction assembled. The code rel16 is applied to instructions whose operand-size attribute is 16 bits. The code rel32 is applied to the instructions with a 32-bit operand-size attribute.

r/m8   A one-byte operand. It is either the contents of a byte from memory or from a byte register—AL, BL, CL, DL, AH, BH, CH, or DH.

r/m16   A word register or memory operand used for instructions whose operand-size attribute is 16 bits. The contents of memory are found at the address provided by the effective address computation. The word registers are AX, BX, CX, DX, SP, BP, SI and DI.

r/m32   A doubleword register or memory operand used for instructions whose operand-size attribute is 32 bits. The contents of memory are found at the address provided by the effective address computation. The doubleword registers are EAX, EBX, ECX, EDX, ESP, EBP, ESI, and EDI.

rrr   When rrr appears in the binary equivalent column, it appears as the last three digits of the binary figure and indicates a particular register is referenced. The rrr translates to the following:

000 = AX/EAX	100 = SP/ESP
001 = CX/ECX	101 = BP/EBP
010 = DX/EDX	110 = SI/ESI
011 = BX/EBX	111 = DI/EDI

Sreg   A segment register. The segment register bit assignments are ES=0, CS=1, SS=2, DS=3, FS=4, and GS=5.

ST or ST(0)   The top element of the Floating-Point Unit (FPU) register stack.

ST(i)   The ith element from the top of the Floating-Point Unit (FPU) register stack; i can range from 1 to 7.

Description of modifiers and specifications

In the descriptions that illustrate each instruction, there are some extensions that show modifiers, register specifications and register/memory specifications. The notation "mm 00 r/m" specifies memory, and "mm 11 r/m" specifies rrr. A further explanation of how those interact with the opcode follows.

disp8 is an 8-byte displacement
disp16 is a 16-byte displacement
disp32 is a 32-byte displacement

8-BIT

rrr	8-bit registers	16- or 32-bit
000	AL	AX, EAX
001	CL	CX, ECX
010	DL	DX, EDX
011	BL	BX, EBX
100	AH	SP, ESP
101	CH	BC, EBP
110	DH	SI, ESI
111	BH	DI, EDI

r/m or mm	00	01	10	11
000	[BX+SI]	+disp8	+disp16	rrr
001	[BX+DI]			
010	[BP+SI]			
011	[BP+DI]			
100	[SI]			
101	[DI]			
110	disp16	[BP]+disp8	[BP]+disp16	[BP]+disp16
111	[BX]	+disp8	+disp16	

32-BIT

r/m & mm	00	01	10	11
000	[EAX]	+disp8	+disp32	rrr
001	[ECX]	+disp8		
010	[EDX]	+disp8		
011	[EBX]	+disp8		
100	SIB Follows			
101	disp32	[ECB]+disp8	[EBP]+disp32	
110	[ESI]	[EBC]+disp8		
111	[EDI]			

SCALED INDEX BYTE (SIB)

Where SS = the scale factor

SS	00	Times 1
	01	Times 2
	10	Times 4
	11	Times 8

Index	Base
000 EAX	000 EAX
001 ECX	001 ECX
010 EDX	010 EDX
011 EBX	011 EBX
100 None	100 ESP
101 EBP	101 Special
110 ESI	110 ESI
111 EDI	111 EDI

Alphabetical listing of instructions

The instruction demonstrations show the various flags. If a flag changes after an instruction executes, that flag is shown in boldface.

AAA   ASCII Adjust After Addition

INSTRUCTION	OPCODE	BINARY
AAA	37	00110111

Purpose: AAA changes the contents of register AL to a valid unpacked decimal number and zeros the top four bits. AAA follows the addition of two unpacked decimal operands in AL, but it can be used for other BCD conversions also. If a decimal carry results from the addition, or the contents of the lower nibble of AL are greater than nine, then AL is incremented by six, AH incremented by one, and the carry flag (CF) and auxiliary carry flag (AF) set to one. If no decimal carry occurred, AH is unchanged, CF and AF set to zero, and the lower four bits of AL are unchanged. Whether or not a decimal carry occurred, the upper four bits of AL are cleared.

Instruction Demonstration: This demonstration of the AAA instruction shows the adjustments made after addition to keep unpacked BCD as BCD even though the addition is binary. The instruction sequence is

```
4C25:0000 B80800   MOV   AX,0008
4C25:0003 80C004   ADD   AL,04
4C25:0006 37       AAA
4C25:0007 80C004   ADD   AL,04
4C25:000A 37       AAA
```

The registers (that change) and flags at the start are

```
EAX=00000000      IP=0000   NV UP EI PL NZ NA PO NC
```

Note an asterisk appears under each flag that has changed in that step.

```
4C25:0000 B80800   MOV       AX,0008

EAX=00000008      IP=0003   NV UP EI PL NZ NA PO NC
```

A pair of BCD digits (0,8) are loaded into AH,AL by the move into AX. The move doesn't affect the flags.

```
4C25:0003 80C004   ADD       AL,04

EAX=0000000C      IP=0006   NV UP EI PL NZ NA **PE** NC
```

The add of 4 only changes the value to 12 (hex C) and the parity flag.

```
4C25:0006 37       AAA

EAX=00000102      IP=0007   NV UP EI PL NZ **AC** PE **CY**
```

The AAA instruction inspects AL for a value greater than 9. If it is, (in our case C, which is) 10 (hex A) is subtracted from AL and 1 is added to

AH. The adjust flag is set as is the carry flag indicating a BCD carry has occurred.

```
4C25:0007 80C004   ADD        AL,04
EAX = 00000106     IP = 000A  NV UP EI PL NZ NA PE NC
```

This add results in neither a carry nor an adjustment. Both flags are reset. The result of the addition is 06 a valid BCD digit.

```
4C25:000A 37       AAA
EAX = 00000106     IP = 000B  NV UP EI PL NZ NA PE NC
```

The result of the AAA is that there is no change—what would be expected because the value doesn't need any.

AAD   ASCII Adjust Register AX Before Division

INSTRUCTION	OPCODE	BINARY
AAD	D5 0A	11010101 00001010

Purpose: AAD modifies the numerator in AH and AL to prepare for the division of two valid unpacked decimal operands. The result of the modification is that the quotient produced by the division is a valid unpacked decimal number. AH should contain the high-order digit and AL the low-order digit. AAD adjusts the value and places the result in AL. AH will contain zero.

Instruction Demonstration: AAD and AAM are demonstrated together because they reverse each other's actions. The effect of each is shown below. The instruction sequence is

```
4C25:0000 B80508   MOV    AX,0805
4C25:0003 D50A     AAD
4C25:0005 D40A     AAM
```

The registers and the flags at the start are

```
EAX = 00000000     IP = 0000  NV UP EI PL NZ NA PO NC
4C25:0000 B80508   MOV        AX,0805
EAX = 00000805     IP = 0003  NV UP EI PL NZ NA PO NC
```

The MOV has loaded two BCD digits into AX. The setting of the flags is unaffected by MOV.

```
4C25:0003 D50A     AAD
EAX = 00000055     IP = 0005  NV UP EI PL NZ NA PE NC
```

The result of the AAD is to combine the BCD digits and convert them to their binary equivalent. (55 Hex = 85 decimal) The zero flag is set according to the result in AL (non-zero in this case) as is the parity flag (to even in this case). If the sign flag were set to negative, it would be set to positive for all valid conversions.

```
4C25:0005 D40A      AAM
EAX = 00000805      IP = 0007    NV UP EI PL NZ NA PE NC
```

The result of the AAM is to convert the value in the AL register into two BCD digits in AH and AL.

AAM   ASCII Adjust AX Register After Multiplication

INSTRUCTION	OPCODE	BINARY
AAM	D4 0A	11010100 00001010

Purpose: Two BCD digits multiplied together could produce an invalid BCD result. AAM corrects the result of a multiplication of two valid unpacked decimal numbers back into a pair of digits in AH and AL. AAM follows the multiplication of two decimal numbers to produce a valid result. The high-order digit is left in AH, the low-order in AL.

Instruction Demonstration: Demonstrated with AAD.

AAS   ASCII Adjust AL Register After Subtraction

INSTRUCTION	OPCODE	BINARY
AAS	3F	00111111

Purpose: AAS changes the contents of register AL to a valid unpacked decimal number and zeros the top four bits. AAS follows the subtraction of one unpacked decimal operand from another in AL. If a decimal borrow results from the subtraction, then AL is decremented by six, AH is decremented by one, and the carry flag (CF) and auxiliary carry flag (AF) flags are set. If no decimal carry occurred, AH is unchanged, CF and AF are set to zero, and the lower four bits of AL are unchanged. Whether a decimal carry occurred or not, the upper four bits of AL are cleared.

Instruction Demonstration: This demonstration of the AAS instruction shows its effect in BCD subtraction. The instruction sequence is

```
4C25:0000 B80500      MOV    AX,0005
4C25:0003 80E804      SUB    AL,04
4C25:0006 3F          AAS
4C25:0007 80E804      SUB    AL,04
4C25:000A 3F          AAS
```

The registers (that change) and flags at the start are

```
EAX = 00000000      IP = 0000   NV UP EI PL NZ NA PO NC
4C25:0000 B80500    MOV         AX,0005
EAX = 00000005      IP = 0003   NV UP EI PL NZ NA PO NC
```

The move changes the register's contents without changing the flags.

```
4C25:0003 80E804    SUB         AL,04
EAX = 00000001      IP = 0006   NV UP EI PL NZ NA PO NC
```

The result of the subtraction is still a positive value.

```
4C25:0006 3F        AAS
EAX = 00000001      IP = 0007   NV UP EI PL NZ NA PO NC
```

The AAS doesn't change the result or the flags because no adjustment is made.

```
4C25:0007 80E804    SUB         AL,04
EAX = 000000FD      IP = 000A   NV UP EI NG NZ AC PO CY
```

This subtract results in a negative value. The sign flag is set, the carry flag is set because of the "borrow" required to set the sign flag. The adjust flag is set because of the borrow from the high nibble of AL.

```
4C25:000A 3F        AAS
EAX = 0000FF07      IP = 000B   NV UP EI NG NZ AC PO CY
```

The result of the AAS is to set the proper decimal value in AL and to subtract one from AH. The carry and auxiliary carry flags are set according to the result (since these flags were set prior to the AAS no change is indicated).

ADC   Add Integers with Carry

INSTRUCTION	OPCODE	BINARY
ADC AL,imm8	14 ib	00010100
ADC AX,imm16	15 iw	00010100
ADC EAX,imm32	15 id	00010101
ADC r/m8,imm8	90 /2 ib	10010000 mm 010 r/m
ADC r/m16,imm16	90 /2 /w	10010000 mm 010 r/m
ADC r/m32,imm32	91 /2 id	10010001 mm 010 r/m
ADC r/m16,imm8	93 /2 ib	10010011 mm rrr r/m
ADC r/m32,imm8	93 /2 ib	10010011 mm rrr r/m
ADC r/m8,r8	10 /r	00010000 mm rrr r/m
ADC r/m16,r16	11 /r	00010001 mm rrr r/m

```
ADC r/m32,r32      11 /r    00010001 mm rrr r/m
ADC r8,r/m8        12 /r    00010010 mm rrr r/m
ADC r16,r/m16      13 /r    00010011 mm rrr r/m
ADC r32,r/m32      13 /r    00010011 mm rrr r/m
```

Purpose: ADC sums the operands, adds one if the carry flag (CF) is set and replaces the destination operand with the result. If CF is cleared, ADC does the same operation as the ADD instruction. An ADD followed by multiple ADC instructions can be used to add numbers longer than 32 bits.

Instruction Demonstration: This demonstration of the ADC instruction shows the effect of the carry flag being set on when the instruction is executed. Note that the carry flag being set adds one to the sum. The instruction sequence is

```
4C25:0000 29C0      SUB   AX,AX
4C25:0002 80C040    ADD   AL,40
4C25:0005 80D040    ADC   AL,40
4C25:0008 80D080    ADC   AL,80
4C25:000B 80D080    ADC   AL,80
```

The registers (that change) and flags at the start are

EAX = 00000000   IP = 0000   NV UP EI PL NZ NA PO NC

First, ensure a clear register.

```
4C25:0000 29C0   SUB        AX,AX
```

EAX = 00000000   IP = 0002   NV UP EI PL **ZR** NA **PE** NC

The sequence of ADCs begins with an ADD that ignores the state of the carry flag. This would normally be the add of the lowest order numbers in the extended summation. The carry flag could have been forced off with the CLC (clear carry) instruction also.

```
4C25:0002 80C040   ADD        AL,40
```

EAX = 00000040   IP = 0005   NV UP EI PL **NZ** NA **PO** NC

ADD changes the value of the register, and the flags change to reflect the result.

```
4C25:0005 80D040   ADC        AL,40
```

EAX = 00000080   IP = 0008   **OV** UP EI **NG** NZ NA PO NC

Note that because the sign bit (the high-order bit of the register) is now set, the minus flag is also set. Also note that the overflow flag has been set, because the result cannot be contained in the target register as a signed quantity.

```
4C25:0008 80D080   ADC        AL,80
```

EAX = 00000000   IP = 000B   OV UP EI **PL ZR** NA **PE CY**

This addition caused a carry out of the register (AL). The carry flag is now set. (Note the effect on the next ADC instruction.) It also left a sum of zero as its result. This caused the zero flag and even parity to be set. Because zero has a sign bit of zero, the sign flag is set to positive.

```
4C25:000B 80D080      ADC      AL,80
EAX=00000081          IP=000E  NV UP EI NG NZ NA PE NC
```

Because the carry flag was on, an additional 1 was added in the operation. This result did not cause a carry, so the carry flag is reset. Because the result is not zero, the zero flag is also reset.

ADD   Add Integers

INSTRUCTION	OPCODE	BINARY
ADD AL,imm8	04 ib	0000100
ADD AX,imm16	05 /w	00000101
ADD EAX,imm32	05 id	00000101
ADD r/m8,imm8	80 /0 ib	10000000 mm 000 r/m
ADD r/m16,imm16	81 /0 iw	10000001 mm 000 r/m
ADD r/m32,imm32	81 /0 id	10000001 mm 000 r/m
ADD r/m16,imm8	83 /0 ib	10000011 mm 000 r/m
ADD r/m32,imm8	83 /0 ib	10000011 mm 000 r/m
ADD r/m8,r8	00 /r	00000000 mm rrr r/m
ADD r/m16,r16	01 /r	00000001 mm rrr r/m
ADD r/m32,r32	01 /r	00000001 mm rrr r/m
ADD r8,r/m8	02 /r	00000010 mm rrr r/m
ADD r16,r/m16	03 /r	00000011 mm rrr r/m
ADD r32,r/m32	03 /r	00000011 mm rrr r/m

Purpose: ADD replaces the destination operation with the sum of the source and destination operands. It sets the carry flag (CF) if there is an overflow. CF is bit zero of the EFLAGS register.

Instruction Demonstration: This demonstration of the ADD instruction shows that it executes its addition without interrogating the carry flag. The instruction sequence is

```
4C13:0000 6629C0      SUB      EAX,EAX
4C13:0003 80C040      ADD      AL,40
4C13:0006 80C040      ADD      AL,40
4C13:0009 80C080      ADD      AL,80
4C13:000C 80C040      ADD      AL,40
```

The registers and flags at the start are

```
EAX=00000000          IP=0000  NV UP EI PL NZ NA PO NC
```

```
4C13:0000 6629C0   SUB      EAX,EAX
EAX = 00000000     IP = 0003   NV UP EI PL ZR NA PE NC
```

The subtract ensures the register contents are zero. It also sets the zero and parity flags.

```
4C13:0003 80C040   ADD      AL,40
EAX = 00000040     IP = 0006   NV UP EI PL NZ NA PO NC
```

The ADD sets the parity flag to odd because the number of bits in the low 8 bits is odd. The zero flag is reset because the result of the addition is not zero.

```
4C13:0006 80C040   ADD      AL,40
EAX = 00000080     IP = 0009   OV UP EI NG NZ NA PO NC
```

The result of the addition cannot be contained as a signed 8-bit number, so the overflow flag is set. The sign bit (of AL) is also set, which causes the sign flag to be set to negative.

```
4C13:0009 80C080   ADD      AL,80
EAX = 00000000     IP = 000C   OV UP EI PL ZR NA PE CY
```

This ADD causes a carry out of the target register. The carry flag is set. Because the result has a zero sign bit, the sign flag changes to positive. The result is a zero register so the zero flag is set.

```
4C13:000C 80C040   ADD      AL,40
EAX = 00000040     IP = 000F   NV UP EI PL NZ NA PO NC
```

This ADD changes the zero flag to non-zero, resets the carry flag, and changes the parity flag to odd. Note that the state of the carry flag does not affect the result of the instruction.

AND   Logical AND

INSTRUCTION	OPCODE	BINARY
AND AL,imm8	24 ib	00100100
AND AX,imm16	25 iw	00100101
AND EAX,imm32	25 id	00100101
AND r/m8,imm8	A0 /4 ib	10100000 mm 100 r/m
AND r/m16,imm16	A1 /4 iw	10100001 mm 100 r/m
AND r/m32,imm32	A1 /4 ib	10100001 mm 100 r/m
AND r/m16,imm8	A3 /4 ib	10100011 mm 100 r/m
AND r/m32,imm8	A3 /4 ib	10100011 mm 100 r/m
AND r/m8,r8	20 /r	00100000 mm rrr r/m

AND r/m16,r16	21 /r	00100001 mm rrr r/m
AND r/m32,r32	21 /r	00100001 mm rrr r/m
AND r8,r/m8	22 /r	00100010 mm rrr r/m
AND r16,r/m16	23 /r	00100011 mm rrr r/m
AND r32,r/m32	23 /r	00100011 mm rrr r/m

Purpose: AND is used to ensure that user-specified bits are off, e.g., the parity bit in an ASCII input stream from a terminal. When AND is used in conjunction with a compare, AND makes certain that the specified bits are on. In use, AND is executed prior to the compare. Both AND and the compare use known masks

Instruction Demonstration: This demonstration of the AND instruction shows its effect as it is used to mask bits of its destination off. The instruction sequence is

```
4C20:0000 66B8EE11F0F0        MOV    EAX,F0F011EE
4C20:0006 81E0FFFF            AND    AX,FFFF
4C20:000A 81E0F5F5            AND    AX,F5F5
4C20:000E 81E0123E            AND    AX,3E12
4C20:0012 676681E0EE11F000    AND    EAX,00F011EE
```

The registers and flags at the start are

```
EAX=00000000              IP=0000    NV UP EI PL NZ NA PO NC
4C20:0000 66B8EE11F0F0     MOV    EAX,F0F011EE
EAX=F0F011EE              IP=0006    NV UP EI PL NZ NA PO NC
```

MOV sets the register value with no changes to the flags.

```
4C20:0006 81E0FFFF         AND        AX,FFFF
EAX=F0F011EE              IP=000A    NV UP EI PL NZ NA **PE** NC
```

Note that ANDing with a mask that has all bits set does not affect the target. It does set the carry flag off, sets the parity flag, and the zero flag according to the result. It also sets overflow off and the sign flag according to the result. Note also that the extended register bits are not affected.

```
4C20:000A 81E0F5F5         AND        AX,F5F5
EAX=F0F011E4              IP=000E    NV UP EI PL NZ NA PE NC
```

This AND has masked off bits 1 and 3 of the low nibble. The result is non-zero with even parity, so no flags change.

```
4C20:000E 81E0123E         AND        AX,3E12
EAX=F0F01000              IP=0012    NV UP EI PL NZ NA PE NC
```

This AND has masked the value in AL to zero, leaving AX with only one bit in AH. Note that the parity calculated on the low eight bits of the result is even. The zero flag is non-zero because it is set based on the total result.

4C20:0012 676681E0EE11F000   AND   EAX,00F011EE
EAX=00F01000   IP=001A   NV UP EI PL NZ NA PE NC

This AND affects the high bits of EAX. Note the address and the width prefixes necessary because of the 16-bit width default that must be over-ridden

---

ARPL   Adjust Requester Privilege Level of Selector

INSTRUCTION	OPCODE	BINARY
ARPL r/m16,r16	63 /r	01100011 mm rrr r/m

Purpose: ARPL is used by systems software to guarantee that selector parameters to a subroutine do not request more privilege than allowed to the caller. ARPL has two operands. The first is a 16-bit word register or memory variable that contains the value of the selector. The second operand is generally a register that contains the caller's CS (code segment) selector value

ARPL checks that the requested privilege level (RPL) of the first operand against the RPL of the second. The RPL is specified in the least significant bits of each operand. If RPL of the first operand is less than that of the second, the zero flag (ZF) is set to one

Instruction Demonstration: The ARPL instruction is used by system software to validate selectors passed as parameter pointers. It checks a selector against a model that contains the maximum privilege allowed (usually the caller's CS selector is used) and adjusts the tested value to the lesser of the privilege levels (highest number). If no change is necessary, the zero flag is reset. If a change was needed, the zero flag is set (a possible attempt to breach security). The instruction sequence is

```
0070:0100 8CCB     MOV     BX,CS
0070:0102 B87300   MOV     AX,0073
0070:0105 63C3     ARPL    BX,AX
```

The registers and flags at the start are

EAX=00000000   EBX=00000000   CS=0070   IP=0100
                                    NV UP EI PL NZ NA PO NC

For the purpose of the demo, we reverse the normal and set CS as the tested value (the demo was done at level 0).

0070:0100 8CCB   MOV   BX,CS
EAX=00000000   EBX=00000070   CS=0070   IP=0102
                                    NV UP EI PL NZ NA PO NC

We set a comparand with a lower privilege (3).

```
0070:0102 B87300                        MOV        AX,0073
EAX=00000073  EBX=00000070  CS=0070    IP=0105
                                        NV UP EI PL NZ NA PO NC
```

The ARPL is issued to adjust the tested descriptor to the least privilege and set the zero flag, because the adjustment was needed.

```
0070:0105 63C3                          ARPL       BX,AX
EAX=00000073  EBX=00000073  CS=0070    IP=0107
                                        NV UP EI PL ZR NA PO NC
```

BOUND Check Array Index Against Bounds

INSTRUCTION	OPCODE	BINARY
BOUND r16,m16&16	62 /r	01100010 mm rrr r/m
BOUND r32,m32&32	62 /r	01100010 mm rrr r/m

Purpose: BOUND verifies that the signed value contained in the specified register lies within specified limits. Interrupt 5 occurs if the value in the register is less than the lower bound or greater than the upper bound. The upper and lower limit values may each be a word or a doubleword.

The block of memory that specifies the lower and upper limits of an array can typically reside just before the array itself. This makes the array bounds accessible at a constant offset from the beginning of the array. Because the address of the array is already present in a register, this avoids extra calculations to obtain the effective address of the array bounds.

BOUND includes two operands. The first specifies the register being tested, and the second contains the effective address of the two signed BOUND limit values. BOUND assumes that the upper limit and the lower limit are in adjacent memory locations. These limit values cannot be register operands; if they are, an invalid opcode exception occurs.

Instruction Demonstration: This demonstration of the BOUND instruction shows the execution of a valid BOUND check. An out of bound check is handled by the routine for INT 5. The instruction sequence is

```
14EB:0100 B84000        MOV       AX,0040
14EB:0103 62060002      BOUND     [0200],AX
14EB:0107 B80101        MOV       AX,0101
14EB:010A 62060002      BOUND     [0200],AX
```

The registers and flags at the start are

```
AX=0040                 DS=14EB   CS=14EB IP=0103
                                  NV UP EI PL NZ NA PO NC
```

```
14EB:0103 62060002      BOUND      [0200],AX
DS:0200=0001
    0202=0100
```

This execution of the bound instruction results in the execution of the next sequential instruction. AX is < = left bound and > = right bound. Note that no flags are affected.

```
AX=0040                 IP=0107    NV UP EI PL NZ NA PO NC
14:EB0107 B80101        MOV        AX,0101
AX=0101                 IP=010A    NV UP EI PL NZ NA PO NC
14EB:010A 62060002      BOUND      [0200],AXDS:0200=0001
    0202=0100
```

This execution of the BOUND instruction causes an INT 5 to be taken because AX is beyond the right bound.

BSF   Bit Scan Forward

INSTRUCTION	OPCODE	BINARY
BSF r16,r/m16	OF BC	00001111 10111100 mm rrr r/m
BSF r32,r/m32	OF BC	00001111 10111100 mm rrr r/m

Purpose: This instruction scans a word or doubleword (from the least significant bit to the most significant bit) for a one-bit and stores the number of the first set bit into a register. The bit string being scanned can be either in a register or in memory. The zero flag (ZF) is set if the entire word is zero (i.e., no set bits are found). ZF is cleared if a *one* bit is found. ZF is bit six of the EFLAGS register.

Note: If no set bit is found, the value of the destination register is undefined.

This instruction was introduced with the 80386; it is useful for scanning allocation bit maps for an allocatable or free bit. Returning the number of the bit provides the relative number of the item within the word being examined.

Instruction Demonstration: This demonstration of the bit scan forward (BSF) instruction shows its operation both when a bit is located and in the case of a zero operand. It should be noted that the operation is on a word of either 16 or 32 bits. The bits are numbered from right to left in the word. The method of storage (low byte to high byte) is ignored. The word is fetched and then scanned.

The **BSR** (bit scan reverse) instruction is demonstrated also to emphasize its difference from BSF. The instruction sequence is

```
4C13:0000 B8144C            MOV  AX,4C14
```

```
4C13:0003 8ED8              MOV    DS,AX
4C13:0005 6629C0            SUB    EAX,EAX
4C13:0008 660FBC061000      BSF    EAX,DWord Ptr [0010]
4C13:000E 660FBC061400      BSF    EAX,DWord Ptr [0014]
4C13:0014 660FBD061000      BSR    EAX,DWord Ptr [0010]
```

The registers and flags at the start:

```
EAX=00000000           DS=4C03 IP=0000    NV UP EI PL NZ NA PO N̄C
4C13:0000 B8144C        MOV                AX,4C14
EAX=00004C14           DS=4C03 IP=0003    NV UP EI PL NZ NA PO NC
```

The move changes only the target register.

```
4C13:0003 8ED8         MOV                DS,AX
EAX=00004C14           DS=4C14 IP=0005    NV UP EI PL NZ NA PO NC
```

DS is now set to the test data's segment.

```
64C13:0005 6629C0      SUB                EAX,EAX
EAX=00000000           IP=0008            NV UP EI PL ZR NA PE NC
```

The subtract clears the register and sets the zero flag and parity even. The data at the start is

```
DS:0010=00030000
DS:0014=00000000
4C13:0008 660FBC061000  BSF                EAX,DWord Ptr [0010]
EAX=00000010           IP=000E            NV UP EI PL NZ NA PO NC
```

The number of the first bit found (16) is placed into the specified register. The zero flag is set non-zero to indicate that a bit was found. Odd parity is also set.

```
4C13:000E 660FBC061400  BSF                EAX,DWord Ptr [0014]
EAX=00000010           IP=0014            NV UP EI PL ZR NA PE NC
```

The scan word without any *one* bits produces no change in the target register. The zero flag is set to indicate that no bit was found. Note that the parity flag is set to even—obviously not the parity of AL.

```
4C13:0014 660FBD061000  BSR                EAX,DWord Ptr [0010]
EAX=00000011           IP=001A            OV UP EI PL NZ NA PE CY
```

The reverse scan locates bit 17 as the first bit in the doubleword. The scan is from bit 31 down to bit 0. The number of the bit located is placed in the target register and the zero flag is set non-zero. The carry flag is changed, but its value is unspecified by Intel (don't count on it!).

BSR   Bit Scan Reverse

INSTRUCTION	OPCODE	BINARY
BSR r16,r/m16	OF BD	00001111 10111101 mm rrr r/m
BSR r32,r/m32	OF BD	00001111 10111101 mm rrr r/m

Purpose: This instruction scans a word or doubleword (from the most significant bit to the least significant bit) for a *one* bit and stores the index of the first set bit into a register. The bit string being scanned can be either in a register or in memory. The zero flag (ZF) is set if the entire word is zero (i.e., no set bits are found). ZF, bit six of the EFLAGS register, is cleared if a *one* bit is found. BSR was introduced with the 80386.

Note: If no set bit is found, the value of the destination register is undefined.

Instruction Demonstration: The demonstration of the BSR instruction is combined with that for BSF.

BSWAP   Byte Swap

INSTRUCTION	OPCODE	BINARY
BSWAP	OF C8/r	00001111 11001rrr

Purpose: BSWAP reverses the byte order of a 32-bit register; it converts a value in "little endian" format to "big endian" format, or vice-versa. (See Note about the big and little endian formats.) It affects no flags.

This instruction is new with the 80486.

Note: Like earlier Intel 86-series microprocessors, the 80486 stores multi-byte data with high-order bits in the highest-address byte. This is called "little endian" format. The "big endian" format has multi-byte data stored in the opposite order: with the high-order bits in the lowest-address byte.

Instruction Demonstration: Not demonstrated.

BT   Bit Test

INSTRUCTION	OPCODE	BINARY
BT r/m16,r16	OF A3	00001111 10100011 mm rrr r/m
BT r/m32,r32	OF A3	00001111 10100011 mm rrr r/m
BT r/m16,imm8	OF BA /r ib	00001111 10111010 mm 100 r/m
BT r/m32,imm8	OF BA /r ib	00001111 10111010 mm 100 r/m

Purpose: BT can determine whether or not a bit in a bit map is set. BT sets the carry flag (CF) to the same value as the bit being tested.

This instruction was introduced with the 80386.

Do not use BT to reference memory-mapped I/O registers directly. Use MOV to load from or store to the memory-mapped device registers and then use the register form of BT.

Instruction Demonstration: This demonstration of the BT instruction shows its action in testing the value of the indicated bit. The instruction sequence is

```
4C13:0000 660FA3060E00    BT      DWord Ptr [000E],EAX
4C13:0006 6640            INC     EAX
4C13:0008 660FA3060E00    BT      DWord Ptr [000E],EAX
```

The registers and flags at the start are

```
EAX=00000014            IP=0000   OV UP EI PL NZ NA PO NC
```

The data area:

```
DS:000E=00200000

4C13:0000 660FA3060E00    BT      DWord Ptr [000E],EAX
EAX=00000014            IP=0006   NV UP EI PL NZ NA PO NC
```

The bit specified in the register (20) is tested and is found to be off. That result is set in the carry flag. If the bit had been set on, the carry flag would also be on.

```
4C13:0006 6640            INC     EAX
EAX=00000015            IP=0008   NV UP EI PL NZ NA PO NC
```

The INC steps the bit number to 21 (a bit that is on).

```
4C13:0008 660FA3060E00    BT      DWord Ptr [000E],EAX
EAX=00000015            IP=000E   NV UP EI PL NZ NA PO **CY**
```

The bit being tested here is on. Carry is set to indicate the state of the bit being tested.

BTC   Bit Test and Complement

INSTRUCTION	OPCODE	BINARY
BTC r/m16,r16	0F BB	00001111 10111011 mm rrr r/m
BTC r/m32,r32	0F BB	00001111 10111011 mm rrr r/m
BTC r/m16,imm8	0F BA /7 ib	00001111 10111010 mm 111 r/m
BTC r/m32,imm8	0F BA /7 ib	00001111 10111010 mm 111 r/m

Purpose: BTC tests a specific bit, copies that bit to the carry flag (CF—bit zero of the EFLAGS register), and inverts the original bit (e.g., if the bit was a one, it's changed to a zero, and CF is set to one).

This instruction was introduced with the 80386.

Do not use BTC to reference memory-mapped I/O registers directly. Use MOV to load from or store to the memory-mapped device registers and then use the register form of BTC.

Instruction Demonstration: This demonstrates the action of the BTC instruction. Note that the first execution finds the bit on, sets the carry on, and sets the bit off. The second execution finds the bit off, sets the carry flag off, and the bit on. The instruction sequence is

```
14EB:0100 0FBB060002    BTC    [0200],AX
14EB:0105 0FBB060002    TC     [0200],AX
```

The data at the start is

```
DS:0200   00 02 00 01 00 00 00 00 . . . . . . . .
```

The registers and flags at the start are

```
AX = 0009                  IP = 0100   NV UP EI PL NZ NA PE NC
14EB:0100 0FBB060002    BTC    [0200],AX
AX = 0009                  IP = 0105   NV UP EI PL NZ NA PE CY
14EB:0200                  00 00 00 01 00 00 00 00 . . . . . . . .
```

The bit was on prior to execution. The bit is copied into the carry flag and then inverted in memory.

```
14EB:0105 0FBB060002    BTC    [0200],AX
AX = 0009                  IP = 010A   NV UP EI PL NZ NA PE NC
14EB:0200                  00 02 00 01 00 00 00 00 . . . . . . . .
```

The bit was off prior to execution. The bit is copied into the carry flag and then inverted in memory.

BTR   Bit Test and Reset

INSTRUCTION	OPCODE	BINARY
BTR r/m16,r16	0F B3	00001111 10110011 mm rrr r/m
BTR r/m32,r32	0F B3	00001111 10110011 mm rrr r/m
BTR r/m16,imm8	0F BA /6 ib	00001111 10111010 mm 110 r/m
BTR r/m32,imm8	0F BA /6 ib	00001111 10111010 mm 110 r/m

Purpose: BTR tests a specific bit, copies that bit to CF, and forces the original bit to zero. This instruction was introduced with the 80386.

Instruction Demonstration: This demonstrates the action of the BTR instruction. Note that the execution copies the bit into the carry flag and sets the bit off. The instruction sequence is

    14EB:0100 0FB3060002   BTR   [0200],AX

The data at the start is

    DS:0200   FF FF 00 01 00 00 00 00. . . . .

The registers and flags at the start are

AX = 0009	IP = 0100	NV UP EI PL NZ NA PE NC
14EB:0100 0FB3060002	BTR	[0200],AX
AX = 0009	IP = 0105	NV UP EI PL NZ NA PE **CY**
DS:0200		FF FD 00 01 00 00 00 00. } . . . . . .

The bit was on prior to execution, as indicated by the carry flag; after execution, it is forced off in memory.

BTS   Bit Test and Set

INSTRUCTION	OPCODE	BINARY
BTS r/m16,r16	0F AB	00001111 10101011 mm rrr r/m
BTS r/m32,r32	0F AB	00001111 10101011 mm rrr r/m
BTS r/m16,imm8	0F BA /5 ib	00001111 10111010 mm 101 r/m
BTS r/m32,imm8	0F BA /5 ib	00001111 10111010 mm 101 r/m

Purpose: BTS tests a specific bit, copies that bit to the carry flag (CF—bit zero of the EFLAGS register), and sets the original bit to one.

This instruction was introduced with the 80386.

Do not use BTC to reference memory-mapped I/O registers directly. Use MOV to load from or store to the memory-mapped device registers and then use the register form of BTS.

Instruction Demonstration: This demonstrates the action of the BTS instruction. Note that the execution copies the bit into the carry flag and sets the bit on. The instruction sequence is

    14EB:0105 0FAB060002   BTS   [0200],AX

The data at the start is

    DS:0200   FF FD 00 01 00 00 00 00 . } . . . . . .

The registers and flags at the start are

AX = 0009	IP = 0105	NV UP EI PL NZ NA PE CY
14EB:0105 0FAB060002	BTS	[0200],AX

AX = 0009   IP = 010A   NV UP EI PL NZ NA PE **NC**
14EB:0200   FF FF 00 01 00 00 00 00 . . . .

The bit was off prior to execution, as indicated by the carry flag (off); after execution, it is forced on in memory.

CALL   Call a Procedure

INSTRUCTION	OPCODE	BINARY
CALL rel16	E8 cw	11101000
CALL r/m16	FF /2	11111111 mm 010 r/m
CALL ptr16:16	9A cd	10011010
CALL m16:16	FF /3	11111111 mm 011 r/m
CALL rel32	E8 cd	11101000
CALL r/m32	FF /2	11111111 mm 010 r/m
CALL ptr16:32	9A cp	10011010
CALL ptr32:32	9A cp	10011010
CALL m16:32	FF /3	11111111 mm 011 r/m

Purpose: CALL transfers control from one code segment location to another. These locations can be within the same code segment (near) or in different ones (far). Prior to actual transfer, CALL saves the address of the instruction following the CALL and the current value of extended instruction pointer (EIP) on the stack.

CALL instructions have relative, direct, and indirect versions. Indirect instructions specify an absolute address in one of two ways: the 80486 can obtain the destination address from a memory operand specified in the instruction, or the program CALLs a location specified by a general register (EAX, EDX, ECX, EBX, EBP, ESI, or EDI).

Instruction Demonstration: The CALL instruction, ENTER instruction, LEAVE instruction, and RET instruction are demonstrated together because they logically "fit" with and complement each other. The CALLed routine's instructions are

    14EB:0110 C80A0001   ENTER   000A,01
    14EB:0114 90   NOP
    14EB:0115 C9   LEAVE
    14EB:0116 C3   RET

The CALL instruction is

    14EB:0101 E80C00   CALL   0110
    14EB:0104 90   NOP

The registers (that change) and flags at the start are

```
SP=EA04 BP=0000   IP=0101   NV UP EI PL NZ NA PO NC
14EB:0101 E80C00      CALL      0110
SP=EA02 BP=0000   IP=0110   NV UP EI PL NZ NA PO NC
```

Issue a CALL NEAR. Note that adding the adjusted IP to the near displacement results in an IP value of 0110. (0104 + 000C = 0110). Note also that SP has decreased by 2. The IP value (0104) was placed on the stack prior to computing its new value.

```
14EB:0110 C80A0001    ENTER     000A,01
SP=E9F4 BP=EA00       IP=0114   NV UP EI PL NZ NA PO NC
```

Note the effect of the ENTER instruction. BP is saved on the stack, set to the resulting value of SP, and then SP is decreased by the first operand's value.

```
14EB:0114 90          NOP
SP=E9F4 BP=EA00       IP=0115   NV UP EI PL NZ NA PO NC
14EB:0115 C9LEAVE
SP=EA02 BP=0000       IP=0116   NV UP EI PL NZ NA PO NC
```

LEAVE reverses the effect of the ENTER. BP is copied to SP, and then BP is POPed off the stack, leaving the SP positioned for the RET.

```
14EB:0116 C3          RET
SP=EA04 BP=0000       IP=0104   NV UP EI PL NZ NA PO NC
```

RET removes the IP value from the stack, which causes the instruction following the CALL to be executed next.

```
14EB:0104 90          NOP
SP=EA04 BP=0000       IP=0105   NV UP EI PL NZ NA PO NC
```

CBW   Convert Byte to Word
CWDE   Convert Word to Doubleword

INSTRUCTION	OPCODE	BINARY
CBW	98	10011000
CWDE	99	10011001

Purpose: These instructions extend the sign bit into the top portion of the larger register so that arithmetic operations can calculate correctly.

The value of bit seven of AX or bit 15 of EAX is placed in every bit of AH or the upper 16 bits of EAX.

Instruction Demonstration: This demonstrates the action of the CBW and CWDE instructions. The instruction sequence is

```
4C13:0000 66B8050F0F0F     MOV     EAX,0F0F0F05
4C13:0006 98               CBW
4C13:0007 6698             CWDE
4C13:0009 B8F104           MOV     AX,04F1
4C13:000C 98               CBW
```

The registers and flags prior to the first CBW are

```
EAX=00000000        IP=0000    NV UP EI PL NZ NA PO NC
4C13:0000 66B8050F0F0F    MOV     EAX,0F0F0F05
EAX=0F0F0F05        IP=0006    NV UP EI PL NZ NA PO NC
```

The move sets the value into the register without changing the flags.

```
4C13:0006 98    CBW
EAX=0F0F0005  IP=0007              NV UP EI PL NZ NA PO NC
```

Note that none of the flags were affected. AX now contains the word equivalent of the value previously in AL. The extension to a word didn't affect the high order 16 bits of the register.

```
4C13:0007 6698    CWDE
EAX=00000005  IP=0009              NV UP EI PL NZ NA PO NC
```

The extension from a word to a doubleword operates the same.

```
4C13:0009 B8F104    MOV     AX,04F1
EAX=000004F1  IP=000C              NV UP EI PL NZ NA PO NC
```

A negative value is placed in AL.

```
4C13:000C 98    CBW
EAX=0000FFF1  IP=000D              NV UP EI PL NZ NA PO NC
```

AX now contains the sign extended negative value. No flags are changed.

CLC   Clear Carry Flag (CF)

INSTRUCTION	OPCODE	BINARY
CLC	F8	11111000

Purpose: This instruction sets the carry flag (CF—bit zero of the EFLAGS register) to zero. No other flags are affected.

Instruction Demonstration: This demonstrates the action of the CLC, CMC and STC instructions. The instruction sequence is

```
14EB:0100 F9   STC
14EB:0101 F8   CLC
14EB:0102 F5   CMC
```

The registers and flags at the start are

```
IP=0100        NV UP EI PL NZ NA PO NC
```

Note that the carry flag is not set.

```
14EB:0100 F9   STC
```
```
IP=0101        NV UP EI PL NZ NA PO CY
```

STC sets the carry flag.

```
14EB:0101 F8   CLC
```
```
IP=0102        NV UP EI PL NZ NA PO NC
```

After the CLC, the carry is set to zero.

```
14EB:0102 F5   CMC
```
```
IP=0103        NV UP EI PL NZ NA PO CY
```

After the CMC, the carry flag is inverted (in this case from zero to non-zero).

CLD   Clear Direction Flag (DF)

INSTRUCTION	OPCODE	BINARY
CLD	FC	11111100

Purpose: CLD sets the direction flag (DF—bit 10 of the EFLAGS register) to zero. No other flags are affected. By setting DF to zero, DF now signals the automatic indexing feature to increment the index registers ESI and EDI. Automatic indexing is used by string instructions.

Instruction Demonstration: This demonstrates the CLD instruction's action as well as STD. The instruction sequence is

```
14EB:0100 FD   STD
14EB:0101 FC   CLD
```

The flags and affected registers at the start are

```
IP=0100        NV UP EI PL NZ NA PO NC
```

Execute the STD to force the direction to down.

    14EB:0100 FD   STD

    IP = 0101   NV **DN** EI PL NZ NA PO NC

Note that the direction flag is set to "down." Then clear the direction flag.

    14EB:0101 FC   CLD

    IP = 0102   NV **UP** EI PL NZ NA PO NC

Note that the direction flag is reset to "up," and the IP register is advanced; these are the only effects of CLD.

CLI   Clear Interrupt Flag (IF)

INSTRUCTION	OPCODE	BINARY
CLI	FA	11111010

Purpose: If the current privilege level is at least as privileged as the input/output privilege level (IOPL—bits 12 and 13 of the EFLAGS register), CLI sets the interrupt flag (IF—bit nine of EFLAGS) to zero. No other flags are affected. An exception is if the program does not have the correct I/O privilege.

Note: External interrupts are ignored at the end of CLI until the interrupt flag is set.

Instruction Demonstration: This demonstrates the action of the CLI and STI instructions. The instruction sequence is

    14EB:0100 FB   STI
    14EB:0101 FA   CLI

The registers (that change) and flags at the start are

    IP = 0100   NV UP DI PL NZ NA PO NC

    14EB:0100 FB   STI

    IP = 0101   NV UP **EI** PL NZ NA PO NC

Note that the interrupt flag now is set (enabled), the IP register is advanced, and no other registers or flags are affected.

    14EB:0101 FA   CLI

    IP = 0102   NV UP **DI** PL NZ NA PO NC

The interrupt flag is reset (disabled), the IP register is advanced, and no other registers or flags are affected.

CLTS   Clear Task-Switched Flag in Control Register Zero (CR0)

INSTRUCTION	OPCODE	BINARY
CLTS	0F 06	00001111 00000110

Purpose: CLTS clears the TS (Task Switched) flag in the CR0 register. This flag is set by the processor every time a task switch occurs. When the TS flag is used to manage processor extensions,

- every execution of an ESC instruction is trapped if the TS flag is set.
- execution of WAIT instruction is trapped if the MP (Math Present) and TS flags are both set.

Thus, if a task switch was made after an ESC instruction began, the Floating-Point Unit's context may need to be saved before a new ESC instruction can be issued. The fault handler saves the context and clears the TS flag.

Note: CLTS is used in systems programming and is a privileged instruction, running at privilege level zero only.

Instruction Demonstration: The CLTS instruction clears the task switched flag in CR0. The CLTS instruction is used by a 80486 dispatcher to indicate to a coprocessor that all the data or results it contains pertain to the current task.

The task switched flag allows delay in saving the coprocessor state (often unnecessary if the switch was to a system task such as a spooler or interrupt handler). No flags are changed in the EFLAGS register. The instructions are

```
0070:0100 0F20C0    MOV      EAX,CR0
0070:0103 0F06      CLTS
0070:0105 0F20C0    MOV      EAX,CR0
```

The registers and flags at the start are

```
EAX=00000000      IP=0100   NV UP EI PL NZ NA PO NC

0070:0100 0F20C0    MOV      EAX,CR0
```

Note that the task switched flag is on in the copy of CR0 copied to EAX.

```
EAX=7FFFFFE9      IP=0103   NV UP EI PL NZ NA PO NC

0070:0103 0F06      CLTS
```

The CLTS instruction makes no visible change.

```
EAX=7FFFFFE9      IP=0105   NV UP EI PL NZ NA PO NC

0070:0105 0F20C0    MOV      EAX,CR0
```

The task switched flag is now reset.

EAX = 7FFFFFE1   IP = 0108   NV UP EI PL NZ NA PO NC

CMC   Complement Carry Flag (CF)

INSTRUCTION	OPCODE	BINARY
CMC	F5	11110101

Purpose: CMC reverses the value of the carry flag (CF—bit zero of the EFLAGS register), e.g., CF becomes a zero if it was a one. No other flags are affected.

Instruction Demonstration: Demonstrated with CLC.

CMP   Compare

INSTRUCTION	OPCODE	BINARY
CMP AL,imm8	3C ib	00111100
CMP AX,imm16	3D iw	00111101
CMP EAX,imm32	3D id	00111101
CMP r/m8,imm8	80 /7 ib	10000000 mm 111 r/m
CMP r/m16,imm16	81 /7 iw	10000001 mm 111 r/m
CMP r/m32,imm32	81 /7 id	10000001 mm 111 r/m
CMP r/m16,imm8	83 /7 ib	10000011 mm 111 r/m
CMP r/m32,imm8	83 /7 ib	10000011 mm 111 r/m
CMP r/m8,r8	38 /r	00111000 mm rrr r/m
CMP r/m16,r16	39 /r	00111001 mm rrr r/m
CMP r/m32,r32	39 /r	00111001 mm rrr r/m
CMP r8,m8	3A /r	00111010 mm rrr r/m
CMP r16,r/m16	3B /r	00111011 mm rrr r/m
CMP r32,r/m32	3B /r	00111011 mm rrr r/m

Purpose: CMP subtracts the source operand from the destination operand but does not store the result. Only the flags are changed. In other words, CMP updates the overflow flag (OF—bit 11 of EFLAGS), the sign flag (SF—bit seven of EFLAGS), the zero flag (ZF—bit six of EFLAGS), the auxiliary carry flag (AF—bit four of EFLAGS), the parity flag (PF—bit two of EFLAGS), and the carry flag (CF—bit 0 of EFLAGS), but does not alter the source and destination operands.

Instruction Demonstration: This demonstrates the action of the CMP instruction. The instruction sequence is

14EB:0100 B8FEFE   MOV   AX,FEFE

```
14EB:0103 BBFD0F     MOV   BX,0FFD
14EB:0106 38E0       CMP   AL,AH
14EB:0108 38F8       CMP   AL,BH
14EB:010A 38D8       CMP   AL,BL
14EB:010C 38C7       CMP   BH,AL
14EB:010E 38C3       CMP   BL,AL
14EB:0110 90         NOP
```

The registers and flags prior to the CMP instruction are

AX=FEFE BX=0FFD   IP=0106   NV UP EI NG NZ AC PO CY

14EB:0106 38E0   CMP   AL,AH

AX=FEFE BX=0FFD   IP=0108   NV UP EI **PL ZR NA PE NC**

The compare of −2 to −2 (FE to FE) results in a zero after the internal subtract. No carry, even parity, no adjust, a zero result, and a positive sign bit are the result. Note that, other than the advance in IP, no other registers are affected.

14EB:0108 38F8   CMP   AL,BH

AX=FEFE BX=0FFD   IP=010A   NV UP EI **NG NZ AC PO** NC

The compare of·15 to −2 (0F to FE) results in a non-zero after the internal subtract of 15 from −2 (−17). This results in the negative flag being set, the zero flag being reset, an adjustment, odd parity (the result EF has 7 bits on), and no carry.

14EB:010A 38D8   MP   AL,BL

AX=FEFE BX=0FFD   IP=010C   NV UP EI **PL** NZ **NA** PO NC

The compare of −3 to −2 (FD to FE) results in a non-zero after the internal subtract of −3 from −2 (1). The positive flag, non-zero flag, adjust, odd parity, and no carry flags are set.

14EB:010C 38C7   CMP   BH,AL

AX=FEFE BX=0FFD   IP=010E   NV UP EI PL NZ NA **PE CY**

The compare of −2 to 15 (FE to 0F) results in a non-zero, positive result after the internal subtract of −2 from 15 (17 or hex 11). The changes in the flags reflect the even parity of the result and the carry because of the borrow.

14EB:010E 38C3   CMP   BL,AL

AX=FEFE BX=0FFD   IP=0110   NV UP EI **NG** NZ **AC** PE CY

The compare of −2 to −3 results in a non-zero negative result after the internal subtraction (−1 or hex FF). A borrow is required, the result having a negative sign and an even (8) number of bits on. Also required is an adjust.

CMPS   Compare String Operands
CMPSB   Compare String—Byte
CMPSW   Compare String—Word
CMPSD   Compare String—Doubleword

INSTRUCTION	OPCODE	BINARY
CMPS m8,m8	A6	10100110
CMPS m16,m16	A7	10100111
CMPS m32,m32	A7	10100111

Note: CMPSB is a common assembler mnemonic for CMPS m8,m8
CMPSW is a common assembler mnemonic for CMPS m16,m16
CMPSD is a common assembler mnemonic for CMPS m32,m32

Purpose: These instructions operate on strings rather than on logical or numeric values. They operate on only one element of a string, which could be a byte, a word, or a doubleword. The string elements are addressed by the registers ESI and EDI. After each string operation, ESI and/or EDI are automatically updated to point to the next element of the string. If DF is zero, the index registers are incremented. If DF is one, they are decremented. The amount incremented or decremented is one, two, or four, depending on the size of the string element.

CMPS subtracts the destination string element (at ES:EDI) from the source string element (at DS:ESI). It then updates the flags auxiliary carry flag (AF—bit four of the EFLAGS register), the sign flag (SF—bit seven of EFLAGS), parity flag (PF— bit two of EFLAGS), the carry flag (CF—bit zero of EFLAGS), and the overflow flag (OF—bit 11 of EFLAGS). If the string elements are equal, ZF is set to one; otherwise, ZF is set to zero. If DF is zero, the 80486 increments the memory pointers ESI and EDI for two strings. The segment register used for the source address can be changed with a segment register override prefix. The destination segment register can *not* be overridden.

The assembler always translates CMPS into one of the other types. CMPSB compares bytes, CMPSW compares words, and CMPSD compares doublewords.

If the REPE or REPNE prefix modifies this instruction, the 80486 compares the value of the destination string element to the value of the source string element. It then steps SI and DI in the direction indicated by DF by the indicated size, until either the REPE/REPNE condition is false or ECX counts to zero.

Instruction Demonstration: This demonstration of the CMPS instruction includes an illustration of the use of the REP instruction prefix (in this case the REPZ prefix). The data being compared is

14EB:0200   41 42 43 41 42 43 41 42-44 41 42 42 41 42 43 00
ABCABCABDABBABC.

to

14EB 0280   41 42 44 41 42 42 41 42-43 41 42 43 41 42 43 00
ABDABBABCABCABC.

The instruction sequence is

```
14EB:0100 BE0002    MOV     SI,0200
14EB:0103 BF8002    MOV     DI,0280
14EB:0106 B90F00    MOV     CX,000F
14EB:0109 F3        REPZ
14EB:010A A6        CMPSB
14EB:010B F3        REPZ
14EB:010C A6        CMPSB
14EB:010D F3        REPZ
14EB:010E A6        CMPSB
14EB:010F F3        REPZ
14EB:0110 A6        CMPSB
14EB:0111 F3        REPZ
14EB:0112 A6        CMPSB
```

The registers and flags at the start are

```
CX=0000 SI=0000 DI=0000 DS=14EB   ES=14EB IP=0100
                                  NV UP EI PL ZR NA PE NC
14EB:0100 BE0002               MOV     SI,0200
CX=0000 SI=0200 DI=0000   IP=0103   NV UP EI PL ZR NA PE NC
14EB:0103 BF8002               MOV     DI,0280
CX=0000 SI=0200 DI=0280   IP=0106   NV UP EI PL ZR NA PE NC
14EB:0106 B90F00               MOV     CX,000F
CX=000F SI=0200 DI=0280   IP=0109   NV UP EI PL ZR NA PE NC
```

The DI, SI, and CX registers are now set for the comparison.

```
14EB:0109 F3                   REPZ
14EB:010A A6                   CMPSB
CX=000C SI=0203 D=0283   IP=010B  NV UP EI NG NZ AC PE CY
```

The first REP group compared the first 3 bytes of the strings at DS:SI
and ES:DI until an unequal occurred. Note that at the end, SI and DI point
at the bytes beyond the unequal one and that CX contains the count of
bytes remaining. This is exactly what is needed to set up for the next REP.
The results of the unequal compare are presented in the flags [C (43 hex)
– D (44 hex) = –1 (FF hex)], setting carry, negative, adjust, and non-zero.
Because the registers are set, continue as

```
14EB:010B F3              REPZ
14EB:010C A6              CMPSB
CX=0009 SI=0206 DI=0286   IP=010D   NV UP EI **PL** NZ **NA PO NC**
```

This brings us to the next unequal comparison. Again, the registers are set to continue. The flags are set by the unequal compare [C (43 hex) − B (42 hex) = 1 (01 hex)], setting positive, non-zero, no adjust, parity odd, and no carry.

Continuing:

```
14EB:010D F3              REPZ
14EB:010E A6              CMPSB
CX=0006 SI=0209 DI=0289   NV UP EI PL NZ NA PO NC
                 IP=010F
```

Here is the next unequal. The flags reflect the results of the D − C subtraction (the same as the C − B above).

Continuing:

```
14EB:010F F3              REPZ
14EB:0110 A6              CMPSB
CX=0003     SI=020C
DI=028C     IP=0111       NV UP EI **NG** NZ **AC PE CY**
```

Here is the final unequal. The flags reflect the results of the B − C subtraction (the same as the C − D above).

Continuing a final time:

```
14EB:0111 F3              REPZ
14EB:0112 A6              CMPSB
CX=0000     SI=020F
DI=028F     IP=0113       NV UP EI **PL ZR NA** PE **NC**
```

The flags are set to the results of an equal comparison. The REP stopped because the count ran out in CX. This is signaled by the zero flag being set when the instruction following the CMPS is executed.

CMPXCHG   Compare and Exchange

INSTRUCTION	OPCODE	BINARY
CMPXCHG r/m8,r8	OF A6 /r	00001111 10100110 mm rrr r/m
CMPXCHG r/m16,r16	OF A7 /r	00001111 10100111 mm rrr r/m
CMPXCHG r/m32,r32	OF A7 /r	00001111 10100111 mm rrr r/m

Purpose: CMPXCHG compares the accumulator (AL, AX, or EAX) with a destination operand. If they are equal, the source is loaded into the destination, and the zero flag (ZF—bit 6 of EFLAGS) is set. Otherwise, the destination operand is loaded into the accumulator, and the zero flag is cleared.

CMPXCHG also updates the overflow flag (OF—bit 11 of EFLAGS), the sign flag (SF—bit 7 of EFLAGS), the auxiliary carry flag (AF—bit 4 of EFLAGS), the parity flag (PF—bit 2 of EFLAGS), and the carry flag (CF—bit 0 of EFLAGS).

This instruction is new with the 80486.

Instruction Demonstration: Not demonstrated.

CWD   Convert Word to Doubleword

CDQ   Convert Doubleword to Quad-Word

CWDE   Convert Word to Doubleword Extended

INSTRUCTION	OPCODE	BINARY
CWD	99	10011001
CDQ	99	10011001

Note: CDQ is for 32-bit mode.

Purpose: CWD doubles the size of the source operand. CWD extends the sign of the word in register AX throughout register DX. CWD can be used to produce a doubleword dividend from a word before a word division.

CWDE extends the sign of the word in register AX throughout EAX.

CDQ extends the sign of the doubleword in EAX throughout EDX. CDQ can be used to produce a quad-word dividend from a doubleword before doubleword division.

Instruction Demonstration: This demonstrates the CWD instruction. The instruction sequence is

```
4C13:0000 B8FFFF          MOV    AX,FFFF
4C13:0003 99              CWD
4C13:0004 66B8FFFFFFFF     MOV    EAX,FFFFFFFF
4C13:000A 6699            CDQ
```

The registers and flags at the start are

```
EAX=00000000 EDX=00000000    IP=0000    NV UP EI PL NZ NA PO NC
4C13:0000 B8FFFF               MOV        AX,FFFF
EAX=0000FFFF EDX=00000000    IP=0003    NV UP EI PL NZ NA PO NC
```

The move changes only the target register.

```
4C13:0003 99                            CWD
```

EAX=0000FFFF EDX=0000FFFF   IP=0004   NV UP EI PL NZ NA PO NC

Note that the only change is to DX, which has had the AX sign bit propagated throughout the register. No flags change. The registers are prepared for a signed, 16-bit division.

    4C13:0004 66B8FFFFFFFF   MOV   EAX,FFFFFFFF

    EAX=FFFFFFFF EDX=0000FFFF   IP=000A   NV UP EI PL NZ NA PO NC

The move sets a −1 into EAX.

    4C13:000A 6699   CDQ

    EAX=FFFFFFFF EDX=FFFFFFFF   IP=000C   NV UP EI PL NZ NA PO NC

The sign bit is extended through the register, forming a signed quadword in preparation for a signed divide.

DAA   Decimal Adjust AL Register After Addition

INSTRUCTION   OPCODE   BINARY
DAA   27   00100111

Purpose: DAA adjusts the result of adding two valid packed-decimal operands in AL. DAA must always follow the addition of two pairs of packed-decimal numbers (one digit in each half-byte) to obtain a pair of valid packed-decimal digits as a result.

If the low nibble of AL is greater than nine, AF is set and six is added to AL. Otherwise AF is reset. If the high nibble is greater than 9h or the carry flag (CF) is set, then add 60h to AL and set CF. Otherwise, CF is reset.

Instruction Demonstration: This demonstrates the DAA instruction. The DAA adjusts packed decimal values after an ADD. The instruction sequence is

    14EB:0100 B011   MOV   AL,11
    14EB:0102 0409   ADD   AL,09
    14EB:0104 27   DAA
    14EB:0105 B099   MOV   AL,99
    14EB:0107 0409   ADD   AL,09
    14EB:0109 27   DAA

Start with the 11 in AL.

    AX=FF11   IP=0102   NV UP EI PL NZ AC PO CY

    14EB:0102 0409   ADD   AL,09

    AX=FF1A   IP=0104   NV UP EI PL NZ **NA** PO **NC**

Note the ADD leaves a non-BCD digit in the low nibble of AL.

```
14EB:0104 27      DAA
AX=FF20           IP=0105   NV UP EI PL NZ **AC** PO NC
```

The DAA corrects the value by adding 6 to AL if the low nibble of AL is greater than 9 or if the adjust flag is set. If 6 is added, AC is set, but otherwise it is cleared. If the high nibble of AL is greater than 9 or if the carry flag is set, 6 is added to the high nibble and the carry flag is set. Otherwise the carry flag is reset. Note that the high digit doesn't need adjustment in this example, so the carry flag is reset.

```
14EB:0105 B099    MOV       AL,99
AX=FF99           IP=0107   NV UP EI PL NZ AC PO NC
```

In order to demonstrate the action taken when both digits need adjustment, 99 is loaded into AL.

```
14EB:0107 0409    ADD       AL,09
AX=FFA2           IP=0109   NV UP EI **NG** NZ AC PO NC
```

Nine is added to the value in AL. The negative and adjust flags are set.

```
14EB:0109 27      DAA
AX=FF08           IP=010A   NV UP EI **PL** NZ AC PO **CY**
```

The values are adjusted, causing a BCD carry that is reflected in the carry flag.

DAS   Decimal Adjust AL Register After Subtraction

INSTRUCTION	OPCODE	BINARY
DAS	2F	00101111

Purpose: DAS adjusts the result of subtracting two valid packed-decimal operands in AL. DAS follows subtraction of one pair of packed-decimal numbers (one digit in each half-byte) from another to obtain a pair of valid packed-decimal digits as a result. If the low nibble of AL is greater than nine, or if auxiliary carry flag (AF—bit four of the EFLAGS register) is set, then AL has six subtracted from it and AF is set. Otherwise, AF is reset. If the high nibble of AL is greater than 9h, or the carry flag (CF—bit zero of EFLAGS) bit is set, then AL has 60h subtracted from it and CF is set. Otherwise, CF is reset.

Instruction Demonstration: The DAS instruction adjusts a packed BCD result after a subtract. Its action is similar to the DAA instruction except that it adjusts by subtracting 6 from the nibbles of AL instead of adding 6. The instruction sequence is

```
14EB:0100 B011          MOV         AL,11
14EB:0102 2C19          SUB         AL,19
14EB:0104 2F            DAS
14EB:0105 B099          MOV         AL,99
14EB:0107 2C09          SUB         AL,09
14EB:0109 2F            DAS
```

After loading 11 into AL,

AX = FF11	IP = 0102	NV UP EI NG NZ NA PE NC
14EB:0102 2C19	SUB	AL,19
AX = FFF8	IP = 0104	NV UP EI NG NZ **AC PO CY**

The subtract sets NG, NZ, PO, and CY as well as AC. AC is the important flag in this case because it triggers the adjust of the 8 in the low nibble.

```
14EB:0104 2F   DAS
AX = FF92       IP = 0105    NV UP EI NG NZ AC PO CY
```

DAS subtracts 6 from the low nibble because the AC flag is set. The high nibble is examined and has 6 subtracted from it because it is greater than 9. Because the high nibble was adjusted, the carry flag is set. If the high nibble had been a valid BCD digit, the carry flag would have triggered the adjustment.

14EB:0105 B099	MOV	AL,99
N05.00AX = FF99	IP = 0107	NV UP EI NG NZ AC PO CY
14EB:0107 2C09	SUB	AL,09
AX = FF90	IP = 0109	NV UP EI NG NZ **NA PE NC**
14EB:0109 2F	DAS	
AX = FF90	IP = 010A	NV UP EI NG NZ NA PE NC

No adjustments are needed in this case, so none are done.

========

DEC   Decrement by One

INSTRUCTION	OPCODE	BINARY
DEC r/m8	FE /1	11111110 mm 001 r/m
DEC r/m16	FF /1	11111111 mm 001 r/m
DEC r/m32	FF /1	11111111 mm 001 r/m
DEC r16	48 + rw	01001rrr
DEC r32	48 + rw	01001rrr

Purpose: DEC subtracts one from the destination operand and replaces the result into the destination operand. DEC does *not* update the carry flag (CF—bit 0 of the EFLAGS register). Use SUB with an operand of one if a carry flag update is desired.

Instruction Demonstration: This demonstrates the DEC instruction and its effect on both the item being decremented and the flags. The instruction sequence is

```
14EB:0100 B80200    MOV    AX,0002
14EB:0103 48        DEC    AX
14EB:0104 48        DEC    AX
14EB:0105 48        DEC    AX
```

Registers and flags after the value 2 is set into AX.

| AX = 0002 | IP = 0103 | NV UP EI NG NZ AC PE NC |

| 14EB:0103 48 | DEC | AX |

| AX = 0001 | IP = 0104 | NV UP EI **PL** NZ **NA PO** NC |

Note that one is subtracted from the target. The sign, zero, adjust, and parity flags are set according to the result.

| 14EB:0104 48 | DEC | AX |

| AX = 0000 | IP = 0105 | NV UP EI PL **ZR** NA **PE** NC |

Note that one is again subtracted from the target. The sign, zero, adjust, and parity flags are set according to the result.

| 14EB:0105 48 | DEC | AX |

| AX = FFFF | IP = 0106 | NV UP EI **NG NZ AC** PE NC |

Note that one is again subtracted from the target. The sign, zero, adjust, and parity flags are set according to the result. Note that the carry flag is not affected.

DIV   Unsigned Integer Divide

INSTRUCTION	OPCODE	BINARY
DIV AL,/m8	F6 /6	11110110 mm 110 r/m
DIV AX,r/m16	F7 /6	11110111 mm 110 r/m
DIV EAX,r/m32	F7 /6	11110111 mm 110 r/m

Purpose: DIV divides an unsigned number in the accumulator by the source operand. The dividend (the accumulator) is twice the size of the divisor (the source operand); the dividend is AX, DX:AX, or EDX:EAX, for divisors of 8, 16, or 32 bits. The quotient and the remainder have the same size as the divisor. The quotient is placed in AL, AX, or EAX for 8-, 16-, or 32-bit operands, respectively. The remainder is in AH, DX, or EDX.

A divisor of zero or a quotient too large for the designated register causes an 80486 interrupt zero (0). Figure 10-3 summarizes the registers and operands of DIV.

Length of Operand 1	Dividend	Divisor	Quotient	Remainder
8	AX	Operand 1	AL	AH
16	DS:AX	Operand 1	AX	DX
32	EDX:EAX	Operand 1	EAX	EDX

10-3 Registers for DIV/IDIV.

Note: Non-integer quotients are truncated to integers. The remainder is always less than the divisor. For unsigned byte division, the largest quotient is 255. For unsigned word division, the largest quotient is 65,535. For unsigned doubleword division, the largest quotient is $2^{32} - 1$.

Intruction Demonstration: This demonstrates the unsigned divide instruction DIV. The instruction sequence is

```
4C13:0000 B80502            MOV     AX,0205
4C13:0003 66BB33000000      MOV     EBX,00000033
4C13:0009 F6F3              DIV     BL
4C13:000B 99                CWD
4C13:000C F7F3              DIV     BX
4C13:000E 66B867FFFF7F      MOV     EAX,7FFFFF67
4C13:0014 6699              CDQ
4C13:0016 66F7F3            DIV     EBX
```

The registers and flags at the start are

```
EAX=00000000   EBX=00000000   EDX=00000000   IP=0000
                                             NV UP EI PL NZ NA PO NC
4C13:0000 B80502            MOV     AX,0205
EAX=00000205   EBX=00000000   EDX=00000000   IP=0003
                                             NV UP EI PL NZ NA PO NC
```

The dividend is placed into AX. Then the divisor is set in EBX (BL).

```
4C13:0003 66BB33000000   MOV    EBX,00000033
EAX=00000205  EBX=00000033  EDX=00000000   IP=0009
                                           NV UP EI PL NZ NA PO NC
4C13:0009 F6F3                DIV    BL
EAX=0000070A  EBX=00000033  EDX=00000000   IP=000B
                                           NV UP EI NG NZ NA PE CY
```

Note that the short divide leaves the quotient in AL (517/51 = 10 with a remainder of 7) and the remainder in AH. The flags might be affected (NG, PE and CY in this example), but their values are undefined.

```
4C13:000B 99                 CWD
EAX=0000070A  EBX=00000033  EDX=00000000   IP=000C
                                           NV UP EI NG NZ NA PE CY
```

CWD extends the sign of AX through DX.

```
4C13:000C F7F3               DIV    BX
EAX=00000023  EBX=00000033  EDX=00000011   IP=000E
                                           NV UP EI PL NZ NA PE NC
```

Note that the long divide leaves the quotient in AX and the remainder in DX. Again, the flags are undefined.

```
4C13:000E        66B867FFFF7F   MOV   EAX,7FFFFF67
```

The move sets a large value in EAX.

```
EAX=7FFFFF67  EBX=00000033  EDX=00000011   IP=0014
                                           NV UP EI PL NZ NA PE NC
4C13:0014 6699               CDQ
```

The sign is extended through EDX. (Because DIV is an unsigned divide, propagating a minus would cause an overflow.)

```
EAX=7FFFFF67  EBX=00000033  EDX=00000000   IP=0016
                                           NV UP EI PL NZ NA PE NC
4C13:0016 66F7F3             DIV    EBX
```

The divide proceeds, placing the remainder in EDX and the quotient in EAX.

```
EAX=0282827F  EBX=00000033  EDX=0000001A   IP=0019
                                           NV UP EI PL NZ NA PO NC
```

ENTER   Make Stack Frame for Procedure Parameter

INSTRUCTION	OPCODE	BINARY
ENTER imm16,0	C8 iw 00	11001000
ENTER imm16,1	C8 /2 01	11001000
ENTER imm16,imm8	C8 iw ib	11001000

Purpose: ENTER creates a stack frame that can be used to implement the rules of block-structured, high-level languages. A LEAVE instruction at the end of the procedure complements the ENTER.

ENTER has two parameters. The first specifies the number of bytes of dynamic storage to be allocated on the stack for the routine being entered. The second parameter corresponds to the lexical nesting level of the routine: 0 to 31. This level determines how many sets of stack frame pointers the CPU copies into the new stack frame from the proceeding frame. This list of stack frames is often called the *display*. Lexical level has *no* relationship to either the protection levels or to the I/O privilege level.

ENTER creates the new display for a procedure. Then it allocates the dynamic storage space for that procedure by decrementing ESP by the number of bytes specified in the first parameter. This new value of ESP serves as the starting point for all PUSH and POP operations within that procedure.

ENTER can be used either nested or non-nested. If the lexical level is zero, the non-nested form is used. The main procedure operates at the highest logical level, level 1. The first procedure it calls operates at the next deeper level, level 2, etc. A level 2 procedure can access the variables in the main program because a program operating at a higher logical level (calling a program at a lower level) requires that the called procedure have access to the variables of the calling program.

A procedure calling another procedure at the *same* level implies that they are parallel procedures and should *not* have access to the variables of the calling program. The new stack frame does not include the pointer for addressing the calling procedure's stack frame. ENTER treats a re-entrant procedure as a procedure calling another procedure at the same level.

Instruction Demonstration: The CALL instruction, ENTER instruction, LEAVE instruction, and RET instruction are demonstrated together because they logically "fit" with each other and complement each other. See the CALL instruction.

ESC   Escape

INSTRUCTION   OPCODE   BINARY

ESC   D8 + TTT   11011TTT mod LLL r/m

(Where TTT and LLL are OPCODE information for the coprocessor.)

Purpose: ESC lets you send instructions to an external coprocessor on the system bus. On the 80386 and earlier processors, this was usually a floating-point chip called a numeric (or math) coprocessor. The 8086 and 8088 work with an Intel 8087 math coprocessor; the 80286 and 80386 work with an 80287 or 80387 coprocessor (respectively). The 80486 has a math coprocessor, called the Floating-Point Unit, on the chip.

The OPCODE for ESC begins with the 5-bit sequence "11011B." This sequence indicates that the rest of the opcode is an instruction meant for a coprocessor, as opposed to an instruction meant for the 80486.

Instruction Demonstration: This instruction is not demonstrated because ESC is the signal that a coprocessor instruction needs decoding. Its action is nondemonstrable, as are the prefixes if no instruction followed them.

F2XM1   Computer $2^x - 1$

INSTRUCTION   OPCODE   BINARY

F2XM1   D9 F0   11011001 11110000

Purpose: F2XM1 replaces the contents of ST with $(2^{ST} - 1)$. ST must be greater than -1 and less than 1; if it is outside this range, F2XM1 produces an unpredictable result. C1 is affected as described in TABLE 1-2; C0, C2, and C3 are undefined.

Instruction Demonstration: Not demonstrated.

FABS   Absolute Value

INSTRUCTION   OPCODE   BINARY

FABS   D9 E1   11011001 11100001

Purpose: FABS replaces the contents of ST with its absolute value (i.e., forces it to a positive value). To do this, FABS clears the sign bit of ST. C1 is affected as described in TABLE 1-2; C0, C2, and C3 are undefined.

Instruction Demonstration: Not demonstrated.

FADD   Add Real
FADDP   Add Real and Pop
FIADD   Add Integer

INSTRUCTION	OPCODE	BINARY
FADD m32real	D8 /0	11011000 mm 000 r/m
FADD m64real	DC /0	11011100 mm 000 r/m
FADD ST,ST(i)	D8 C0+i	11011000 11000iii
FADD ST(i),ST	DC C0+i	11011100 11000iii
FADDP ST(i),ST	DE C0+i	11011110 11000iii
FADD	DE C1	11011110 11000001
FIADD m32int	DA /0	11011010 mm 000 r/m
FIADD m16int	DE /0	11011110 mm 000 r/m

Purpose: These instructions add the source operand to the destination operand, as follows:

Instruction	Action
FADD m32real	Add m32real to ST
FADD m64real	Add m64real to ST
FADD ST,ST(i)	Add ST(i) to ST
FADD ST(i),ST	Add ST to ST (i)
FADDP ST(i),ST	Add ST to ST(i) and pop ST
FADD	Add ST to St(1) and pop ST
FIADD m32int	Add m32int to ST
FIADD m16int	Add m16int to ST

C1 is affected as described in TABLE 1-2; C0, C2, and C3 are undefined.

You can use the following instruction to double the operand at the top of the stack:

```
FADD   ST,ST(0)
```

Note: If the source operand is in memory, it is converted to extended-real format automatically.

Instruction Demonstration: The following program adds a table of single-precision numbers in memory. The table starts at location Table, the element count is in location Count, the sum is stored at location Sum.

```
          MOV    CX,Count     ;Load count into CX
          JCXZ   Done         ;If count is zero, quit
          FLDZ                ;To start, set sum to zero
          MOV    BX,0         ;Set index to zero
AddLoop   FADD   Table[BX]    ;Add next number to sum
          ADD    BX,4         ;Point to next number
```

```
        LOOP    AddLoop      ;Decrement CX, quit when CX=0
Done    FSTP    Sum          ;Done, store sum in memory
```

FBLD   Load BINARY-Coded Decimal

INSTRUCTION	OPCODE	BINARY
FBLD m80dec	D8 /4	11011000 mm 100 r/m

Purpose: FBLD converts the packed decimal source operand into extended-real format, and pushes it onto the FPU stack. C1 is affected as described in TABLE 1-2; C0, C2, and C3 are undefined.

Notes: FBLD assumes that the operand contains packed decimal digits in the range 0 to 9. If your operand contains anything else, FBLD produces unpredictable results.

ST(7) must be empty; if it is not, the 80486 receives an invalid-operation exception. To empty ST(7), execute an FFREE ST(7) instruction.

Instruction Demonstration: Not demonstrated.

FBSTP   Store BINARY-Coded Decimal and Pop

INSTRUCTION	OPCODE	BINARY
FBSTP m80dec	DF /6	11011111 mm 110 r/m

Purpose: FBLD converts the value in ST into a packed decimal integer, and stores the result at the specified memory location. It then pops ST.

C1 is affected as described in TABLE 1-2; C0, C2, and C3 are undefined.

Note: If ST contains a non-integral value, FBSTP rounds it according to the RC (Rounding Control) field of the control word.

Instruction Demonstration: Not demonstrated.

FCHS   Change Sign

INSTRUCTION	OPCODE	BINARY
FCHS	D9 E0	11011001 11100000

Purpose: FCHS inverts the sign bit of ST. Thus, it converts a positive number into a negative number, or vice versa. C1 is affected as described in TABLE 1-2; C0, C2, and C3 are undefined.

Instruction Demonstration: Not demonstrated.

FCLEX   Clear Floating-Point Exceptions (with Error Check)
FNCLEX   Clear Floating-Point Exceptions

INSTRUCTION	OPCODE	BINARY
FCLEX	9B DB E2	10011011 11011011 11100010
FNCLEX	DB E2	11011011 11100010

Purpose: These instructions clear the floating-point exception flags, the exception status flag, and the Busy flag of the FPU status word. Before clearing the exception flags, FCLEX checks for unmasked floating-point error conditions (using an FWAIT instruction); FNCLEX does not make this check. These instructions leave C0, C1, C2, and C3 undefined.

FCLEX or FNCLEX can be used by an exception handler after it has processed an exception. If the exception flags are not cleared, a second interrupt request would be issued immediately.

Instruction Demonstration: Not demonstrated.

FCOM   Compare Real
FCOMP   Compare Real and Pop
FCOMPP   Compare Real and Pop Twice

INSTRUCTION	OPCODE	BINARY
FCOM m32real	D8 /2	11011000 mm 010 r/m
FCOM m64real	DC /2	11011100 mm 010 r/m
FCOM ST(i)	D8 D0+i	11011000 11010iii
FCOM	D8 D1	11011000 11010001
FCOMP m32real	D8 /3	11011000 mm 011 r/m
FCOMP m64real	DC /3	11011100 mm 011 r/m
FCOMP ST(i)	D8 D8+i	11011000 11011iii
FCOMP	D8 D9	11011000 11011001
FCOMPP	DE D9	11011110 11011001

Purpose: These instructions compare the stack top to a single- or double-real memory operand, or to a register. They operate as follows:

Instruction	Action
FCOM m32real	Compare ST with m32real
FCOM m64real	Compare ST with m64real
FCOM ST(i)	Compare ST with ST(i)
FCOM	Compare ST with ST(1)

FCOMP m32real	Compare ST with m32real and pop ST
FCOMP m64real	Compare ST with m64real and pop ST
FCOMP ST(i)	Compare ST with ST(i) and pop ST
FCOMP	Compare ST with ST(1) and pop ST
FCOMPP	Compare ST with ST(1) and pop ST twice

Following the instruction, the condition codes reflect the relationship between ST and the source operand. C1 is affected as described in TABLE 1-2. C0, C2, and C3 are affected as follows:

FPU Flags	EFLAGS
C_0	CF
C_1	(none)
C_2	PF
C_3	ZF

Notes: If ST contains a NaN or has an undefined format, or a stack fault occurs, the invalid-operation exception is raised and the condition bits are set to "unordered."

The sign of zero is ignored, so that $-0.0 = - + 0.0$.

See also the Compare Integer instructions (FICOM and FICOMP) and the Unordered Compare Real instructions (FUCOM, FUCOMP, and FUCOMPP).

Instruction Demonstration: Not demonstrated.

FCOS   Cosine

INSTRUCTION	OPCODE	BINARY
FCOS	D9 FF	11011001 11111111

Purpose: FCOS replaces the contents of ST with cos(ST). ST, expressed in radians, must be an absolute number that is less than 2^{63}.

C1 and C2 are affected as described in TABLE 1-2; C0 and C3 are undefined.

FCOS was introduced with the 80387; it does not exist in the 8087 and 80287.

Notes: If the operand is outside the acceptable range, the C2 flag is set and ST remains unchanged.

The 80486 checks for interrupts while executing this instruction. It will abort FCOS to service an interrupt.

If you want the sine as well as the cosine, use FSINCOS instead of FCOS.

Instruction Demonstration: Not demonstrated.

FDECSTP   Decrement Stack-Top Pointer

INSTRUCTION	OPCODE	BINARY
FDECSTP	D9 F6	11011001 11110110

Purpose: FDECSTP subtracts 1 from the three-bit TOP field of the FPU status word. In effect, FDECSTP rotates the stack. C1 is affected as described in TABLE 1-2; C0, C2, and C3 are undefined.

Instruction Demonstration: Not demonstrated.

FDIV   Divide Real
FDIVP   Divide Real and Pop
FIDIV   Divide Integer

INSTRUCTION	OPCODE	BINARY
FDIV m32real	D8 /6	11011000 mm 110 r/m
FDIV m64real	DC /6	11011100 mm 110 r/m
FDIV ST,ST(i)	D8 F0+i	11011000 11110iii
FDIV ST(i),ST	DC F8+i	11011100 11111iii
FDIVP ST(i),ST	DE F8+i	11011100 11111iii
FDIV	DE F9	11011110 11111001
FIDIV m32int	DA /6	11011010 mm 110 r/m
FIDIV m16int	DE /6	11011110 mm 110 r/m

Purpose: These instructions divide the stack top by an operand and return the quotient to the destination. They operate as follows:

Instruction	Action
FDIV m32real	Divide ST by m32real
FDIV m64real	Divide ST by m64real
FDIV ST,ST(i)	Divide ST by ST(i)
FDIV ST(i),ST	Divide ST by ST(i), put quotient in ST(i)
FDIVP ST(i),ST	Divide ST by ST(i), put quotient in ST(i), and pop ST
FDIV	Divide ST by ST(1), put quotient in ST(1), and pop ST
FIDIV m32int	Divide ST by m32int
FIDIV m16int	Divide ST by m16int

C1 is affected as described in TABLE 1-2; C0, C2, and C3 are undefined.
Note: If the source operand is in memory, it is converted to extended-real format automatically.

Instruction Demonstration: Not demonstrated.

FDIVR Reverse Divide Real
FDIVPR Reverse Divide Real and Pop
FIDIVR Reverse Divide Integer

INSTRUCTION	OPCODE	BINARY
FDIVR m32real	D8 /7	11011000 mm 111 r/m
FDIVR m64real	DC /7	11011100 mm 111 r/m
FDIVR ST,ST(i)	D8 F8+i	11011000 11111iii
FDIVR ST(i),ST	DC F0+i	11011100 11110iii
FDIVPR ST(i),ST	DE F0+i	11011100 11110iii
FDIVR	DE F1	11011110 11110001
FIDIVR m32int	DA /7	11011010 mm 111 r/m
FIDIVR m16int	DE /7	11011110 mm 111 r/m

Purpose: These instructions divide an operand by the stack top and return the quotient to the destination. They operate as follows:

Instruction	Action
FDIVR m32real	Divide m32real by ST, put quotient in ST
FDIVR m64real	Divide m64real by ST, put quotient in ST
FDIVR ST,ST(i)	Divide ST(i) by ST, put quotient in ST
FDIVR ST(i),ST	Divide ST(i) by ST
FDIVPR ST(i),ST	Divide ST(i) by ST, pop ST
FDIVR	Divide ST(1) by ST, pop ST
FIDIVR m32int	Divide m32int by ST, put quotient in ST
FIDIVR m16int	Divide m16int by ST, put quotient in ST

C1 is affected as described in TABLE 1-2; C0, C2, and C3 are undefined.

Notes: To divide an operand by 2, 4, or some other power of 2, you can use the FSCALE instruction.

If the source operand is in memory, it is converted to extended-real format automatically.

Instruction Demonstration: Not demonstrated.

FFREE Free Floating-Point Register

INSTRUCTION	OPCODE	BINARY
FFREE	DD C0+i	11011101 11000iii

Purpose: FFREE tags the destination register as empty. C0, C1, C2, and C3 are undefined.

Note: FFREE does not affect the contents of the destination register. Nor does it affect the floating-point stack-top pointer (TOP).

Instruction Demonstration: Not demonstrated.

FICOM   Compare Integer
FICOMP   Compare Integer and Pop

INSTRUCTION	OPCODE	BINARY
FICOM m16real	DE /2	11011110 mm 010 r/m
FICOM m32real	DA /2	11011010 mm 010 r/m
FICOMP m16int	DE /3	11011110 mm 011 r/m
FICOMP m32int	DA /3	11011010 mm 011 r/m

Purpose: These instructions compare the stack top to a word- or short-integer operand. After doing the compare, FICOMP pops ST. C1 is affected as described in TABLE 1-2. C0, C2, and C3 are affected as follows:

FPU Flags	**EFLAGS**
C_0	CF
C_1	(none)
C_2	PF
C_3	ZF

Note: See also the Compare Real instructions, FCOM, FCOMP, and FCOMPP.

Instruction Demonstration: Not demonstrated.

FILD   Load Integer

INSTRUCTION	OPCODE	BINARY
FILD m16int	DF /0	11011111 mm 000 r/m
FILD m32int	DB /0	11011011 mm 000 r/m
FILD m64int	DF /5	11011111 mm 101 r/m

Purpose: FILD converts the source signed integer into extended-real format and pushes it onto the FPU stack. C1 is affected as described in TABLE 1-2. C0, C2, and C3 are undefined.

Note: ST(7) must be empty; if it is not, the 80486 receives an invalid-operation exception. To empty ST(7), execute a FFREE ST(7) instruction.

Instruction Demonstration: Not demonstrated.

FINCSTP   Increment Stack-Top Pointer

INSTRUCTION	OPCODE	BINARY
FINCSTP	D9 F7	11011001 11110111

Purpose: FINCSTP adds 1 to the three-bit TOP field of the FPU status word. In effect, FINCSTP rotates the stack. C1 is affected as described in TABLE 1-2; C0, C2, and C3 are undefined.

Instruction Demonstration: Not demonstrated.

FINIT Initialize Floating-Point Unit (with Error Check)
FNINIT Initialize Floating-Point Unit

INSTRUCTION	OPCODE	BINARY
FINIT	9B DB E3	10011011 11011011 11100011
FNINIT	DB E3	11011011 11100011

Purpose: These instructions put the FPU in a known state, unaffected by any previous activity. In fact, FINIT and FNINIT affect the FPU in the same way as a hardware RESET signal with Built-In Self-Test.

Before initializing the FPU, FINIT checks for unmasked floating-point error conditions (using an FWAIT instruction); FNINIT does not make this check. These instructions do the following tasks:

- Set the FPU control word to 037FH (i.e., round to nearest, 64-bit precision, all exceptions masked).
- Clear the status word (no exception flags set and stack register R0 = stack-top).
- Tag all stack registers as empty.
- Clear instruction and error data pointers. (The 80387 math coprocessor's FINIT and FNINIT instructions do not clear these pointers.)

Instruction Demonstration: Not demonstrated.

FIST Store Integer
FISTP Store Integer and Pop

INSTRUCTION	OPCODE	BINARY
FIST m16int	DF /2	11011111 mm 010 r/m
FIST m32int	DB /2	11011011 mm 010 r/m
FISTP m16int	DF /3	11011111 mm 011 r/m
FISTP m32int	DB /3	11011011 mm 011 r/m
FISTP m64int	DF /7	11011111 mm 111 r/m

Purpose: FIST converts the value in ST into a signed integer (according to the RC field of the control word) and transfers the result to the destination; ST is unchanged. FISTP does the same thing as FIST, but pops ST after the transfer. C1 is affected as described in TABLE 1-2; C0, C2, and C3 are undefined.

Note: If the value in ST is too large to represent an integer, an invalid-operation exception is raised. The masked response is to write the most negative integer to memory.

Instruction Demonstration: Not demonstrated.

FLD   Load Real

INSTRUCTION	OPCODE	BINARY
FLD m32real	D9 /0	11011001 mm 000 r/m
FLD m64real	DD /0	11011101 mm 000 r/m
FLD m80real	DB /5	11011011 mm 101 r/m
FLD ST(i)	D9 C0+i	11011001 11000iii

Purpose: FLD pushes the source operand onto the FPU stack and is the basic instruction for moving data into the FPU.

If the source is a register, the register number used is that before the stack-top pointer is decremented. For example, you can use the following instruction to duplicate the stack top:

    FLD   ST(0)

C1 is affected as described in TABLE 1-2; C0, C2, and C3 are undefined.

Notes: If the source operand is in single- or double-real format, FLD converts it to extended-real format automatically.

ST(7) must be empty; if it is not, the 80486 receives an invalid-operation exception. To empty ST(7), execute a FFREE ST(7) instruction.

Instruction Demonstration: Not demonstrated.

FLD1	Push +1.0 onto the FPU Stack
FLDL2T	Push $\log_2 10$ onto the FPU Stack
FLDL2E	Push $\log_e 10$ onto the FPU Stack
FLDPI	Push pi onto the FPU Stack
FLDLG2	Push $\log_{10} 2$ onto the FPU Stack
FLDLN2	Push $\log_e 2$ onto the FPU Stack
FLDZ	Push +0.0 onto the FPU Stack

INSTRUCTION	OPCODE	BINARY
FLD1	D9 E8	11011001 11101000

FLDL2T	D9 E9	11011001 11101001
FLDL2E	D9 EA	11011001 11101010
FLDPI	D9 EB	11011001 11101011
FLDLG2	D9 EC	11011001 11101100
FLDLN2	D9 ED	11011001 11101101
FLDZ	D9 EE	11011001 11101110

Purpose: Each of these instructions pushes a commonly-used value (in extended-real format) onto the FPU stack. C1 is affected as described in TABLE 1-2; C0, C2, and C3 are undefined.

Instruction Demonstration: FLDZ is demonstrated with FADD. FLDLG2 and FLDLN2 are demonstrated with FYL2X.

FLDCW   Load Control Word

INSTRUCTION	OPCODE	BINARY
FLDCW	D9 /5	11011001 mm 101 r/m

Purpose: FLDCW replaces the current value of the FPU control word with the value contained in the specified memory word; it is used to change the FPU's mode of operation. FLDCW can, for example, change the rounding control.

C0, C1, C2, and C3 are undefined.

Note: If an exception bit in the status word is set, loading a new control word will produce a floating-point error condition. To avoid this problem, you should clear any pending exceptions before loading the new control word.

Instruction Demonstration: Not demonstrated.

FLDENV   Load FPU Environment

INSTRUCTION	OPCODE	BINARY
FLDENV m14byte	D9 /4	11011001 mm 100 r/m
FLDENV m28byte	D9 /4	11011001 mm 100 r/m

Purpose: FLDENV reloads the FPU environment from the memory area defined by the source operand. This data should have been written by a previous FSTENV or FNSTENV instruction.

The FPU environment consists of the FPU control word, status word, tag word, and error pointers (both data and instruction). The environment layout in memory depends on the operand size and the current operating mode of the processor (real or protected). The USE attribute of the current code segment determines the operand size. The 14-byte operand applies to a USE16 segment; the 28-byte operand applies to a USE32 segment. Figures 1-13 and 1-14 in Chapter 1 show the environment layouts for the 32-bit and 16-bit operand sizes (respectively) in both real mode and protected mode.

Notes: FLDENV should be executed in the same operating mode as the corresponding FSTENV or FNSTENV.

If the environment image contains an unmasked exception, loading it will produce a floating-point error condition.

To reload both the FPU environment and register stack, use the FRSTOR instruction.

Instruction Demonstration: Not demonstrated.

FMUL — Multiply Real
FMULP — Multiply Real and Pop
FIMUL — Multiply Integer

INSTRUCTION	OPCODE	BINARY
FMUL m32real	D8 /1	11011000 /1
FMUL m64real	DC /1	11011100 /1
FMUL ST,ST(i)	D8 C8+i	11011000 11001iii
FMUL ST(i),ST	DC C8+i	11011100 11001iii
FMULP ST(i),ST	DE C8+i	11011100 11001iii
FMUL	DE C9	11011110 11001001
FIMUL m32int	DA /1	11011010 /1
FIMUL m16int	DE /1	11011110 /1

Purpose: These instructions multiply the destination operand by the source operand and return the product to the destination. They operate as follows:

Instruction	Action
FMUL m32real	Multiply ST by m32real
FMUL m64real	Multiply ST by m64real
FMUL ST,ST(i)	Multiply ST by ST(i)
FMUL ST(i),ST	Multiply ST(i) by ST
FMULP ST(i),ST	Multiply ST(i) by ST and pop ST
FMUL	Multiply ST(1) by ST and pop ST
FIMUL m32int	Multiply ST by m32int
FIMUL m16int	Multiply ST by m16int

C1 is affected as described in TABLE 1-2; C0, C2, and C3 are undefined.

Notes: To multiply the operand by 2 (double), 4 (quadruple), or some other power of 2, you can use the FSCALE instruction.

If the source operand is in memory, it is converted to extended-real format automatically.

Instruction Demonstration: Not demonstrated.

FNOP   No Operation

INSTRUCTION	OPCODE	BINARY
FNOP	D9 D0	11011001 11010000

Purpose: FNOP performs no operation. It only advances INSTRUCTION pointer. C0, C1, C2, and C3 are undefined.

Instruction Demonstration: Not demonstrated.

FPATAN   Partial Arctangent

INSTRUCTION	OPCODE	BINARY
FPATAN	D9 F3	11011001 11110011

Purpose: FPATAN computes the arctangent of ST(1) divided by ST, and puts the result (in radians) in ST. It then pops ST. The result has the same sign as the operand from ST(1), and a magnitude less than pi. C1 is affected as described in TABLE 1-2; C0, C2, and C3 are undefined.

You can also use FPATAN to compute other trigonometric functions. For example, arcsin(x) is the arctangent of x divided by $SQRT(1-x^2)$. To compute arcsin(x), follow these steps:

1. Push x onto the FPU stack
2. Compute the square root of $(1-x^2)$ and push the result onto the stack
3. Execute FPATAN

Notes: There is no restriction on the range of arguments that FPATAN can accept.

The 80486 checks for interrupts while executing this instruction. It will abort FPATAN to service an interrupt.

Instruction Demonstration: Not demonstrated.

FPREM   Partial Remainder
FPREM1   IEEE Standard Partial Remainder

INSTRUCTION	OPCODE	BINARY
FPREM	D9 F8	11011001 11111000
FPREM1	D9 F5	11011001 11110101

Purpose: These instructions divide ST by ST(1), and put the remainder in ST. The sign of the remainder is the same as the sign of the original dividend in ST. FPREM is supported for compatibility with the 8087 and 80287 math coprocessors. The FPREM1 instruction is the remainder operation specified in IEEE Standard 754. FPREM1 was introduced with the 80387; it does not exist in the 8087 and 80287.

C0, C1, C2, and C3 are affected as described in TABLE 1-2.

An important use of FPREM/FPREM1 is to reduce the arguments of periodic functions. When the reduction is complete, FPREM/FPREM1 provides the three least-significant bits of the quotient in flags C3, C1, and C0. This is important in argument reduction for the tangent function (using a modulus of pi/4), because it locates the original angle in the correct one of eight sectors of the unit circle.

Note: FPREM and FPREM1 produce an exact result; the precision (inexeact) exception does not occur and the rounding control has no effect.

Instruction Demonstration: Not demonstrated.

FPTAN   Partial Tangent

INSTRUCTION	OPCODE	BINARY
FPTAN	D9 F2	11011001 11110010

Purpose: FPTAN replaces the contents of ST with tan(ST) and then pushes 1.0 onto the FPU stack. ST, expressed in radians, must be an absolute number that is less than 2^{63}. C1 and C2 are affected as described in TABLE 1-2; C0 and C3 are undefined.

FPTAN pushes 1.0 onto the FPU stack to maintain compatibility with the 8087 and 80287 math coprocessors, simplifying the calculation of other trigonometric functions. For example, you can produce the cotangent (the reciprocal of the tangent) by executing FPTAN, then FDIVR.

Notes: If the operand is outside the acceptable range, the C2 flag is set and ST remains unchanged.

The 80486 checks for interrupts while executing this instruction. It will abort FPTAN to service an interrupt.

ST(7) must be empty to avoid an invalid-operation exception. To empty ST(7), execute an FFREE ST(7) instruction.

Instruction Demonstration: Not demonstrated.

FRNDINT   Round to Integer

INSTRUCTION	OPCODE	BINARY
FRNDINT	D9 FC	11011001 11111100

Purpose: FRNDINT rounds the value in ST to an integer according to the RC (Rounding Control) field of the FPU control word.

C1 is affected as described in TABLE 1-2; C0, C2, and C3 are undefined.

Instruction Demonstration: Not demonstrated.

FRSTOR   Restore FPU State

INSTRUCTION	OPCODE	BINARY
FRSTOR m94byte	DB /4	11011011 mm 100 r/m
FRSTOR m108byte	DB /4	11011011 mm 100 r/m

Purpose: FRSTOR reloads the FPU state (environment and register stack) from the memory area defined by the source operand. This data should have been written by a previous FSAVE or FNSAVE instruction.

The FPU environment consists of the FPU control word, status word, tag word, and error pointers (both data and instruction). The environment layout in memory depends on the operand size and the current operating mode of the processor (real or protected). The USE attribute of the current code segment determines the operand size. The 94-byte operand applies to a USE16 segment; the 108-byte operand applies to a USE32 segment. Figures 1-13 and 1-14 in Chapter 1 show the environment layouts for the 32-bit and 16-bit operand sizes (respectively) in both real mode and protected mode.

The stack registers, ST and ST(1) through ST(7), are in the 80 bytes that follow the environment image.

C0, C1, C2, and C3 are affected as loaded.

Notes: FRSTOR should be executed in the same operating mode as the corresponding FSAVE or FNSAVE.

You should precede, FRSTOR with an FWAIT instruction, to ensure that the storage operation is complete.

If the state image contains an unmasked exception, loading it will produce a floating-point error condition.

To reload just the FPU environment, use the FLDENV INSTRUCTION.

Instruction Demonstration: Not demonstrated.

FSAVE   Store FPU State (with Error Check)
FNSAVE   Store FPU State

INSTRUCTION	OPCODE	BINARY
FSAVE m94byte	9B DD /6	10011011 11011101 mm 110 r/m
FSAVE m108byte	9B DD /6	10011011 11011101 mm 110 r/m
FNSAVE m94byte	DD /6	11011101 mm 110 r/m
FNSAVE m108byte	DD /6	11011101 mm 110 r/m

Purpose: These instructions write the current FPU state (environment and register stack) to the specified destination, then reinitialize the FPU. FSAVE checks for unmasked floating-point error conditions before writing the state; FNSAVE does not make this check.

The FPU environment consists of the FPU control word, status word, tag word, and error pointers (both data and instruction). The state layout in memory depends on the operand size (16 or 32 bits) and the current operating mode of the processor (real or protected). The USE attribute of the current code segment determines the operand size. The 94-byte operand applies to a USE16 segment; the 108-byte operand applies to a USE32 segment. Figures 1-13 and 1-14 in Chapter 1 show the environment layouts for the 32-bit and 16-bit operand sizes (respectively) in both real mode and protected mode.

The stack registers, ST and ST(1) through ST(7), are stored in the 80 bytes that follow the environment image.

C0, C1, C2, and C3 are cleared.

FSAVE and FNSAVE are typically used when an operating system needs to perform a context switch, an exception handler needs to use the FPU, or an application program wants to "clean" the FPU before a subroutine uses it.

Notes: FSAVE and FNSAVE do not store the FPU state until all FPU activity has finished.

To restore a saved state, use the FRSTOR instruction.

If a program is to read from the state's memory image following a save instruction, it must issue an FWAIT instruction to ensure that the storage operation is complete.

Instruction Demonstration: Not demonstrated.

FSCALE Scale by a Power of 2

INSTRUCTION	OPCODE	BINARY
FSCALE	D9 FD	11011001 11111101

Purpose: FSCALE interprets the contents of ST(1) as an integer, and uses it as an exponent of 2 with which to multiply the contents of ST. That is, FSCALE performs this operation:

$$ST = ST \times 2^{ST(1)}$$

Thus, FSCALE provides a quick way to multiply or divide by a power of 2.

C1 is affected as described in TABLE 1-2; C0, C2, and C3 are undefined.

Instruction Demonstration: Not demonstrated.

FSIN Sine

INSTRUCTION	OPCODE	BINARY
FSIN	D9 FE	11011001 11111110

Purpose: FSIN replaces the contents of ST with sin(ST). ST, expressed in radians, must be an absolute number that is less than 2^{63}. C1 and C2 are affected as described in TABLE 1-2; C0 and C3 are undefined.

FSIN was introduced with the 80387; it does not exist in the 8087 and 80287.

Notes: If the operand is outside the acceptable range, the C2 flag is set and ST remains unchanged.

The 80486 checks for interrupts while executing this instruction. It will abort FSIN to service an interrupt.

If you want the cosine as well as the sine, use FSINCOS instead of FSIN.

Instruction Demonstration: Not demonstrated.

FSINCOS Sine and Cosine

INSTRUCTION	OPCODE	BINARY
FSINCOS	D9 FB	11011001 11111011

Purpose: FSINCOS computes both sin(ST) and cos(ST). It replaces ST with the sine and then pushes the cosine onto the FPU stack. ST, expressed in radians, must be an absolute number that is less than 2^{63}.

C1 and C2 are affected as described in TABLE 1-2; C0 and C3 are undefined.

FSINCOS was introduced with the 80387; it does not exist in the 8087 and 80287.

Notes: If the operand is outside the acceptable range, the C2 flag is set and ST remains unchanged.

The 80486 checks for interrupts while executing this instruction. It will abort FSINCOS to service an interrupt.

It is faster to execute FSINCOS than to execute both FSIN and FCOS.

Instruction Demonstration: Not demonstrated.

FSQRT   Square Root

INSTRUCTION	OPCODE	BINARY
FSQRT	D9 FA	11011001 11111010

Purpose: FSQRT replaces the value in ST with its square root. C1 is affected as described in TABLE 1-2; C0, C2, and C3 are undefined.

Note: The square root of -0 is -0.

Instruction Demonstration: Not demonstrated.

FST   Store Real
FSTP   Store Real and Pop

INSTRUCTION	OPCODE	BINARY
FST m32real	D9 /2	11011001 mm 010 r/m
FST m64real	DD /2	11011101 mm 010 r/m
FST ST(i)	DD D0+i	11011001 11010iii
FSTP m32real	D9 /3	11011001 mm 011 r/m
FSTP m64real	DD /3	11011101 mm 011 r/m
FSTP m80real	DB /7	11011011 mm 111 r/m
FSTP ST(i)	DD D8+i	11011001 11011iii

Purpose: FST copies the value in ST to the destination, which can be another register or a single- or double-real memory operand. FSTP copies and then pops ST; it also accepts extended-real memory operands. These instructions operate as follows:

Instruction	Action
FST m32real	Copy ST to m32real
FST m64real	Copy ST to m64real
FST ST(i)	Copy ST to ST(i)
FSTP m32real	Copy ST to m32real and pop ST
FSTP m64real	Copy ST to m64real and pop ST
FSTP m80real	Copy ST to m80real and pop ST
FSTP ST(i)	Copy ST to ST(i) and pop ST

C1 is affected as described in TABLE 1-2; C0, C2, and C3 are undefined.

Notes: If the destination is single- or double-real, the significand is rounded to the width of the destination (according to the RC field of the control word) and the exponent is converted to the width and bias of the destination format. The instructions also check for the over/underflow condition.

If ST contains zero, infinity, or a NaN, the significand is not rounded but chopped on the right to fit the destination. The exponent is also chopped on the right. These operations preserve the value's identity as infinity or NaN (exponent all ones).

The invalid operation exception is not raised when the destination is a nonempty stack element.

Instruction Demonstration: FSTP is demonstrated with FADD.

FSTCW   Store Control Word (with Error Check)
FNSTCW   Store Control Word

INSTRUCTION	OPCODE	BINARY
FSTCW m2byte	9B D9 /7	10011011 11011001 mm 111 r/m
FNSTCW m2byte	D9 /7	11011001 mm 111 r/m

Purpose: These instructions write the current value of the FPU control word to the specified destination. FSTCW checks for unmasked floating-point error conditions before storing the control word; FNSTCW does not make this check.

C0, C1, C2, and C3 are undefined.

Instruction Demonstration: Not demonstrated.

FSTENV   Store FPU State (with Error Check)
FNSTENV   Store FPU State

INSTRUCTION	OPCODE	BINARY
FSTENV m14byte	9B D9 /6	10011011 11011001 mm 110 r/m
FSTENV m28byte	9B D9 /6	10011011 11011001 mm 110 r/m
FNSTENV m14byte	D9 /6	11011001 mm 110 r/m
FNSTENV m28byte	D9 /6	11011001 mm 110 r/m

Purpose: These instructions write the current FPU environment to the specified destination and then mask all floating-point exceptions. FSTENV checks for unmasked floating-point error conditions before writing the state; FNSTENV does not make this check.

The FPU environment consists of the FPU control word, status word, tag word, and error pointers (both data and instruction). The state layout in memory depends on the operand size and the current operating mode of the processor (real or protected). The USE attribute of the current code segment determines the operand size. The 14-byte operand applies to a USE16 segment; the 28-byte operand applies to a USE32 segment. Figures 1-13 and 1-14 in Chapter 1 show the environment layouts for the 32-bit and 16-bit operand sizes (respectively) in both real mode and protected mode.

C0, C1, C2, and C3 are undefined.

FSTENV and FNSTENV are often used by exception handlers because they provide access to the FPU error pointers. The environment is typically saved onto the memory stack. After saving the environment, FSTENV and FNSTENV set all the exception masks in the FPU control word, preventing floating-point errors from interrupting the exception handler.

Notes: FSTENV and FNSTENV do not store the FPU state until all FPU activity has finished.

To restore a saved environment, use the FLDENV instruction.

If a program is to read from the environment's memory image following a save instruction, it must issue an FWAIT instruction to ensure that the storage operation is complete.

Instruction Demonstration: Not demonstrated.

FSTSW   Store Status Word (with Error Check)
FNSTSW   Store Status Word

INSTRUCTION	OPCODE	BINARY
FSTSW m2byte	9B DF /7	10011011 11011111 mm 111 r/m
FSTSW	9B DF E0	10011011 11011111 11100000
FNSTSW m2byte	DF /7	11011111 mm 111 r/m
FNSTSW AX	DF E0	11011111 11100000

Purpose: These instructions write the current value of the FPU status word to the specified destination, which can be either a two-byte location in memory or the AX register. FSTSW checks for unmasked floating-point error conditions before storing the status word; FNSTSW does not make this check.

C0, C1, C2, and C3 are undefined.

FSTSW and FNSTSW are primarily used for conditional branching after a comparison instruction (FPREM, FPREM1, or FXAM). They can also be used to invoke exception handlers (by polling the exception bits) in environments that do not use interrupts.

Instruction Demonstration: Not demonstrated.

FSUB   Subtract Real
FSUBP   Subtract Real and Pop
FISUB   Subtract Integer

INSTRUCTION	OPCODE	BINARY
FSUB m32real	D8 /4	11011000 mm 100 r/m
FSUB m64real	DC /4	11011100 mm 100 r/m
FSUB ST,ST(i)	D8 E0+i	11011000 11100iii
FSUB ST(i),ST	DC E8+i	11011100 11101iii
FSUBP ST(i),ST	DE E8+i	11011110 11101iii
FSUB	DE E9	11011110 11101001
FISUB m32int	DA /4	11011010 mm 100 r/m
FISUB m16int	DE /4	11011110 mm 100 r/m

Purpose: These instructions subtract an operand from the stack top and return the result to the destination. They operate as follows:

Instruction	Action
FSUB m32real	Subtract m32real from ST
FSUB m64real	Subtract m64real from ST
FSUB ST,ST(i)	Subtract ST(i) from ST
FSUB ST(i),ST	Replace ST(i) with ST − ST (i)
FSUBP ST(i),ST	Replace ST(i) with ST − ST (i); pop ST
FSUB	Replace ST(1) with ST − ST(1); pop ST
FISUB m32int	Subtract m32int from ST
FISUB m16int	Subtract m16int from ST

C1 is affected as described in TABLE 1-2; C0, C2, and C3 are undefined.

Notes: If the source operand is in memory, it is converted to extended-real format automatically.

To subtract the stack top from an operand, use a reverse subtract instruction: FSUBR, FSUBPR, or FISUBR.

Instruction Demonstration: Not demonstrated.

FSUBR   Reverse Subtract Real
FSUBPR   Reverse Subtract Real and Pop
FISUBR   Reverse Subtract Integer

INSTRUCTION	OPCODE	BINARY
FSUBR m32real	D8 /5	11011000 mm 101 r/m
FSUBR m64real	DC /5	11011100 mm 101 r/m
FSUBR ST,ST(i)	D8 E8+i	11011000 11101iii
FSUBR ST(i),ST	DC E0+i	11011100 11100iii
FSUBPR ST(i),ST	DE E0+i	11011110 11100iii
FSUBR	DE E1	11011110 11100001
FISUBR m32int	DA /5	11011010 mm 101 r/m
FISUBR m16int	DE /5	11011110 mm 101 r/m

Purpose: These instructions subtract the stack top from an operand and return the result to the destination. They operate as follows:

Instruction	Action
FSUBR m32real	Replace ST with m32real − ST
FSUBR m64real	Replace ST with m64real − ST
FSUBR ST,ST(i)	Replace ST with ST(i) − ST
FSUBR ST(i),ST	Subtract ST from ST (i)
FSUBPR ST(i),ST	Subtract ST from ST(i) and pop ST
FSUBR	Subtract ST from St(1) and pop ST
FISUBR m32int	Replace ST with m32int − ST
FISUBR m16int	Replace ST with m16int − ST

C1 is affected as described in TABLE 1-2; C0, C2, and C3 are undefined.

Notes: If the source operand is in memory, it is converted to extended-real format automatically.

To subtract an operand from the stack top, use a subtract instruction: FSUB, FSUBP, or FISUB.

Instruction Demonstration: Not demonstrated.

FTST   Test

INSTRUCTION	OPCODE	BINARY
FTST	D9 E4	11011001 11100100

Purpose: FTST compares the stack top to 0.0. Following the instruction, the condition codes reflect the relationship between ST and 0.0. C1 is affected as described in TABLE 1-2. C0, C2, and C3 are affected as follows:

FPU Flags	**EFLAGS**
C_0	CF
C_1	(none)
C_2	PF
C_3	ZF

Notes: If ST contains a NaN or has an undefined format, or a stack fault occurs, the invalid-operation exception is raised and the condition bits are set to "unordered."

The sign of zero is ignored, so that $-0.0 = - + 0.0$.

Instruction Demonstration: Not demonstrated.

FUCOM   Unordered Compare Real
FUCOMP   Unordered Compare Real and Pop
FUCOMPP   Unordered Compare Real and Pop Twice

INSTRUCTION	OPCODE	BINARY
FUCOM ST(i)	DD E0+i	11011101 11100iii
FUCOM	DD E1	11011101 11100001
FUCOMP ST(i)	DD E8+i	11011101 11101iii
FUCOMP	DD E9	11011101 11101001
FUCOMPP	DA E9	11011010 11101001

Purpose: These instructions compare the stack top to a register. They operate as follows:

Instruction	**Action**
FUCOM ST(i)	Compare ST with ST(i)
FUCOM	Compare ST with ST(1)
FUCOMP ST(i)	Compare ST with ST(i) and pop ST
FUCOMP	Compare ST with ST(1) and pop ST
FUCOMPP	Compare ST with ST(1) and pop ST twice

Following the instruction, the condition codes reflect the relationship between ST and the source operand. C1 is affected as described in TABLE 1-2. C0, C2, and C3 are affected as follows:

FPU Flags	EFLAGS
C_0	CF
C_1	(none)
C_2	PF
C_3	ZF

Notes: If either operand is an SNaN or has an undefined format, or a stack fault occurs, the invalid-operation exception is raised and the condition bits are set to "unordered."

If either operand is a QSNaN, the condition bits are set to "unordered." Unlike the regular Compare instructions (FCOM, and so on), the Unordered Compare instructions do not raise the invalid-operation exception due to a QNaN operand.

These instructions were introduced with the 80387; they do not exist in the 8087 and 80287.

The sign of zero is ignored, so that $-0.0 = - + 0.0$.

See also the Compare Integer instructions (FICOM and FICOMP) and the Compare Real instructions (FCOM, FCOMP, and FCOMPP).

Instruction Demonstration: Not demonstrated.

FWAIT   Wait

INSTRUCTION	OPCODE	BINARY
FWAIT	9B	10011011

Purpose: FWAIT causes the processor to check for pending unmasked numeric exceptions before processing. C0, C1, C2, and C3 are undefined.

Notes: FWAIT is an alternate mnemonic for WAIT.

Coding FWAIT after an ESC instruction ensures that any unmasked floating-point exceptions the instruction may cause are handled before the processor can modify the instruction's results.

Instruction Demonstration: Not demonstrated.

FXAM   Examine

INSTRUCTION	OPCODE	BINARY
FXAM	D9 E5	11011001 11100101

Purpose: FXAM reports on the contents of the ST register by setting the condition codes as follows:

FPU Flags	EFLAGS
C_0	CF
C_1	(none)
C_2	PF
C_3	ZF

Instruction Demonstration: Not demonstrated.

FXCH   Exchange Register Contents

INSTRUCTION	OPCODE	BINARY
FXCH ST(i)	D9 C8+i	11011001 11001iii
FXCH	D9 C9	11011001 11001001

Purpose: FXCH swaps the contents of the destination and stack-top registers. If you omit the operand, FXCH swaps ST and ST(1).

C1 is affected as described in TABLE 1-2; C0, C2, and C3 are undefined.

Many numeric instructions operate only on the stack-top. FXCH provides a handy way to operate on lower stack elements. For example, the following takes the square root of the fourth register from the top:

```
FXCH    ST(4)
FSQRT
FXCH    ST(4)
```

Instruction Demonstration: FXCH is demonstrated with FYL2X.

FXTRACT   Extract Exponent and Significand

INSTRUCTION	OPCODE	BINARY
FXTRACT	D9 F4	11011001 11110100

Purpose: FXTRACT separates out the exponent and significand of the value in ST. It puts the exponent into ST and then pushes the significand onto the stack. (Both are represented as real numbers.) C1 is affected as described in TABLE 1-2; C0, C2, and C3 are undefined.

Notes: FXTRACT performs a superset of the IEEE-recommended logb(x) function.

If the original operand is zero, FXTRACT leaves negative infinity as the exponent in ST(1) and sets ST to zero with the same sign as the original operand. The zero-divide exception is raised in this case.

ST(7) must be empty to avoid an invalid-operation exception. To empty ST(7), execute a FFREE ST(7) instruction.

Instruction Demonstration: Not demonstrated.

FYL2X   Compute y times $\log_2 x$

INSTRUCTION   OPCODE   BINARY

FYL2X   D9 F1   11011001 11110001

Purpose: FYL2X computes the base-2 logarithm of ST, multiplies the logarithm by ST(1), and puts the result in ST(1). Then it pops ST. The operand in ST cannot be negative.

C1 is affected as described in TABLE 1-2; C0, C2, and C3 are undefined.

Notes: If the operand in ST is negative, the invalid-operation exception is raised.

You can use the instructions FLDL2T and FLDL2E to load the constants $\log_2 10$ and $\log_2 e$, respectively.

If the operand is very close to 1, use the FYL2XP1 instruction instead of FYL2X.

The 80486 checks for interrupts while executing this instruction. It will abort FYL2X to service an interrupt.

Instruction Demonstration: Many math applications require natural logarithms (log base e) or common logarithms (log base 10). These are easy to calculate by using the following equation to change the base of a logarithm to a new base n:

$$\log_n X = \log_n 2 \times \log_2 X$$

In this case, n is e or 10. The following programs assume that X is on the top of the stack; they replace X with its logarithm.

The program that produces natural logs is

```
FLDLN2  ;Push log base e of 2
FXCH    ;Swap ST and ST(1)
FYL2X   ;Pop ST, replace it with natural log
```

The program that produces common logs is

```
FLDLG2  ;Push log base e of 10
FXCH    ;Swap ST and ST(1)
FYL2X   ;Pop ST, replace it with common log
```

FYL2XP1   Compute y times $\log_2(x + 1)$

INSTRUCTION	OPCODE	BINARY
FYL2XP1	D9 F1	11011001 11110001

Purpose: FYL2XP1 computes the base-2 logarithm of (ST + 1.0), multiplies the logarithm by ST(1), and puts the result in ST(1). Then it pops ST. The operand in ST cannot be negative. The absolute value of the operand in ST must be greater than zero and less than SQRT(2)/2.

C1 is affected as described in TABLE 1-2; C0, C2, and C3 are undefined.

Notes: If the operand in ST is outside the acceptable range, the result of FYL2XP1 is undefined.

FYL2XP1 is more accurate than FYL2X when computing the logarithm of numbers very close to 1.

The 80486 checks for interrupts while executing this instruction. It will abort FYL2XP1 to service an interrupt.

Instruction Demonstration: Not demonstrated.

HLT   Halt

INSTRUCTION	OPCODE	BINARY
HLT	F4	11110100

Purpose: HALT stops the execution of all instructions and places the 80486 in a HALT state. An NMI, reset, or an enabled interrupt will resume execution. A HLT would normally be the last instruction in a sequence that shuts down the system, i.e., for a checkpoint after a power failure is detected.

Instruction Demonstration: Not demonstrated, because this instruction stops the processor.

IDIV   Signed Divide

INSTRUCTION	OPCODE	BINARY
IDIV r/m8	F6 /7	11110110 mm 111 r/m
IDIV AX,r/m16	F7 /7	11110111 mm 111 r/m
IDIV EAX,r/m32	F7 /7	11110111 mm 111 r/m

Purpose: IDIV does signed division. The dividend, quotient, and remainder are implicitly allocated to fixed registers (see FIG. 10-4), while only the divisor is given as an explicit r/m (register or memory) operand. The divisor determines which registers are used. The figure shows which registers to use for IDIV. Nonintegral quotients are truncated toward zero. Remainders are always the same sign as the dividend and always have less magnitude than the divisor.

Size (bits)	Divisor	Quotient	Remainder	Dividend
Byte (8)	r/m 8	AL	AH	AX
Word (16)	r/m 16	AX	DX	DX:AX
Dword (32)	r/m 32	EAX	EDX	EDX:EAX

10-4   Registers to use for IDIV.

An 80486 interrupt zero (0) is taken if a zero divisor or a quotient too large for the destination register is generated. If a divide-by-zero occurs, the quotient and remainder are undefined.

Instruction Demonstration: This demonstrates the signed divide instruction IDIV. The instruction sequence is

```
4C13:0000 B80502              MOV    AX,0205
4C13:0003 66BB33000000        MOV    EBX,00000033
4C13:0009 F6FB                IDIV   BL
4C13:000B 99                  CWD
4C13:000C F7FB                IDIV   BX
4C13:000E 66B867FFFFFF        MOV    EAX,FFFFFF67
4C13:0014 6699                CDQ
4C13:0016 66F7FB              IDIV   EBX
```

The registers and flags at the start are

EAX = 00000000 EBX = 00000000 EDX = 00000000   IP = 0000
                                                NV UP EI PL NZ NA PO NC

4C13:0000 B80502   MOV   AX,0205

EAX = 00000205 EBX = 00000000 EDX = 00000000   IP = 0003
                                                NV UP EI PL NZ NA PO NC

The dividend is placed into AX. Then set the divisor in EBX (BL).

4C13:0003 66BB33000000   MOV   EBX,00000033

EAX = 00000205 EBX = 00000033 EDX = 00000000   IP = 0009
                                                NV UP EI PL NZ NA PO NC

4C13:0009 F6FB   IDIV   BL

EAX = 0000070A EBX = 00000033 EDX = 00000000   IP = 000B
                                                NV UP EI **NG** NZ NA **PE CY**

Note that the short divide leaves the quotient in AL (517/51 = 10 with a remainder of 7) and the remainder in AH. The flags might be affected (NG, PE and CY in this example), but their values are undefined. Note that the signed and unsigned divide operate the same on positive values.

4C13:000B 99   CWD

EAX = 0000070A EBX = 00000033 EDX = 00000000   IP = 000C

NV UP EI NG NZ NA PE CY

CWD extends the sign of AX through DX.

4C13:000C F7FB   IDIV   BX

EAX = 00000023 EBX = 00000033 EDX = 00000011   IP = 000E

NV UP EI NG NZ **AC** PE CY

Note that the long divide leaves the quotient in AX and the remainder in DX. Again, the flags are undefined and the operation on positive values is the same as DIV.

4C13:000E 66B867FFFFFF   MOV   EAX,FFFFFF67

The move sets a negative 153 in EAX.

EAX = FFFFFF67 EBX = 00000033 EDX = 00000011   IP = 0014

NV UP EI NG NZ AC PE CY

4C13:0014 6699   CDQ

The sign is extended through EDX in order to preserve the negative or positive sign for the signed divide.

EAX = FFFFFF67 EBX = 00000033 EDX = FFFFFFFF   IP = 0016

NV UP EI NG NZ AC PE CY

4C13:0016 66F7FB   IDIV EBX

The divide proceeds, placing the remainder (0) in EDX and the quotient (−3) in EAX.

EAX = FFFFFFFD EBX = 00000033 EDX = 00000000   IP = 0019

NV UP EI **PL ZR** AC PE CY

IMUL   Signed Integer Multiply

INSTRUCTION	OPCODE	BINARY
IMUL r/m8	F6 /5	11110110 mm 101 r/m
IMUL r/m16	F7 /5	11110111 mm 101 r/m
IMUL r/m32	F7 /5	11110111 mm 101 r/m
IMUL r16,r/m16	OF AF /r	00001111 10101111 mm rrr r/m

IMUL r32,r/m32	0F AF /r	00001111 10101111 mm rrr r/m
IMUL r16,r/m16,imm8	6B /r ib	01101011 mm rrr r/m
IMUL r32,r/m32,imm8	6B /r ib	01101011 mm rrr r/m
IMUL r16,imm8	6B /r ib	01101011 mm rrr r/m
IMUL r32,imm8	6B /r ib	01101011 mm rrr r/m
IMUL r16,r/m16,imm16 69	/r iw	01101001 mm rrr r/m
IMUL r32,r/m32,imm32 69	/r id	01101001 mm rrr r/m
IMUL r16,imm16	69 /r iw	01101001 mm rrr r/m
IMUL r32,imm32	69 /r id	01101001 mm rrr r/m

Purpose: IMUL performs a signed multiplication operation. This instruction has three variations:

- *One-operand form.* The operand could be a byte, word, or double-word located in memory or in a general register. IMUL uses EAX and EDX as implicit operands in the same way that MUL does.
- *Two-operand form.* One of the source operands might be in any general register while the other might be either in memory or in a general register. The product replaces the general-register operand. If the result is within the range of the first operand, CF and OF are zero. Otherwise, CF and OF are set to 1.
- *Three-operand form.* The second and third operands are sources, and first operand is the destination. One of the source operands is an immediate value stored in the instruction. The second might be in memory or in any general register. The product can be stored in any general register. The immediate operand is treated as signed. If the immediate operand is a byte, the processor automatically sign-extends it to the size of the second operand before doing the multiplication. If the result is within the range of the first operand, CF and OF are zero. Otherwise, CF and OF are set to 1.

Instruction Demonstration: This demonstrates signed multiplication. In some cases, various flags change as a result of the IMUL instruction; in these cases, the flags become undefined. In essence, their new status is meaningless to the programmer. The instruction sequence is

```
4D69:0000 66B8EEFFFFFF    MOV    EAX, - 18
4D69:0006 66BB70000000    MOV    EBX,112
4D69:000C F6EB            IMUL   BL
4D69:000E 66B8EEFFFFFF    MOV    EAX, - 18
4D69:0014 F7EB            IMUL   BX
4D69:0016 66B8EEFFFFFF    MOV    EAX, - 18
4D69:001C 66F7EB          IMUL   EBX
```

The registers and flags at the start are

EAX = 00000000 EBX = 00000000 EDX = 00000000   IP = 0000

NV UP EI PL NZ NA PO NC

Set up the registers for the multiply:

```
4D69:0000 66B8EEFFFFFF              MOV         EAX, – 18
EAX=FFFFFFEE EBX=00000000 EDX=00000000  IP=0006
                                        NV UP EI PL NZ NA PO NC
```

Load a – 18 into EAX (AX, and AL).

```
4D69:0006 66BB70000000              MOV         EBX,112
EAX=FFFFFFEE EBX=00000070 EDX=00000000  IP=000C
                                        NV UP EI PL NZ NA PO NC
```

A positive multiplier of 112 into EBX (BX, and BL).

```
4D69:000C F6EB                      IMUL        BL
EAX=FFFFF820 EBX=00000070 EDX=00000000  IP=000E
                                        OV UP EI NG NZ AC PO CY
```

The negative product is formed in AX – 2016. Restoring the value in AX,

```
4D69:000E 66B8EEFFFFFF              MOV         EAX, – 18
EAX=FFFFFFEE EBX=00000070 EDX=00000000  IP=0014
                                        OV UP EI NG NZ AC PO CY
```

and multiplying by the word value in BX

```
4D69:0014 F7EB                      IMUL        BX
EAX=FFFFF820 EBX=00000070 EDX=0000FFFF  IP=0016
                                        NV UP EI NG NZ AC PO NC
```

forms the product in the DX – AX register pair (in this case by extending the negative sign through DX).
Restoring the value in EAX

```
4D69:0016 66B8EEFFFFFF              MOV         EAX, – 18
EAX=FFFFFFEE EBX=00000070 EDX=0000FFFF  IP=001C
                                        NV UP EI NG NZ AC PO NC
```

and multiplying by the doubleword value in EBX

```
4D69:001C 66F7EB                    IMUL        EBX
EAX=FFFFF820 EBX=00000070 EDX=FFFFFFFF  IP=001F
                                        NV UP EI NG NZ AC PO NC
```

forms the product in the EDX – EAX register pair (again by extending the negative sign through EDX).

IN   Input from Port

INSTRUCTION	OPCODE	BINARY
IN AL,imm8	E4 ib	11100100
IN AX,imm8	E5 ib	11100101
IN EAX,imm8	E5 ib	11100101
IN AL,DX	EC	11101100
IN AX,DX	ED	11101101
IN EAX,DX	ED	11101101

Purpose: IN brings a byte, word, or dword from a specified port and stores it in a register AL, AX, or EAX, respectively. The port is specified by the second operand and is in the range of 0 to 64K – 1. The port is accessed by using an immediate operand or by placing its number into the DX register and using an IN instruction with DX as the second parameter. The immediate byte allows access to ports 0–255, in which case the upper bits of the port are always zero. The register form (DX) allows for the full range to be used. An exception occurs if the current task has insufficient privilege for the I/O.

Instruction Demonstration: The IN, INS, OUT, and OUTS instructions are demonstrated together because of their relationship with each other. This demonstrates the use of the input and output group of instructions. The instruction sequence is

```
14EB:0000 E440        IN      AL,40
14EB:0102 E640        OUT     40,AL
14EB:0104 BA7803      MOV     DX,0378
14EB:0107 EC          IN      AL,DX
14EB:0108 EE          OUT     DX,AL
14EB:0109 BF0002      MOV     DI,0200
14EB:010C 6C          INSB
14EB:010D 6D          INSW
14EB:010E BE0002      MOV     SI,0200
14EB:0111 6E          OUTSB
14EB:0112 6F          OUTSW
```

The registers and flags at the start are

```
EAX=00000000 EDX=00000000 ESI=00000000
EDI=00000000     IP=0000          NV UP EI PL NZ NA PO NC
14EB:0000 E440   IN               AL,40
EAX=0000001A
EDX=00000000
ESI=00000000
EDI=00000000     IP=0102          NV UP EI PL NZ NA PO NC
```

Read a byte value from port X"40" or 64 into AL.

```
14EB:0102 E640    OUT              40,AL
EAX=0000001A
EDX=00000000
ESI=00000000
EDI=00000000     IP=0104          NV UP EI PL NZ NA PO NC
```

Output the byte in AL to port 40.

```
14EB:0104 BA7803    MOV     DX,0378
EAX=0000001A EDX=00000378 ESI=00000000
EDI=00000000     IP=0107          NV UP EI PL NZ NA PO NC
14EB:0107 EC        IN              AL,DX
EAX=000000AA EDX=00000378 ESI=00000000
EDI=00000000     IP=0108          NV UP EI PL NZ NA PO NC
```

Read a byte from the port addressed by DX into AL. Note that the port address is above hex FF (the largest port addressable in an 8-bit immediate value).

```
14EB:0108 EE        OUT              DX,AL
EAX=000000AA EDX=00000378 ESI=00000000
EDI=00000000     IP=0109          NV UP EI PL NZ NA PO NC
```

Output the byte to the port that has its address in DX.

```
14EB:0109 BF0002    MOV     DI,0200
EAX=000000AA EDX=00000378 ESI=00000000
EDI=00000200     IP=010C          NV UP EI PL NZ NA PO NC
14EB:010C 6C        INSB
EAX=000000AA EDX=00000378 ESI=00000000
EDI=00000201     IP=010D          NV UP EI PL NZ NA PO NC
```

Note that the index (DI) has been stepped by one.

```
14EB:010D 6D        INSW
EAX=000000AA EDX=00000378 ESI=00000000
EDI=00000203     IP=010E          NV UP EI PL NZ NA PO NC
```

Again, DI is stepped but this time by the size of the word that was read.

```
14EB:010E BE0002    MOV     SI,0200
EAX=000000AA EDX=00000378 ESI=00000200
EDI=00000203     IP=0111          NV UP EI PL NZ NA PO NC
```

```
14EB:0111 6E          OUTSB
EAX = 000000AA EDX = 00000378 ESI = 00000201
EDI = 00000203     IP = 0112          NV UP EI PL NZ NA PO NC
```

Note that the SI value has been incremented by the size of the value output.

```
14EB:0112 6F          OUTSW
EAX = 000000AA EDX = 00000378 ESI = 00000203
EDI = 00000203     IP = 0113          NV UP EI PL NZ NA PO NC
```

Again the output pointer is incremented, this time by 2 for the size of a word. The data read with the INS instructions is

```
DS:0200AA    AA 7F
```

INC   Increment by 1

INSTRUCTION	OPCODE	BINARY
INC r/m8	FE /0	11111110 mm 000 r/m
INC r/m16	FF /0	11111111 mm 000 r/m
INC r/m32	FF /0	11111111 mm 000 r/m
INC r16	40 + rw	01000rrr
INC r32	40 + rd	01000rrr

Purpose: INC adds one to the destination operand, but (unlike ADD) INC does not affect CF. Other flags are set according to the result. Use ADD with an operand of 1 if the carry flag update is desired.

Instruction Demonstration: This demonstrates the effects of the INC instruction. The instruction sequence is

```
4D69:0000 66B8FE000000    MOV    EAX,000000FE
4D69:0006 FEC0            INC    AL
4D69:0008 FEC0            INC    AL
4D69:000A FEC0            INC    AL
```

The registers and flags at the start are

```
EAX = 00000000          IP = 0000    NV UP EI NG NZ AC PO NC
```

Load a −2 into AL:

```
4D69:0000 66B8FE000000    MOV        EAX,000000FE
EAX = 000000FE          IP = 0006    NV UP EI NG NZ AC PO NC
4D69:0006 FEC0            INC        AL
EAX = 000000FF          IP = 0008    NV UP EI NG NZ NA PE NC
```

Increment AL to – 1. Note that the flags normally affected by an arithmetic instruction are also affected by INC.

4D69:0008		FEC0	INC AL
EAX = 00000000		IP = 000A	NV UP EI **PL ZR AC** PE NC

In incrementing from – 1 to zero, a carry should have formed. In this way—not affecting the carry flag—INC differs from normal arithmetic instructions.

4D69:000A		FEC0	INC AL
EAX = 00000001		IP = 000C	NV UP EI PL **NZ NA PO** NC

In incrementing from zero to one, the flags reflect the change.

INS   Input String from Port
INSB   Input Byte
INSW   Input Word
INSD   Input Doubleword

INSTRUCTION	OPCODE	BINARY
INS r/m8,DX	6C	01101100
INS r/m16,DX	6D	01101101
INS r/m32,DX	6D	01101101

Note: INSB is a common assembler mnemonic for INS r/m8, DX
INSW is a common assembler mnemonic for INS r/m16,DX
INSD is a common assembler mnemonic for INS r/m32,DX

Purpose: These instructions allow a read from a specified device into memory (ES:EDI)—the input device being specified in the DX register. After the transfer is made, EDI is updated to point to the next string location, depending on how DF (the direction flag) is set. If DF = 0, EDI increments by 1, 2, or 4. If DF = 1, EDI is decremented by 1, 2, or 4. The data is read into the segment specified by ES, and no segment override is possible. INS does *not* allow port number specification as an immediate value. The port must be addressed through DX.

These instructions normally use a REP prefix to indicate the reading of the number of bytes as specified in CX. An exception is raised if the current task has insufficient privilege to perform I/O.

Instruction Demonstration: The IN, INS, OUT, and OUTS instructions are demonstrated together because of their relationship with each other. See the IN instruction.

INT   Call to Interrupt Procedure
INTO   Interrupt on Overflow

INSTRUCTION	OPCODE	BINARY
INT 3	CC	11001100
INT imm8	CD ib	11001101
INTO	CE	11001110

Purpose: INT transfers control from one code segment location to another. These locations can be within the same code segment (near) or in different code segments (far). INT is a software-generated interrupt that allows a programmer to transfer control to an interrupt service routine from within a program.

When any of the INTs are used, the flags register, the code segment register, and the instruction pointer are pushed onto the stack. When CS is PUSHed onto the stack, a full 32-bit word is PUSHed. This keeps the stack aligned, which improves the 80486 performance.

INT n activates the interrupt service that corresponds to the number coded in the instruction. INT can specify any interrupt type. Note that interrupts 0 through 31 are reserved by Intel. INTn returns control at the end of the service routine with an IRET.

INTO invokes interrupt 4 if the overflow flag (OF) is set, and interrupt 4 is reserved for this purpose. OF is set by several arithmetic, logical, and string instructions. INT 3 is a single-byte form (the breakpoint instruction) that is useful for debugging.

Instruction Demonstration: The INT and IRET instructions are demonstrated together because of their interrelationship. This demonstrates the INT and IRET instructions. INTO functions the same as INT 4 if an overflow is detected and is provided as a shorthand for the sequence:

```
JNO       around    ; Skip if no overflow
INT       4         ; Call overflow handler
around:   NOP
```

which would follow each arithmetic instruction that could overflow. The instruction sequence is (interrupt 42 legitimately taken from MS-DOS):

```
14EB:0100 BA0002    MOV   DX,0200
14EB:0103 B042      MOV   AL,42
14EB:0105 B425      MOV   AH,25
14EB:0107 CD21      INT   21
14EB:0109 90        NOP
14EB:010A 90        NOP
14EB:010B CD42      INT   42
14EB:010D 90        NOP
```

The interrupt handling routine is

```
14EB:0200 90   NOP
14EB:0201 CF   IRET
```

The registers and flags at the start are

```
AX=0000 DX=0000 SP=EA04 DS =14EB CS=14EB IP=0100
                                  NV UP EI PL NZ NA PO NC
14EB:0100 BA0002    MOV        DX,0200
AX=0000 DX=0200 SP=EA04 DS =14EB CS=14EB IP=0103
                                  NV UP EI PL NZ NA PO NC
```

MS-DOS is told where our handler is located (DS:DX),

```
14EB:0103 B042     MOV        AL,42
AX=0042 DX=0200 SP=EA04 DS =14EB CS=14EB IP=0105
                                  NV UP EI PL NZ NA PO NC
```

which interrupt is desired,

```
14EB:0105 B425     MOV        AH,25
AX=2542 DX=0200 SP=EA04 DS =14EB CS=14EB IP=0107
                                  NV UP EI PL NZ NA PO NC
```

and that a set vector operation is desired.

```
14EB:0107 CD21     INT        21
AX=2542 DX=0200 SP=EA04 DS =14EB CS=14EB IP=0109
                                  NV UP EI PL NZ NA PO NC
```

Then call MS-DOS with a DOS CALL INT.

```
14EB:0109 90       NOP
AX=2542 DX=0200 SP=EA04 DS =14EB CS=14EB IP=010A
                                  NV UP EI PL NZ NA PO NC
```

The results:

```
INT Vector   40   41   42   43
0000:010059 EC 00 F0 20 00 3D 08-00 02 EB 14 FC 80 00 F0
14EB:010A 90       NOP
AX=2542 DX=0200 SP=EA04 DS =14EB CS=14EB IP=010B
                                  NV UP EI PL NZ NA PO NC
14EB:010B CD42     INT        42
AX=2542 DX=0200 SP=E9FE DS =14EB CS=14EB IP=0200
                                  NV UP DI PL NZ NA PO NC
```

The INT places the flags, CS, and IP registers on the stack for use in returning.

14EB:39FE 0D 01 EB 14 02 72
14EB:0200 90   NOP
AX = 2542 DX = 0200 SP = E9FE DS = 14EB CS = 14EB IP = 0201
                              NV UP DI PL NZ NA PO NC

The interrupt is handled:

14EB:0201 CF   IRET
AX = 2542 DX = 0200 SP = EA04 DS = 14EB CS = 14EB IP = 010D
                              NV UP EI PL NZ NA PO NC

and returned. Note that IP and SP have been adjusted. Also note that the flags are not changed throughout the sequence.

INVD   Invalidate Data Cache

INSTRUCTION	OPCODE	BINARY
INVD	OF 08	00001111 00001000

Purpose: INVD flushes the internal cache of the 80486, and issues a special-function bus cycle, to indicate that external caches should also be flushed. Data held in write-back external caches is discarded. INVD affects no flags.

This instruction is new with the 80486.

Note: See also the WBINVD (Write-Back and Invalidate Cache) instruction.

Instruction Demonstration: Not demonstrated.

INVLPG   Invalidate TLB Entry

INSTRUCTION	OPCODE	BINARY
INVLPG m	OF 01 /7	00001111 00000001 mm 111 r/m

Purpose: INVLPG is used to invalidate a single entry in the Translation Lookaside Buffer (TLB), the cache used for page table entries. If the TLB contains a valid entry that maps the address of the memory operand, that TLB entry is marked invalid. INVLPG affects no flags.

This instruction is new with the 80486.

Instruction Demonstration: Not demonstrated.

IRET   Return from Interrupt
IRETD   Return from Interrupt—32-bit Mode

INSTRUCTION	OPCODE	BINARY
IRET	CF	11001111
IRETD	CF	11001111

Purpose: IRET returns control to an interrupted procedure. In the Real Address Mode, IRET pops the instruction counter, the CS register, and the flags register from the stack. The 80486 then resumes the interrupted procedure.

In Protected Mode, IRET's action depends on the setting of the NT (Nested Task) bit in the flags register:

- If NT = 0, the IRET instruction returns from an interrupt procedure without a task switch. The code returned to must be equally- or less-privileged than the interrupt routine, as indicated by the RPL bits of the CS selector popped from the stack. If the destination code is less-privileged, IRET also pops the stack pointer and SS from the stack.
- If NT = 1, The IRET instruction reverses the operation of a CALL or INT that caused a task switch. The updated state of the task executing the IRET is saved in its Task State Segment (TSS). If the task is reentered later, the 80486 executes the code that follows the IRET instruction.

Note: In the case of IRET, the flags register is Flags. If IRETD is used, then it's the EFLAGS register.

Instruction Demonstration: The INT and IRET instructions are demonstrated together because of their interrelationship. See the INT instruction.

JMP   Jump
Jcc   Jump on some Condition code

INSTRUCTION	OPCODE	BINARY
JMP rel8	EB cb	11101011
JMP rel16	E9 cw	11101001
JMP r/m16	FF /4	11111111 mm 100 r/m
JMP ptr16:16	EA cd	11101010
JMP m16:16	FF /5	11111111 mm 101 r/m
JMP rel32	E9 cd	11101001

JMP r/m32	FF /4	11111111 mm 100 r/m
JMP ptr16:32	EA cp	11101010
JMP m16:32	FF /5	11111111 mm 101 r/m
JA rel8	77 cb	01110111
JAE rel8	73 cb	01110011
JB rel8	72 cb	01110010
JBE rel8	76 cb	01110110
JC rel8	72 cb	01110010
JCXZ rel8	E3 cb	11100011
JECXZ rel8	E3 cb	11100011
JE rel8	74 cb	01110100
JZ rel8	74 cb	01110100
JG rel8	7F cb	01111111
JGE rel8	7D cb	01111101
JL rel8	7C cb	01111100
JLE rel8	7E cb	01111110
JNA rel8	76 cb	01110110
JNAE rel8	72 cb	01110010
JNB rel8	73 cb	01110011
JNBE rel8	77 cb	01110111
JNC rel8	73 cb	01110011
JNE rel8	75 cb	01110101
JNG rel8	7E cb	01111110
JNGE rel8	7C cb	01111100
JNL rel8	7D cb	01111101
JNLE rel8	7F cb	01111111
JNO rel8	71 cb	01110001
JNP rel8	7B cb	01111011
JNS rel8	79 cb	01111001
JNZ rel8	75 cb	01110101
JO rel8	70 cb	01110000
JP rel8	7A cb	01111010
JPE rel8	7A cb	01111010
JPO rel8	7B cb	01111011
JS rel8	78 cb	01111000
JZ rel8	74 cb	01110100
JA rel16/32	0F 87 cw/cd	00001111 10000111
JAE rel16/32	0F 83 cw/cd	00001111 10000011
JB rel16/32	0F 82 cw/cd	00001111 10000010
JBE rel16/32	0F 86 cw/cd	00001111 10000110
JC rel16/32	0F 82 cw/cd	00001111 10000010
JE rel16/32	0F 84 cw/cd	00001111 10000100
JZ rel16/32	0F 84 cw/cd	00001111 10000100
JG rel16/32	0F 8F cw/cd	00001111 10001111
JGE rel16/32	0F 8D cw/cd	00001111 10001101

JL rel16/32	OF 8C cw/cd	00001111 10001100
JLE rel16/32	OF 8E cw/cd	00001111 10001110
JNA rel16/32	OF 86 cw/cd	00001111 10000110
JNAE rel16/32	OF 82 cw/cd	00001111 10000010
JNB rel16/32	OF 83 cw/cd	00001111 10000011
JNBE rel16/32	OF 87 cw/cd	00001111 10000111
JNC rel16/32	OF 83 cw/cd	00001111 10000011
JNE rel16/32	OF 85 cw/cd	00001111 10000101
JNG rel16/32	OF 8E cw/cd	00001111 10001110
JNGE rel16/32	OF 8C cw/cd	00001111 10001100
JNL rel16/32	OF 8D cw/cd	00001111 10001101
JNLE rel16/32	OF 8F cw/cd	00001111 10001111
JNO rel16/32	OF 81 cw/cd	00001111 10000001
JNP rel16/32	OF 8B cw/cd	00001111 10001011
JNS rel16/32	OF 89 cw/cd	00001111 10001001
JNZ rel16/32	OF 85 cw/cd	00001111 10000101
JO rel16/32	OF 80 cw/cd	00001111 10000000
JP rel16/32	OF 8A cw/cd	00001111 10001010
JPE rel16/32	OF 8A cw/cd	00001111 10001010
JPO rel16/32	OF 8B cw/cd	00001111 10001011
JS rel16/32	OF 88 cw/cd	00001111 10001000
JZ rel16/32	OF 84 cw/cd	00001111 10000100

Purpose: JMP transfers control from one code segment location to another. The Jcc jumps depend on the flags, as shown below. These locations can be within the same code segment (near) or in different code segments (far). JMP unconditionally transfers control to the target location and is a one-way transfer. JMP does *not* save a return address on the stack as CALL does.

JMP's implementation varies depending on whether the address is directly specified within the instruction or indirectly through a register or memory. A direct JMP includes the destination address as part of the instruction. An indirect JMP gets the destination address through a register or a pointer variable. An indirect JMP specifies an absolute address by one of the following ways:

- a register modifies the address of the memory pointer to select a destination address
- the program can JMP to a location specified by a general register (EAX, EDX, ECX, EBX, EBP, ESI, or ECI)—the 80386 moves this 32-bit value into EIP and resumes execution, or
- the 80486 obtains the destination address from a memory operand specified in the instruction.

The following Jcc conditional transfer instructions may or may not transfer control, depending on the state of the flags when the instruction executes. The flags are assumed to have been set in some meaningful way by proceeding instruction(s).

JA/JNBE	Above, not below nor equal	CF=0, ZF=0
JAE/JNB	Above or equal, not below	CF=0
JB/JNAE	Below, not above nor equal	CF=1
JBE/JNA	Below or equal, not above	CF=1, ZF=1
JC	Carry	CF=1
JE/JZ	Equal, zero	ZF=1
JNC	Not carry	CF=0
JNE/JNZ	Not equal, not zero	ZF=0
JNP/JPO	Not parity, parity odd	PF=0
JP/JPE	Parity, parity even	PF=1

The following Jcc instructions are signed control transfers:

JG/JNLE	Greater, not less nor equal	ZF=0, SF=OF
JGE/JNL	Greater or equal, not less	SF=OF
JL/JNGE	Less, not greater nor equal	SF=OF
JLE/JNG	Less or equal, not greater	SF=OF, SF=1
JNO	Not overflow	OF=0
JNS	Not sign	SF=0
JO	Overflow	OF=1
JS	Sign (negative)	SF=1

JCXZ (Jump if CX is zero) and JECXZ (Jump if ECX is zero) branch to the label specified in the instruction if CX or ECX contains a value of zero. These instructions are useful for designing a loop that gets bypassed if the count in the register is initialized to zero. When used with repeated string scan and compare instructions, JCXZ/JECXZ determines whether the repetitions ended due to a zero in CX/ECX or due to scan or compare conditions being satisfied.

Note: JCXZ and JECXZ take longer to execute than a two-instruction sequence comprised of a compare and a conditional jump. For example, while the count is nonzero, each execution of JECXZ Label takes 8 clock cycles, but

```
CMP    ECX,0
JZ     Label
```

takes only 4 cycles.

Instruction Demonstration #1: This demonstrates the unconditional JMP instruction. The instruction sequence is

```
14EB:0100 29C0    SUB    AX,AX
14EB:0102 750C    JNZ    0110
14EB:0104 EB0A    JMP    0110
```

The affected registers and flags are

```
        AX = 0000              IP = 0100   NV UP EI PL NZ NA PE NC
        14EB:0100 29C0    SUB          AX,AX
```

Note that the subtract set the zero flag.

```
        AX = 0000              IP = 0102   NV UP EI PL **ZR** NA PE NC
        14EB:0102 750C    JNZ          0110
        AX = 0000              IP = 0104   NV UP EI PL ZR NA PE NC
```

The JNZ tests for the condition NZ, which is false. IP advances to the next sequential instruction.

```
        14EB:0104 EB0A    JMP          0110
        AX = 0000              IP = 0110   NV UP EI PL ZR NA PE NC
```

The JMP instruction alters program flow unconditionally. No flags or other conditions are tested.

Instruction Demonstration #2: This demonstrates the conditional jump instruction. The instruction sequence is

```
        14EB:0100 29C0    SUB          AX,AX
        14EB:0102 750C    JNZ          0110
        14EB:0104 740A    JZ           0110
```

The affected registers and flags are

```
        AX = 0000              IP = 0100   NV UP EI PL NZ NA PE NC
        14EB:0100 29C0    SUB          AX,AX
```

Note that the subtract set the zero flag.

```
        AX = 0000              IP = 0102   NV UP EI PL **ZR** NA PE NC
```

A conditional jump is encountered, the JNZ.

```
        14EB:0102 750C    JNZ          0110
        AX = 0000              IP = 0104   NV UP EI PL ZR NA PE NC
```

Note that the instruction pointer advances to the next sequential instruction because the tested condition is false. The condition tested by the JZ instruction is true, however. Note the resulting effect on the instruction pointer.

```
        14EB:0104 740A    JZ           0110
        AX = 0000              IP = 0110   NV UP EI PL ZR NA PE NC
```

The sequential flow of instructions has been altered.

Instruction Demonstration #3: The JCXZ instruction tests the value in the CX register and jumps if the CX contains zeros. The importance of this instruction lies in the sting REP instruction prefix and the LOOP instruction. Both use the CX register as a counter. The JCXZ provides a single instruction escape at the beginning of a sequence. The instruction sequence is

14EB:0100 E302	JCXZ	0104
14EB:0102 EBFC	JMP	0100
14EB:0104 B90100	MOV	CX,0001
14EB:0107 E3FB	JCXZ	0104

The registers and flags at the start are

CX=0000	IP=0100	NV UP EI PL ZR NA PE NC

Note that CX is zero.

14EB:0100 E302	JCXZ	0104
CX=0000	IP=0104	NV UP EI PL ZR NA PE NC

The JCXZ instruction transfers to the MOV, bypassing the next instruction (the JMP to 100).

14EB:0104 B90100	MOV	CX,0001
CX=0001	IP=0107	NV UP EI PL ZR NA PE NC

The value in CX is set non-zero.

14EB:0107 E3FB	JCXZ	0104
CX=0001	IP=0109	NV UP EI PL ZR NA PE NC

Because of this, the JCXZ allows sequential execution of the instructions that follow it.

LAHF   Load Flags into AH Register

INSTRUCTION	OPCODE	BINARY
LAHF	9F	10011111

Purpose: Though specific instructions exist to alter CF and DF, there is no direct way of altering the other applications-oriented flags. The flag transfer instructions (LAHF and SAHF) allow a program to alter the other flag bits with the bit manipulation instructions after transferring these flags to the stack or the AH register.

LAHF copies SF, ZF, AF, PF, and CF to AH bits 7, 6, 4, 2, and 0, respectively. The contents of the remaining bits (5, 3, and 1) are undefined. The flags remain unaffected. See FIG. 10-5 for the layout of the flags in the flags register, the low 16 bits of EFLAGS.

Instruction Demonstration: The LAHF instruction copies the low byte of the flags word to AH. The instruction sequence is

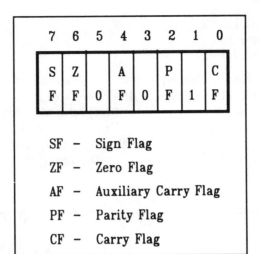

7	6	5	4	3	2	1	0
S F	Z F	0	A F	0	P F	1	C F

SF – Sign Flag

ZF – Zero Flag

AF – Auxiliary Carry Flag

PF – Parity Flag

CF – Carry Flag

10-5 Low byte of the Flags register.

```
14EB:0100 29C0   SUB    AX,AX
14EB:0102 9F     LAHF
```

The subtract sets the sign, zero, and parity flags are

```
AX = 0000      IP = 0102   NV UP EI PL ZR NA PE NC
14EB:0102 9F   LAHF
AX = 4600      IP = 0103   NV UP EI PL ZR NA PE NC
```

The LAHF instruction copies the flags into AH. Note that 46 is 01000110 in binary and that the flags are PL ZR xx NA xx PE xx NC.

LAR   Load Access Rights Byte

INSTRUCTION	OPCODE	BINARY
LAR r16,r/m16	OF 02 /r	00001111 00000010 mm rrr r/m
LAR r32,r/m32	OF 02 /r	00001111 00000010 mm rrr r/m

Purpose: If you specify a 32-bit register as the destination operand, LAR reads a segment descriptor and puts the following bits into the register:

- Granularity, bit 23.
- Default Operation Size, bit 22.
- Programmer-available, bit 20.
- Segment Present, bit 15.
- DPL, bits 13-14.

- Segment, bit 12.
- Type, bits 9-11.
- Accessed, bit 8.

If you specify a 16-bit register as the destination, LAR puts descriptor bits 8 through 15 (the Access Rights Byte) into the register.

The segment attribute field is simply the high-order four bytes of the descriptor ANDed with 00FxFF00h, where x indicates that bits 16 through 19 are undefined in the value loaded by LAR.

Note: Only the following are valid special-segment and gate-descriptor types as shown in FIG. 10-6.

Type	Name
0	Undefined, invalid
1	Available 80286 TSS
2	Load Descriptor Table
3	Busy 80286 TSS
4	80286 call gate
5	80286/386/486 task gate
6	80286 interrupt gate
7	80286 trap gate
8	Undefined, invalid
9	Available 80386/486 TSS
A	Undefined, invalid
B	Busy 80386/486 TSS
C	80386/486 call gate
D	Undefined, invalid
E	80386/486 interrupt gate
F	80386/486 trap gate

Note that types 0, 8, A, and D are invalid.

10-6 Valid special segment and gate descriptor types.

The descriptor specified by the selector in the first operand must be within the descriptor table limits, have a valid type field, and be accessible at both CPL (current privilege level) and RPL (requestor's privilege level) of the selector in the second operand compared to DPL (descriptor privilege level). If so, ZF is set to 1 and the segment attributes are loaded to operand 1. If not, ZF is set to zero and the first operand is unmodified.

Instruction Demonstration: The LAR instruction loads a masked image of the second doubleword of the descriptor selected by the second operand into the register specified by the first operand. The instruction sequence is

```
0070:0100 6629C0      SUB    EAX,EAX
0070:0103 B84000      MOV    AX,0040h
0070:0106 6689C3      MOV    EBX,EAX
0070:0109 660F02C3    LAR    EAX,EBX
```

The registers and flags at the start are

```
EAX=00000000 EBX=00000000    IP=0100   NV UP EI PL NZ NA PE NC
0070:0100 6629C0                SUB       EAX,EAX
EAX=00000000 EBX=00000000    IP=0103   NV UP EI PL ZR NA PE NC
```

Set a selector into EAX:

```
0070:0103 B84000                          MOV       AX,0040h
EAX=00000400 EBX=00000000    IP=0106   NV UP EI PL ZR NA PE NC
```

and into EBX:

```
0070:0106 6689C3                          MOV       EBX,EAX
EAX=00000040 EBX=00000040    IP=0109   NV UP EI PL ZR NA PE NC
```

Check the access rights for the descriptor thus selected:

```
Descriptor 0040 67 00 98 E8 00 8B 00 00
(Our active TSS segment)
0070:0109 660F02C3                         LAR       EAX,EBX
00FxFF00 is the mask
EAX=00008B00 EBX=00000040    IP=010D   NV UP EI PL ZR NA PE NC
```

The zero flag is set. If the descriptor were not accessible either because of privilege or GDT or LDT limits, the access bytes are not loaded and the zero flag is reset.

LEA   Load Effective Address

INSTRUCTION	OPCODE	BINARY
LEA r16,m	8D /r	10001101 mm rrr r/m
LEA r32,m	8D /r	10001101 mm rrr r/m

Purpose: LEA transfers the offset of the source operand, rather than its value, to the destination operand. The source operand must be a memory operand. The destination operand must be a general register. LEA is particularly useful for initializing registers before the execution of the string primitives or the XLAT.

Instruction Demonstration: The LEA instruction loads the offset portion of the address into the register specified. The instruction sequence is

```
4C13:0000 66BB20000000            MOV    EBX,00000020
4C13:0006 66B905000000            MOV    ECX,00000005
4C13:000C 668D060002              LEA    EAX,DWord Ptr [0200]
4C13:0011 668D870001              LEA    EAX,DWord Ptr [BX+0100]
4C13:0016 67668D8300200000        LEA    EAX,DWordPtr [EBX+00000200]
4C13:001E 67668D044B              LEA    EAX,DWord Ptr [EBX+2*ECX]
```

The registers and flags at the start are

EAX = 00000000 EBX = 00000000 EXC = 00000000 IP = 0000
                              NV UP EI PL NZ NA PO NC

4C13:0000 66BB20000000   MOV   EBX,00000020

EAX = 00000000 EBX = 00000020 ECX = 00000000 IP = 0006
                              NV UP EI PL NZ NA PO NC

The move sets a base into EBX.

4C13:0006 66B905000000   MOV   ECX,00000005

EAX = 00000000 EBX = 00000020 EXC = 00000005 IP = 000C
                              NV UP EI PL NZ NA PO NC

An index value is placed into ECX.

4C13:000C 668D060002   LEA   EAX,DWord Ptr [0200]

EAX = 00000200 EBX = 00000020 ECX = 00000005 IP = 0011

                              NV UP EI PL NZ NA PO NC

This displacement from DS is loaded into EAX.

4C13:0011 668D870001   LEA   EAX,DWord Ptr [BS+0100]

EAX = 00000120 EBX = 00000020 ECX = 00000005 IP = 0016
                              NV UP EI PL NZ NA PO NC

The base is added to the displacement to provide the effective total displacement from DS.

4C13:0016 67668D8300200000   LEA   EAX,DWord Ptr [EBX
                                                        +00000200]

EAX = 00000220 EBX = 00000020 ECX = 00000005 IP = 001E
                              NV UP EI PL NZ NA PO NC

The base is added to the doubleword displacement to provide the total offset from DS.

4C13:001E 67668D044B   LEA   EAX,DWord Ptr [EBX + 2$*ECX]
EAX = 0000002A EBX = 00000020 ECX = 00000005 IP = 0023
                                  NV UP EI PL NZ NA PO NC

The base is added to the scaled index to provide the total offset from DS.

LEAVE   High Level Procedure Exit

INSTRUCTION	OPCODE	BINARY
LEAVE	C9	11001001

Purpose: LEAVE reverses the action of a previous ENTER and does not use any operands. LEAVE copies EBP to ESP to release all stack space allocated to the procedure by the most recent ENTER. Then LEAVE POPs the old value of EBP from the stack. A subsequent RET can then remove any arguments that were pushed on the stack by the calling program for use by the called procedure.

Instruction Demonstration: The CALL instruction, ENTER instruction, LEAVE instruction, and RET instruction are demonstrated together because they logically "fit" with each other and complement each other. See the CALL instruction.

LGDT   Load Global Descriptor Table Register
LIDT   Load Interrupt Descriptor Table Register

INSTRUCTION	OPCODE	BINARY
LGDT m16&32	0F 01 /2	00001111 00000001 mm 010 r/m
LIDT m16&32	0F 01 /3	00001111 00000001 mm 011 r/m

Purpose: LGDT loads the global descriptor table register (GDTR) from the 48-bit pseudo-descriptor given in the instruction. These 48 bits have two components: the limit and base. The 16-bit limit is stored at the low word and the 32-bit base at the high doubleword.

LIDT tells the hardware where to go in case of interrupts. LIDT loads the interrupt descriptor table register (IDTR) from the 48-bit pseudo-descriptor given in the instruction. These 48-bits have two components: the limit and base. The 16-bit limit is stored at the low word and the 32-bit base at the high doubleword.

Both the global descriptor table (GDT) and the interrupt descriptor table (IDT) are loaded at system reset (initialization of the operating system). This generally happens at the beginning of the work session.

Instruction Demonstration: See the program in Appendix E.

LGS	Load Full Pointer
LSS	Load Pointer Using SS
LDS	Load Pointer Using DS
LES	Load Pointer Using ES
LFS	Load Pointer Using FS

INSTRUCTION	OPCODE	BINARY
LDS r16,m16:16	C5 /r	11000101 mm rrr r/m
LDS r32,m16:32	C5 /r	11000101 mm rrr r/m
LSS r16,m16:16	0F B2 /r	00001111 10110010 mm rrr r/m
LSS r32,m16:32	0F B2 /r	00001111 10110010 mm rrr r/m
LES r16,m16:16	C4 /r	11000100 mm rrr r/m
LES r32,m16:32	C4 /r	11000100 mm rrr r/m
LFS r16,m16:16	0F B4 /r	00001111 10110100 mm rrr r/m
LFS r32,m16:32	0F B4 /r	00001111 10110100 mm rrr r/m
LGS r16,m16:16	0F B5 /r	00001111 10110101 mm rrr r/m
LGS r32,m16:32	0F B5 /r	00001111 10110101 mm rrr r/m

Purpose: The data pointer instructions load a pointer that consists of a segment selector and an offset into a segment register and a general register.

LDS transfers a pointer variable from the source operand to DS and the destination register. The source operand must be a memory operand. The destination operand must be a general register. DS receives the segment-selector of the pointer. The destination register receives the offset part of the pointer that points to a specific location within the segment.

The other instructions use the various registers, as noted in the instruction mnemonic.

LSS is particularly important because it allows the two registers that identify the stack (SS:ESP) to be changed in one uninterruptible operation.

Instruction Demonstration: See the program in Appendix E.

LLDT   Load Local Descriptor Table Register

INSTRUCTION	OPCODE	BINARY
LLDT r/m16	OF 00 /2	00001111 00000000 mm 010 r/m

Purpose: The local descriptor table (LDT) is loaded whenever a task or major subsystem gains or regains control of the system. LLDT loads the local descriptor table register (LDTR). The operand (memory or register) should hold a selector to the global descriptor table (GDT). The descriptor registers are not affected and the LDT field in the task state segment does not change. The first operand might be a null selector that causes the LDT to be marked invalid. Loading a selector naming an LDT segment raises a segment load exception if LDTR contains a null selector.

Instruction Demonstration: The LLDT instruction transfers the contents of a 16-bit register or memory word into the local descriptor table register. No flags are affected. The operand size attribute has no effect on the operation of LLDT.

```
0070:0100 0F00D0    LLDT      AX
```

The registers and flags at the start are

```
AX=0010              IP=0100   NV UP EI PL NZ NA PO NC
```

Transfer the LDT selector from AX to the LDTR.

```
0070:0100 0F00D0    LLDT      AX
AX=0010              IP=0103   NV UP EI PL NZ NA PO NC
```

LMSW   Load Machine Status Word

INSTRUCTION	OPCODE	BINARY
LMSW r/m16	OF 01 /6	00001111 00000001 mm 110 r/m

Purpose: LMSW loads the machine status word (MSW) into CR0 from the source as specified in the first operand. The MSW is the low-order 16 bits of control register zero (CR0) (see FIG. 10-7). LMSW can be used to switch to protected mode by setting the PE (protection enable) bit to 1. If so, the instruction queue must be flushed and LMSW followed by an intrasegment jump instruction. LMSW will *not* switch back to real address mode; you cannot alter the PE bit to zero with an LMSW.

For compatibility with the 80286, the ET (extension type) bit of MSW is not altered by the LMSW instruction. 80386 and 80486 programs should use MOV CR0.

```
3  2                    1   1 1                          5 4 3 2 1 0
1  9                    8   6 5
┌─┬─┬─┬─────────────────┬─┬─┬─┬─────────────────┬─┬─┬─┬─┬─┬─┐
│P│C│N│0 0 0 0 0 0 0 0 0│A│0│W│0 0 0 0 0 0 0 0 0│N│E│T│E│M│P│
│G│D│W│                 │M│ │P│                 │E│T│S│M│P│E│
└─┴─┴─┴─────────────────┴─┴─┴─┴─────────────────┴─┴─┴─┴─┴─┴─┘
                            └────── Machine Status Word ──────┘
```

Control Register Zero (CR0)

PG – Paging Enable	ET – Extension Type
CD – Cache Disable	TS – Task Switched
NW – Not Write-through	EM – Emulation
AM – Alignment Mask	MP – Math Present
WP – Write Protect	PE – Protection Enable
NE – Numeric Error	

10-7 Machine Status Word.

Instruction Demonstration: This demonstrates the LMSW instruction by setting the machine status word part of CR0 from the specified source. AX was set using SMSW. The instruction is

    14EB:0100 0F01F0   LMSW   AX

The registers and flags at the start are

    AX = FFE0   IP = 0100   NV UP EI PL NZ NA PO NC

    14EB:0100 0F01F0   LMSW   AX

    AX = FFE0   IP = 0103   NV UP EI PL NZ NA PO NC

LOCK   Assert LOCK# Signal Prefix

INSTRUCTION	OPCODE	BINARY
LOCK	F0	11110000

Purpose: LOCK asserts a hold on shared memory so that the 80486 has exclusive use of it during the instruction that immediately follows the LOCK. LOCK's integrity is not affected by memory field alignment. LOCK will only work with

BT, BTS, BTR, BTC	memory, reg/imm
ADD, OR, ADC, SBB, AND, SUB, XOR	memory, reg/imm
NOT, NEG, INC, DEC	memory
XCHG	reg, memory or memory, reg
CMPXCHG, XADD	reg, reg or memory, reg

An undefined opcode trap is generated if LOCK is used with any instruction not listed here. Note that XCHG always asserts LOCK# whether or not it has the LOCK prefix.

Note: LOCK is *not* assured if another 80486 is concurrently executing an instruction that has any of the following characteristics:

- If it is not one of the instructions in the previous list.
- If it is not preceded by a LOCK prefix.
- If it specifies a memory operand that does not *exactly* overlap the destination operand. LOCK is not guaranteed for partial overlap, even if one memory is contained wholly within the other.

Instruction Demonstration: Not demonstrated.

LODS	Load String Operand
LODSB	Load Byte
LODSW	Load Word
LODSD	Load Doubleword

INSTRUCTION	OPCODE	BINARY
LODS m8	AC	10101100
LODS m16	AD	10101101
LODS m32	AD	10101101

Purpose: These instructions operate on strings rather than on logical or numeric values. They operate on one element of a string that could be a byte, a word, or a doubleword. The string elements are addressed by the DS (default) and ESI registers. After each string operation, ESI is automatically updated to point to the next element of the string. If DF = 0, the index register is incremented. If DF = 1, it is decremented. The amount incremented or decremented is 1, 2, or 4, depending on the size of the string element.

LODS places the source string element at ESI into AL for byte strings, AX for word strings, and in EAX for doubleword strings. LODS increments or decrements ESI according to DF.

The operand specifies the length of the operand, e.g., AH specifies 8 bits, AX is 16, and EAX is 32. The actual transfer is always done with the address specified in ESI. A segment override prefix can be specified in the operand, which is applied to [ESI].

Instruction Demonstration: This demonstration of the LODS instruction shows it in a loop where it might naturally reside. The instruction sequence is

```
14EB:0100 B90500    MOV      CX,0005
14EB:0103 BE0002    MOV      SI,0200
14EB:0106 E307      JCXZ     010F
14EB:0108           AC       LODSB
14EB:0109 3C00      CMP      AL,00
14EB:010B E0FB      LOOPNZ   0108
14EB:010D EBF7      JMP      0106
```

The registers and flags at the start are

AX = FFA4 CX = 0000 SI = 0000 DS = 14EB CS = 14EB IP = 0100

NV UP EI PL NZ NA PE CY

14EB:0100 B90500   MOV   CX,0005

AX = FFA4 CX = 0005 SI = 0000 DS = 14EB CS = 14EB IP = 0103

NV UP EI PL NZ NA PE CY

Move the count into CX.

14EB:0103 BE0002   MOV   SI,0200

AX = FFA4 CX = 0005 SI = 0200 DS = 14EB CS = 14EB IP = 0106

NV UP EI PL NZ NA PE CY

Set the data displacement into SI.

14EB:0106 E307   JCXZ   010F

AX = FFA4 CX = 0005 SI = 0200 DS = 14EB CS = 14EB IP = 0108

NV UP EI PL NZ NA PE CY

Because CX is non-zero, the jump is not taken.

14EB:0108 AC   LODSB

AX = FF41 CX = 0005 SI = 0201 DS = 14EB CS = 14EB IP = 0109

NV UP EI PL NZ NA PE CY

A byte is loaded using SI, and SI is incremented.

14EB:0109 3C00   CMP   AL,00

AX = FF41 CX = 0005 SI = 0201 DS = 14EB CS = 14EB IP = 010B

NV UP EI PL NZ NA PE **NC**

Compare the byte for a null value (a common end of string indicator).

14EB:010B E0FB   LOOPNZ   0108

AX = FF00 CX = 0001 SI = 0204 DS = 14EB CS = 14EB IP = 010D

NV UP EI PL **ZR** NA PE NC

The LOOPNZ was executed three times with the NZ condition. It decremented the CX register each time and fell through on the fourth byte because of the condition code. (See the following data.)

```
14EB:010D EBF7                  JMP        0106
AX=FF00 CX=0001 SI=0204 DS=14EB CS=14EB IP=0106
                                   NV UP EI PL ZR NA PE NC
```

For this demonstration, jump to extract the next string.

```
14EB:0106 E307                  JCXZ       010F
AX=FF00 CX=0001 SI=0204 DS=14EB CS=14EB IP=0108
                                   NV UP EI PL ZR NA PE NC
```

CX is not yet zero, so we enter the loop again.

```
14EB:0108 AC                    LODSB
AX=FF43 CX=0001 SI=0205 DS=14EB CS=14EB IP=0109
                                   NV UP EI PL ZR NA PE NC
```

Load the next byte (which is not null).

```
14EB:0109 3C00                  CMP        AL,00
AX=FF43 CX=0001 SI=0205 DS=14EB CS=14EB IP=010B
                                   NV UP EI PL **NZ** NA **PO** NC
```

Compare to set an NZ condition code.

```
14EB:010B E0FB                  LOOPNZ 0108
AX=FF43 CX=0000 SI=0205 DS=14EB CS=14EB IP=010D
                                   NV UP EI PL NZ NA PO NC
```

There is a fall-through in the LOOPNZ even though the condition code is NZ, because the count in CX ran out. The NZ condition would normally be tested to determine the reason for the fall-through.

```
14EB:010D EBF7                  JMP        0106
AX=FF43 CX=0000 SI=0205 DS=14EB CS=14EB IP=0106
                                   NV UP EI PL NZ NA PO NC
```

Jump back to the guard instruction just before the loop.

```
14EB:0106 E307                  JCXZ       010F
AX=FF43 CX=0000 SI=0205 DS=14EB CS=14EB IP=010F
                                   NV UP EI PL NZ NA PO NC
```

It detects that the CX register is zero and bypasses the loop. (Note the value in IP.)

The data being tested is

```
14EB:0200 41 42 43 00 43 42 41 00   ABC.CBA.
```

LOOP	Loop Control While EXC Counter Not Zero
LOOP	cond
LOOPE	Loop while Equal
LOOPZ	Loop while Zero
LOOPNE	Loop while Not Equal
LOOPNZ	Loop while Not Zero

INSTRUCTION	OPCODE	BINARY
LOOP rel8	E2 cb	11100010
LOOPE rel8	E1 cb	11100001
LOOPNE rel8	E0 cb	11100001

Note: LOOPZ is an alternate mnemonic for LOOPE

LOOPNZ is an alternate mnemonic for LOOPNE

Purpose: The LOOP instructions are conditional jumps that use a value stored in ECX to specify the number of times a section of software loops to a label. All LOOPs automatically decrement ECX and terminate when ECX=0. LOOP is placed at the bottom of the loop and the label at the top.

LOOP first decrements ECX before testing ECX for the branch condition. If ECX is not zero, the program branches to the target label specified in the instruction. If ECX=0, control transfers to the instruction immediately following the LOOP. ECX is decremented without affecting any of the flags.

LOOPE and LOOPZ are synonymous. These instructions decrement ECX before testing ECX and ZF (zero flag) for branch condition. If ECX is non-zero and ZF=1, the program branches to the target label as specified in the instruction. If LOOPE and LOOPZ finds ECX=0 *or* ZF=0, control transfers to the instruction immediately following the LOOPE or LOOPZ.

LOOPNE and LOOPNZ are synonymous. These instructions decrement ECX before testing ECX *or* ZF for branch conditions. If ECX is non-zero and ZF=0, the program branches to the target label specified by the instruction. If ECX=0 or ZF=1, control transfers to the instruction immediately following LOOPNE or LOOPNZ.

Note: The unconditional LOOP instruction takes longer to execute than a two-instruction sequence that decrements the count register, then jumps if the count does not equal zero. For example, while the count is nonzero, each execution of LOOP Start takes 6 clock cycles, but

```
DEC   ECX
JNZ   Start
```

takes only 4 cycles.

Instruction Demonstration: Demonstrated with LODS.

LSL   Load Segment Limit

INSTRUCTION	OPCODE	BINARY
LSL r16,r/m16	OF 03 /r	00001111 00000011 mm rrr r/m
LSL r32,r/m32	OF 03 /r	00001111 00000011 mm rrr r/m

Purpose: LSL loads a user-specified register with a segment limit. The limit comes from the descriptor for the segment specified by the selector in the second operand. If the source selector is visible at the CPL and the descriptor is a type accepted by LSL (see FIG. 10-8), LSL sets ZF to 1. Otherwise, LSL sets ZF to 0 and keeps the destination register unchanged.

Type	Name
0	Undefined, invalid
1	Available 80286 TSS
2	Load Descriptor Table
3	Busy 80286 TSS
4	80286 call gate
5	80286/386/486 task gate
6	80286 interrupt gate
7	80286 trap gate
8	Undefined, invalid
9	Available 80386/486 TSS
A	Undefined, invalid
B	Busy 80386/486 TSS
C	80386/486 call gate
D	Undefined, invalid
E	80386/486 interrupt gate
F	80386/486 trap gate

Note that types 0, 8, A, and D are invalid.

10-8   Valid system segments and gates for LSL.

The 32-bit forms of LSL store the 32-bit granular limit in the 16-bit destination register. Note that this segment limit is a byte granular value. If the descriptor uses a page granular (the G bit = 1) segment limit, LSL translates that value to a byte limit (shifts it left 12 bits and fills the low 12 bits with 1s) and then loads it into the destination register.

Instruction Demonstration: The instruction sequence is

```
0070:0100 6629C0      SUB   EAX,EAX
0070:0103 6689C3      MOV   EBX,EAX
0070:0106 BB7800      MOV   BX,0078H
0070:0109 660F03C3    LSL   EAX,EBX
0070:010D 90          NOP
```

The registers and flags at the start are

EAX=00000000 EBX=00000000	IP=0100	NV UP EI PL NZ NA PO NC
0070:0100 6629C0	SUB	EAX,EAX
EAX=00000000 EBX=00000000	IP=0103	NV UP EI PL **ZR** NA **PE** NC
0070:0103 6689C3	MOV	EBX,EAX
EAX=00000000 EBX=00000000	IP=0106	NV UP EI PL ZR NA PE NC
0070:0106 BB7800	MOV	BX,0078H

The selector is in EBX and EAX is cleared.

EAX=00000000 EBX=00000078	IP=0109	NV UP EI PL ZR NA PE NC
0070:0109 660F03C3	LSL	EAX,EBX

LSL loads the limit value from the selected descriptor. If the limit was not loaded into a 32-bit register (i.e., into AX instead of EAX), the low-order 16 bits of the limit would be loaded.

EAX=000FFFFF EBX=00000078   IP=010D NV UP EI PL ZR NA PE NC

Descriptor 0078 = FF FF 00 AB 01 93 0F 00

LTR   Load Task Register

INSTRUCTION	OPCODE	BINARY
LTR r/m16	0F 00 /3	00001111 00000000 mm 011 r/m

Purpose: The operand of LTR specifies the source register or memory location that contains information for the task register. LTR loads data from that location into the task register. The loaded TSS is marked busy; however, a task switch does *not* occur. The given selector must point to a global descriptor table (GDT) entry that is of the descriptor type TSS (task state segment). If this is the case, the task register (TR) is loaded.

Instruction Demonstration: See the program listing in Appendix E.

MOV   Move Data

INSTRUCTION	OPCODE	BINARY
MOV r/m8,r8	88 /r	10001000 mm rrr r/m
MOV r/m16,r16	89 /r	10001001 mm rrr r/m
MOV r/m32,r32	89 /r	10001001 mm rrr r/m
MOV r8,r/m8	8A /r	10001010 mm rrr r/m
MOV r16,r/m16	8B /r	10001011 mm rrr r/m
MOV r32,r/m32	8B /r	10001011 mm rrr r/m
MOV r/m16,sreg	8C /r	10001100 mm rrr r/m
MOV Sreg,r/m16	8D /r	10001101 mm rrr r/m
MOV AL,moffs8	A0	10100000
MOV AX,moffs16	A1	10100001
MOV EAX,moffs32	A1	10100001
MOV moffs8,AL	A2	10100010
MOV moffs16,AX	A3	10100011
MOV moffs32,EAX	A3	10100011
MOV reg8,imm8	B0 + rb	10110rrr
MOV reg16,imm16	B8 + rw	10111rrr
MOV reg32,imm32	B8 + rd	10111rrr
MOV r/m8,imm8	C6	11000110 mm rrr r/m
MOV r/m16,imm16	C7	11000111 mm rrr r/m
MOV r/m32,imm32	C7	11000111 mm rrr r/m

Purpose: MOV transfers a byte, word, or doubleword from the source operand to the destination operand. MOV is useful for transferring data along these paths:

- Immediate data to a memory
- Immediate data to a register
- Between general registers
- To a register from memory
- To memory from a register

Some variations of MOV operate on segment registers, which is how the segment registers are initialized in programs in this book.

Note: MOV cannot move from memory to memory or from segment register to segment register. Memory to memory can be done with the string move MOVS.

Instruction Demonstration: See MOV To/From Special Registers and MOVS.

MOV   Move To/From Special Registers

INSTRUCTION	OPCODE	BINARY
MOV r32,C0/C2/C3	OF 20 /r	00001111 00100000 mm ccc r/m
MOV C0/C2/C3,r32	OF 22 /r	00001111 00100010 mm ccc r/m
MOV r32,TR3-7	OF 24 /r	00001111 00100100 mm ttt r/m
MOV TR3-7,r32	OF 26 /r	00001111 00100110 mm ttt r/m
MOV r32,DR0-3/6/7	OF 21 /r	00001111 00100001 mm ddd r/m
MOV DR0-3/6/7,r32	OF 23 /r	00001111 00100011 mm ddd r/m

Purpose: These forms of MOV load or store special registers to or from
a general register. They are particularly designed for the control registers
(C0, C2, C3), test registers (TR3 through TR7), and debug registers (DR0
through DR3, DR6, and DR7).

The forms that involve TR3, TR4, and TR5 are new with the 80486.

Instruction Demonstration #1: This demonstrates the movement
of the control registers to EAX. The values in the control registers are
those for real address mode. The instruction sequence is

```
4C13:0000 0F20C0    MOV    EAX,CR0
4C13:0003 0F20D0    MOV    EAX,CR2
4C13:0006 0F20D8    MOV    EAX,CR3
```

The registers and flags at the start are

```
EAX = 00000000      IP = 0000    NV UP EI PL NZ NA PO NC
```

Get CR0 to EAX

```
4C13:0000 0F20C0    MOV          EAX,CR0
EAX = 7FFFFFE0      IP = 0003    NV UP EI PL NZ NA PO NC
```

Now CR2

```
4C13:0003 0F20D0    MOV          EAX,CR2
EAX = 00000000      IP = 0006    NV UP EI PL NZ NA PO NC
```

and CR3

```
4C13:0006 0F20D8    MOV          EAX,CR3
EAX = 00000000      IP = 0009    NV UP EI PL NZ NA PO NC
```

Instruction Demonstration #2: This demonstrates the movement
of the test registers into EAX. The instruction sequence is

```
4C13:0009 0F24F0    MOV          EAX,tr6
4C13:000C 0F24F8    MOV          EAX,tr7
```

The registers and flags at the start are

```
EAX = 00000000      IP = 0009    NV UP EI PL NZ NA PO NC
```

Move test register 6 into EAX.

```
4C13:0009 0F24F0     MOV          EAX,tr6
EAX = FFFFFFFF        IP = 000C    NV UP EI PL NZ NA PO NC
```

Then test register 7.

```
4C13:000C 0F24F8     MOV          EAX,tr7
EAX = 7FFFF01C        IP = 000F    NV UP EI PL NZ NA PO NC
```

Instruction Demonstration #3: This demonstrates the movement of the debug registers into EAX. The instruction sequence is

```
4C13:000F 0F21C0     MOV          EAX,DR0
4C13:0012 0F21C8     MOV          EAX,DR1
4C13:0015 0F21D0     MOV          EAX,DR2
4C13:0018 0F21D8     MOV          EAX,DR3
4C13:001B 0F21F0     MOV          EAX,DR6
4C13:001E 0F21F8     MOV          EAX,DR7
```

The registers and flags at the start are

```
EAX = 7FFFF01C        IP = 000F    NV UP EI PL NZ NA PO NC
```

First move DR0,

```
4C13:000F 0F21C0     MOV          EAX,DR0
EAX = 00000000        IP = 0012    NV UP EI PL NZ NA PO NC
```

then DR1,

```
4C13:0012 0F21C8     MOV          EAX,DR1
EAX = 00000000        IP = 0015    NV UP EI PL NZ NA PO NC
```

then DR2,

```
4C13:0015 0F21D0     MOV          EAX,DR2
EAX = 00000000        IP = 0018    NV UP EI PL NZ NA PO NC
```

then DR3,

```
4C13:0018 0F21D8     MOV          EAX,DR3
EAX = 00000000        IP = 001B    NV UP EI PL NZ NA PO NC
```

then DR6,

```
4C13:001B 0F21F0     MOV          EAX,DR6
EAX = FFFF4FF0        IP = 001E    NV UP EI PL NZ NA PO NC
```

and DR7.

```
4C13:001E 0F21F8     MOV          EAX,DR7
EAX = 00000400        IP = 0021    NV UP EI PL NZ NA PO NC
```

MOVS   Move Data from String to String
MOVSB   Move String Byte
MOVSW   Move String Word
MOVSD   Move String Doubleword

INSTRUCTION	OPCODE	BINARY
MOVS m8,m8	A4	10100100
MOVS m16,m16	A5	10100101
MOVS m32,m32	A5	10100101

Note: MOVSB is a common assembler mnemonic for MOVS m8,m8.
MOVSW is a common assembler mnemonic for MOVS m16,m16.
MOVSD is a common assembler mnemonic for MOVS m32,m32.

Purpose: These instructions operate on strings rather than on logical or numeric values. They operate on one element of a string (addressed by ESI) that could be a byte, a word, or a doubleword and move it to the area addressed by ES:EDI. After each string operation, ESI and/or EDI are automatically updated to point to the next element of the string. If the direction (DF) is 0, the index registers are incremented. If DF = 1, they are decremented. The amount incremented or decremented is 1, 2, or 4, depending on the size of the string element.

When prefixed by REP, MOVS operates as a memory-to-memory block transfer and repeats for the number of times specified by the value stored in ECX. To set this up, your program must first initialize ECX and the register pairs ESI and EDI. ECX specifies the number of bytes, words or doublewords in the block. If the direction flag (DF) is 0, the program must point ESI to the first element of the source string and point EDI to the destination address for the first element. If DF = 1, the program points these two registers to the last element of the source string and to the destination address for the last element, respectively.

Instruction Demonstration: This demonstrates the string move instruction MOVSB. The instruction can move a byte, word, or doubleword at a time. This demonstration uses the byte width movement. The instruction sequence is

```
4C13:0000 BE0002    MOV   SI,0200
4C13:0003 BF0003    MOV   DI,0300
4C13:0006 B92000    MOV   CX,0020
4C13:0009 F3A4      REP   MOVSB
```

The data at SI is

```
4C13:0200   01 02 03 04 05 06 07 08-09 0A 0B 0C 0D 0E 0F
            10
```

4C13:0210   11 12 13 14 15 16 17 18-19 1A 1B 1C 1D 1E 1F
            20

The data at DI is

4C13:0300   00 00 00 00 00 00 00 00-00 00 00 00 00 00 00 00

4C13:0310   00 00 00 00 00 00 00 00-00 00 00 00 00 00 00 00

The registers and flags at the start are

ECX=00000000 ESI=00000000 EDI=00000000 DS=4C13 ES=4C13
            IP=0000   NV UP EI PL NZ NA PO NC

Note that the direction flag is UP.

4C13:0000 BE0002   MOV   SI,0200
ECX=00000000 ESI=00000200 EDI=00000000 DS=4C13 ES=4C13
            IP=0003   NV UP EI PL NZ NA PO NC
4C13:0003 BF0003   MOV   DI,0300
ECX=00000000 ESI=00000200 EDI=00000300 DS=4C13 ES=4C13
            IP=0006   NV UP EI PL NZ NA PO NC
4C13:0006 B92000   MOV   CX,0020
ECX=00000020 ESI=00000200 EDI=00000300 DS=4C13 ES=4C13
            IP=0009   NV UP EI PL NZ NA PO NC

The registers are now set.

4C13:0009 F3A4   REP   MOVSB
ECX=0000001E ESI=00000202 EDI=00000302 DS=4C13 ES=4C13
            IP=0009   NV UP EI PL NZ NA PO NC

Partially executed, IP points to the REP, the indicies are incremented
(because the direction is up), and the count in CX is decremented.

4C13:0009 F3A4   REP   MOVSB
ECX=00000000 ESI=00000220 EDI=00000320 DS=4C13 ES=4C13
            IP=000B   NV UP EI PL NZ NA PO NC

The repeated move continues until CX bytes are moved.
The data at SI

C13:0200   01 02 03 04 05 06 07 08-09 0A 0B 0C 0D 0E 0F 10

4C13:0210   11 12 13 14 15 16 17 18-19 1A 1B 1C 1D 1E 1F 20

has been moved to DI without change to the source.

4C13:0300   01 02 03 04 05 06 07 08-09 0A 0B 0C 0D 0E 0F 10

4C13:0310   11 12 13 14 15 16 17 18-19 1A 1B 1C 1D 1E 1F 20

MOVSX   Move with Sign Extension

INSTRUCTION	OPCODE	BINARY
MOVSX r16,r/m8	OF BE /r	00001111 10111110 mm rrr r/m
MOVSX r32,r/m8	OF BE /r	00001111 10111110 mm rrr r/m
MOVSX r32,r/m16	OF BF /r	00001111 10111111 mm rrr r/m

Purpose: MOVSX extends the sign of an 8-bit value to a 16-bit value and an 8-bit or 16-bit value to 32-bit value. If both operands are words, a normal move occurs. This instruction was introduced with the 80386.

Instruction Demonstration: The MOVSX instruction moves a byte to a word or doubleword or a word to a doubleword with sign extension. The demonstration moves a byte from BL to AX and EAX extending the sign. It also includes the demonstration of the MOVZX instruction for contrast. The instruction sequence is

```
4C13:0000 66BBF0000000    MOV     EBX,000000F0
4C13:0006 0FBEC3          MOVSX   AX,BL
4C13:0009 0FB6C3          MOVZX   AX,BL
4C13:000C 660FBEC3        MOVSX   EAX,BL
4C13:0010 660FB6C3        MOVZX   EAX,BL
```

The registers and flags at the start are

```
EAX=00000000 EBX=00000000   IP=0000
                               NV UP EI PL NZ NA PO NC
4C13:0000 66BBF0000000       MOV      BX,000000F0
EAX=00000000 EBX=000000F0   IP=0006
                               NV UP EI PL NZ NA PO NC
```

First, set BL to – 16 (or to 240 as an unsigned value).

```
4C13:0006 0FBEC3                 MOVSX   AX,BL
EAX=0000FFF0 EBX=000000F0   IP=0009
                               NV UP EI PL NZ NA PO NC
```

Note the sign extension into AH making the AX value – 16.

```
4C13:0009 0FB6C3                 MOVZX   AX,BL
EAX=000000F0 EBX=000000F0   IP=000C
                               NV UP EI PL NZ NA PO NC
```

In this case, zero extension forms an AX value of 240.

```
4C13:000C 660FBEC3               MOVSX   EAX,BL
EAX=FFFFFFF0 EBX=000000F0   IP=0010
                               NV UP EI PL NZ NA PO NC
```

Sign extension provides an EAX value of – 16,

```
4C13:0010 660FB6C3            MOVZX   EAX,BL
EAX=000000F0 EBX=000000F0    IP=0014
                             NV UP EI PL NZ NA PO NC
```

while zero extension forms a doubleword value of 240.

MOVZX   Move with Zero Extension

INSTRUCTION	OPCODE	BINARY
MOVZX r16,r/m8	0F B6 /r	00001111 10110110 mm rrr r/m
MOVZX r32,r/m8	0F B6 /r	00001111 10110110 mm rrr r/m
MOVZX r32,r/m16	0F B7 /r	00001111 10110111 mm rrr r/m

Purpose: MOVZX extends an 8-bit value to a 16-bit value, and an 8- or 16-bit value to 32-bit value by padding with high-order zeros. This instruction was introduced with the 80386.

Instruction Demonstration: This instruction moves a byte to a word or doubleword, or from a word to a doubleword, with zero extension. It is demonstrated with MOVSX.

MUL   Unsigned Integer Multiply of AL, AX, or EAX

INSTRUCTION	OPCODE	BINARY
MUL AL,r/m8	F6 /4	11110110 mm 100 r/m
MUL AX,r/m16	F7 /4	11110111 mm 100 r/m
MUL EAX,r/m32	F7 /4	11110111 mm 100 r/m

Purpose: MUL multiplies the numbers in the source operand and the accumulator (AL, AX, or EAX). If the source is a byte, the 80486 multiplies it by the contents of AL and returns the double-length result in AH and AL. If the source operand is a word, the 80486 multiplies it by the contents of AX and returns the double-length result to DX and AX. If the source is a doubleword, the processor multiplies it by the contents of EAX and returns the 64-bit result in EDX and EAX. MUL sets CF (carry flag) and OF (overflow flag) to zero if AH, DX, or EDX is all zeros for 8-, 16-, or 32-bit operations. Otherwise, CF and OF are set to 1.

Instruction Demonstration: This demonstration shows how MUL works. Compare it with the IMUL instruction. The instruction sequence is

```
14EB:0100 B033   MOV   AL,33
14EB:0102 B381   MOV   BL,81
14EB:0104 F6E3   MUL   BL
```

The registers and flags at the start are

    EAX = 00000D8C EBX = 00000044   IP = 0100
                                           OV UP EI PL NZ NA PE CY

Load AL with hex 33 (51 decimal).

    14EB:0100 B033   MOV   AL,33
    EAX = 00000D33 EBX = 00000044   IP = 0102
                                           OV UP EI PL NZ NA PE CY

Then load BL with hex 81 (129 decimal).

    14EB:0102 B381   MOV   BL,81
    EAX = 00000D33 EBX = 00000081   IP = 0104
                                           OV UP EI PL NZ NA PE CY

The unsigned multiplication produces the product 19B3 hex (6579 decimal), treating BL as an unsigned 8-bit value.

    14EB:0104 F6E3   MUL   BL
    EAX = 000019B3 EBX = 00000081   IP = 0106
                                           OV UP EI PL NZ NA PE CY

NEG   Negate (Two's Complement)

INSTRUCTION	OPCODE	BINARY
NEG r/m8	F6 /3	11110110 mm 011 r/m
NEG r/m16	F7 /3	11110111 mm 011 r/m
NEG r/m32	F7 /3	11110111 mm 011 r/m

Purpose: NEG subtracts a signed integer operand from zero, making a positive into a negative or vice versa. In other words, NEG forms a two's complement of a given operand, which is subtracted from zero; the result is placed in the operand. The carry flag (CF) is set to 1, except when the operand prior to the NEG was zero.

Instruction Demonstration: This demonstrates the action of the NEG instruction. It takes the two's complement of the value being acted on. The instruction sequence is

    14EB:0100 B80002   MOV   AX,0200
    14EB:0103 F7D8   NEG   AX

The registers and flags at the start are

    EAX = 00000000   IP = 0100   OV UP EI PL NZ NA PE NC

Set a value into AX.

    14EB:0100 B80002   MOV   AX,0200

EAX=00000200   IP=0103   OV UP EI PL NZ NA PE NC

The value in AX is replaced with its two's complement.

    14EB:0103 F7D8   NEG   AX

    EAX=0000FE00   IP=0105   **NV** UP EI **NG** NZ NA PE **CY**

The flags are set according to the result of the negation. Carry is set unless the operand is zero, in which case it is reset.

NOP   No Operation

INSTRUCTION	OPCODE	BINARY
NOP	90	10010000

Purpose: NOP occupies a byte of storage. It affects nothing but the instruction pointer, EIP. NOP is useful for providing space in "fixing up" branch addresses, i.e., the address might require an 8- or 16-bit displacement—if 16 bits are reserved, an 8-bit displacement and an NOP can be used to fill the 16 bits.

Instruction Demonstration: NOP is often used simply as a placeholder in an instruction stream and only affects IP. The instruction sequence is

    14EB:0100 90 NOP

The registers and flags at the start are

    IP=0100   OV UP EI PL NZ NA PE CY

Execute the NOP.

    14EB:0100 90 NOP

    IP=0101   OV UP EI PL NZ NA PE CY

IP is advanced, but no other changes are made.

NOT   Negate (One's Complement)

INSTRUCTION	OPCODE	BINARY
NOT r/m8	F6 /2	11110110 mm 010 r/m
NOT r/m16	F7 /2	11110111 mm 010 r/m
NOT r/m32	F7 /2	11110111 mm 010 r/m

Purpose: NOT inverts the bits in the specified operand to form a one's complement of the operand. NOT is a unary operation (refers to an arithmetic operator having only one term) that uses a single operand in a register or memory. The result is stored in the operand. NOT has no effect on flags.

Instruction Demonstration: This demonstrates the NOT instruction. This instruction takes the one's complement of its operand. The instruction sequence is

14EB:0100 B80002	MOV	AX,0200
14EB:0103 F7D0	NOT	AX

The registers and flags at the start are

EAX = 00000000	IP = 0100	NV UP EI NG NZ NA PE CY

After setting AX:

14EB:0100 B80002	MOV	AX,0200

EAX = 00000200	IP = 0103	NV UP EI NG NZ NA PE CY

14EB:0103 F7D0	NOT	AX

EAX = 0000FDFF	IP = 0105	NV UP EI NG NZ NA PE CY

The NOT instruction inverts each bit of its operand. No flags are affected.

OR   Logical Inclusive OR

INSTRUCTION	OPCODE	BINARY
OR AL,imm8	0C ib	00001100
OR AX,imm16	0D iw	00001101
OR EAX,imm32	0D id	00001101
OR r/m8,imm8	80 /1 ib	10000000 mm 001 r/m
OR r/m16,imm16	81 /1 iw	10000001 mm 001 r/m
OR r/m32,imm32	81 /1 id	10000001 mm 001 r/m
OR r/m16,imm8	83 /1 ib	10000011 mm 001 r/m
OR r/m32,imm8	83 /1 ib	10000011 mm 001 r/m
OR r/m8,r8	08 /r	00001000 mm 001 r/m
OR r/m16,r16	09 /r	00001001 mm 001 r/m
OR r/m32,r32	09 /r	00001001 mm 001 r/m
OR r8,r/m8	0A /r	00001010 mm rrr r/m
OR r16,r/m16	0B /r	00001011 mm rrr r/m
OR r32,r/m32	0B /r	00001011 mm rrr r/m

Purpose: OR compares its two operands. If each corresponding bit in the operands are zeros, the result is a zero; otherwise, the result is a 1.

Operand   10011
Operand   20110
Result   0111

The result is stored in the operand.

Instruction Demonstration: The OR instruction combines two values bit by bit. If a bit is on in either or both of the operands, it is set in the result. The instruction sequence is

```
14EB:0100 B80002    MOV    AX,0200
14EB:0103 0C3F       OR     AL,3F
14EB:0105 0D000A     OR     AX,0A00
```

The registers and flags at the start are

EAX = 00000000   IP = 0100   NV UP EI PL NZ NA PE NC

```
14EB:0100 B80002    MOV         AX,0200
```

After setting AX:

EAX = 00000200   IP = 0103   NV UP EI PL NZ NA PE NC

The overflow and carry flags are forced to zero by the OR instruction. Note that ORing *one* bits against zero bits sets the bits in the result, and that zero bits against zero bits leave the bits zero.

```
14EB:0103 0C3F       OR          AL,3F
```

EAX = 0000023F   IP = 0105   NV UP EI PL NZ NA PE NC

ORing bits that are on against bits that are also on doesn't change their value.

```
14EB:0105 0D000A     OR          AX,0A00
```

EAX = 00000A3F   IP = 0108   NV UP EI PL NZ NA PE NC

OUT   Output to Port

INSTRUCTION	OPCODE	BINARY
OUT imm8,AL	E6 ib	11100110
OUT imm8,AX	E7 ib	11100111
OUT imm8,EAX	E7 ib	11100111
OUT DX,AL	EE	11101110
OUT DX,AX	EF	11101111
OUT DX,EAX	EF	11101111

Purpose: OUT transfers data from a register to an output port. The source is a register (AL, AX, or EAX) and is given as the second operand. The output port is specified in the first operand. To output data to any port from 0 to 65536, the portnumber is placed in the DX register. OUT is then used with DX as the first operand. If the instruction contains an 8-bit port ID, the value is zero-extended to 16 bits in DX. If the immediate 8 is used, only ports from 0 to 255 are valid. In this case, the upper bits of the port address are zero.

Note: I/O ports 00F8 through 00FF are reserved by Intel.

Instruction Demonstration: The IN, INS, OUT, and OUTS instructions are demonstrated together because of their relationship with each other. See the IN instruction.

OUTS   Output String to Port
OUTSB   Output Byte
OUTSW   Output Word
OUTSD   Output Doubleword

INSTRUCTION	OPCODE	BINARY
OUTS DX,r/m8	6E	01101110
OUTS DX,r/m16	6F	01101111
OUTS DX,r/m32	6F	01101111

Note: OUTSB is a common assembler mnemonic for OUTS DX,r/m8
OUTSW is a common assembler mnemonic for OUTS DX,r/m16
OUTSD is a common assembler mnemonic for OUTS DX,r/m32

Purpose: OUTS operates much like OUT in that it transfers data (memory byte, word, or doubleword) at the source-index register to the output port addressed by the DX register. After the data transfer, the source-index register (SI or ESI, see below) is either incremented or decremented. If the DF is 0 (CLD was executed), the index is incremented. If DF is 1 (STD was executed), it is decremented. The amount it is changed depends on the size of the output: a 1 if it's a byte, a 2 if it's a word, or 4 if it's a doubleword.

The source data address is determined by the contents of a source-index register. The correct index value must be loaded into either SI or ESI prior to executing these instructions. SI is used for the source-index register if the address size attribute for these instructions is 16 bits. Otherwise, ESI is used and the address size attribute is 32 bits.

The port must be addressed through the DX register value. OUTS does *not* allow specification of the port number as an immediate value.

OUTS can be preceded by the REP prefix. In this case, ECX bytes, words, or dwords are transferred.

Instruction Demonstration: The IN, INS, OUT, and OUTS instructions are demonstrated together because of their relationship with each other. See the IN instruction.

POP   Pop a Word from the Stack

INSTRUCTION	OPCODE	BINARY
POP m16	8F /0	10001111 mm 000 r/m
POP m32	8F /0	10111111 mm 000 r/m
POP r16	58 + rw	01011rrr
POP r32	58 + rd	01011rrr
POP DS	1F	00011111
POP ES	07	00000111
POP SS	17	00010111
POP FS	0F A1	00001111 10100001
POP GS	0F A9	00001111 10101001

Purpose: POP transfers the word or doubleword at the current top of stack (indicated by SS:ESP) to the destination operand. It then increments SS:ESP to point to the new top of stack. When POPing 16-bit operands, avoid misaligning the stack, which causes performance degradation. See FIG. 10-9 for an overview of how stacks PUSH and POP.

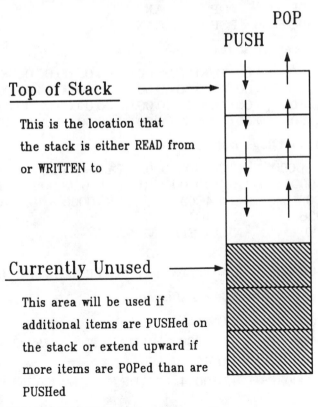

10-9   Representation of stack processing.

Note: Using a POP instruction with an operand in memory takes one more clock cycle to execute than an equivalent two-instruction sequence that moves the operand through a register before pushing it onto the stack. For example, POP MemOp takes 6 cycles, but

```
POP    EAX
MOV    MemOp,EAX
```

takes 5 cycles.

Instruction Demonstration: This demonstration shows the action of the PUSH, PUSHA, POP, and POPA instructions. They are demonstrated together because of their logical interaction. The instruction sequence is

```
4C13:0000 6650    PUSH     EAX
4C13:0002 50      PUSH     AX
4C13:0003 1E      PUSH     DS
4C13:0004 60      PUSHA
4C13:0005 6660    PUSHAD
4C13:0007 6661    POPAD
4C13:0009 61      POPA
4C13:000A 1F      POP      DS
4C13:000B 58      POP      AX
4C13:000C 6658    POP      EAX
```

The stack area at the start is

```
4C26:03C0    00 00 00 00 00 00 00 00-00 00 00 00 00 00 00 00
4C26:03D0    00 00 00 00 00 00 00 00-00 00 00 00 00 00 00 00
4C26:03E0    00 00 00 00 00 00 00 00-00 00 00 00 00 00 00 00
4C26:03F0    00 00 00 00 00 00 00 00-00 00 00 00 00 00 00 00
```

The registers and flags at the start are

```
EAX=80000001    EBX=40000002    ECX=20000004    EDX=10000008
ESP=00000400    EBP=08000010    ESI=04000020    EDI=02000040
DS=4C03         ES=4C03         FS=0000         GS=0000
SS=4C26         CS=4C13
IP=0000         NV UP EI PL NZ NA PO NC
4C13:0000 6650  PUSH      EAX
ESP=000003FC    IP=0002   NV UP EI PL NZ NA PO NC
```

SP and IP are the only registers affected.

```
4C13:0002 50        PUSH     AX
ESP=000003FA    IP=0003   NV UP EI PL NZ NA PO NC
4C13:0003 1E        PUSH     DS
ESP=000003F8    IP=0004   NV UP EI PL NZ NA PO NC
```

4C13:0004 60	PUSHA	
ESP = 000003E8	IP = 0005	NV UP EI PL NZ NA PO NC
4C13:0005 6660	PUSHAD	
ESP = 000003C8	IP = 0007	NV UP EI PL NZ NA PO NC

The stack is

4C26:03C0	40 00 00 02 20 00 00 04
4C26:03D0	10 00 00 08 E8 03 00 00-02 00 00 40 08 00 00 10
4C26:03E0	04 00 00 20 01 00 00 80-40 00 20 00 10 00 F8 03
4C26:03F0	02 00 08 00 04 00 01 00-03 4C 01 00 01 00 00 80

4C13:0007 6661	POPAD	
ESP = 000003E8	IP = 0009	NV UP EI PL NZ NA PO NC
4C13:0009 61	POPA	
ESP = 000003F8	IP = 000A	NV UP EI PL NZ NA PO NC
4C13:000A 1F	POP	DS
ESP = 000003FA	IP = 000B	NV UP EI PL NZ NA PO NC
4C13:000B 58	POP	AX
ESP = 000003FC	IP = 000C	NV UP EI PL NZ NA PO NC
4C13:000C 6658	POP	EAX

EAX = 80000001	EBX = 40000002	ECX = 20000004	EDX = 10000008
ESP = 00000400	EBP = 08000010	ESI = 040000020	EDI = 02000040
DS = 4C03	ES = 4C03	FS = 0000	GS = 0000
SS = 4C26	CS = 4C13		
IP = 000E	NV UP EI PL NZ NA PO NC		

POPA   PopAll Registers
POPAD   PopAll Registers—32-bit Mode

INSTRUCTION	OPCODE	BINARY
POPA	61	01100001
POPAD	61	01100001

Purpose: POPA restores the eight general-purpose registers saved on the stack by PUSHA. It discards the saved value of ESP. The order the registers are POPed is DI, SI, BP, SP, BX, DX, CX, and AX for POPA, or EDI, ESI, EBP, ESP, EBX, EDX, ECX, and EAX for POPAD.

Instruction Demonstration: The PUSH, PUSHA, POP, and POPA instructions are demonstrated together because of their logical interaction. See the demonstration under POP.

POPF   PopStack into FLAGS or EFLAGS Register
POPFD   PopStack—32-bit Mode

INSTRUCTION	OPCODE	BINARY
POPF	9D	10011101
POPFD	9D	10011101

Purpose: POPF transfers specific bits from the word at the top of stack into the low-order byte of EFLAGS. Then POPF increments ESP by two. POPFD transfers the 16 or 32 bits and increments ESP by four. The RF and VM flags are not changed by either POPF or POPFD.

PUSHF and POPF are useful for storing the flags in memory where they can be examined and modified. They can also preserve the state of the flags register while executing a procedure.

The IOPL (I/O privilege level) flag will only be altered if the current privilege level (CPL) is 0. If not 0, IOPL is not altered and no exception results. If CPL is as privileged or more privileged than the current IOPL, the interrupt enable flag (IF) is altered. If not, IF is unchanged and no exception results.

Instruction Demonstration: This demonstrates the effects of the PUSHF and POPF instructions. The flags are PUSHed twice, POPed into AX and inverted. Then AX is PUSHed and the value POPed into the flags. Finally, the original flags are restored. The instruction sequence is

```
14EB:0101 9C      PUSHF
14EB:0102 9C      PUSHF
14EB:0103 58      POP     AX
14EB:0104 F7D0    NOT     AX
14EB:0106 50      PUSH    AX
14EB:0107 9D      POPF
14EB:0108 9D      POPF
```

The registers and flags at the start are

```
EAX=00000000 SP=EA04   IP=0101   NV UP EI PL ZR NA PE NC
14EB:0101 9C           PUSHF
EAX=00008DB9 SP=EA02   IP=0102   NV UP EI PL ZR NA PE NC
14EB:0102 9C           PUSHF
EAX=00008DB9 SP=EA00   IP=0103   NV UP EI PL ZR NA PE NC
```

The flags have been PUSHed twice.

```
14EB:0103 58           POP       AX
EAX=00007246 SP=EA02   IP=0104   NV UP EI PL ZR NA PE NC
```

There is one copy off the stack into AX.

```
14EB:0104 F7D0              NOT     AX
EAX=00008DB9 SP=EA02   IP=0106   NV UP EI PL ZR NA PE NC
```

Flip all the bits.

```
14EB:0106 50               PUSH    AX
EAX=00008DB9 SP=EA00   IP=0107   NV UP EI PL ZR NA PE NC
```

Put the inverted bits on the stack.

```
14EB:0107 9D               POPF
EAX=00008DB9 SP=EA02   IP=0108   OV DN DI NG NZ AC PO CY
```

Then they are put into the flag register. Note that all are changed.

```
14EB:0108 9D               POPF
EAX=00008DB9 SP=EA04   IP=0109   NV UP EI PL ZR NA PE NC
```

Then restore the original flags.

PUSH   Push Operand onto the Stack

INSTRUCTION	OPCODE	BINARY
PUSH m16	FF /6	11111111 mm 110 r/m
PUSH m32	FF /6	11111111 mm 110 r/m
PUSH r16	50 + /r	01010rrr
PUSH r32	50 + /r	01010rrr
PUSH imm8	6A	01101010
PUSH imm16	68	01101000
PUSH imm32	68	01101000
PUSH CS	0E	00001110
PUSH SS	16	00010110
PUSH DS	1E	00011110
PUSH ES	06	00000110
PUSH FS	0F A0	00001111 10100000
PUSH GS	0F A8	00001111 10101000

Purpose: PUSH decrements the stack pointer (ESP) and transfers the source operand to the top of stack (TOS) indicated by ESP. PUSH is often used to place parameters on the stack before calling a procedure. It also provides a means of storing temporary variables on the stack. PUSH operates on memory operands, register operands (including segment registers), and immediate operands. Immediate data is always considered to be 32 bits in size, although it might be encoded in the instruction as an 8-bit immediate.

Be careful when PUSHing 16-bit operands. Avoid misaligning the stack, which causes performance degradation.

Note: Using a PUSH instruction with an operand in memory takes two more clock cycles to execute than an equivalent two-instruction sequence that moves the operand through a register before pushing it onto the stack. For example, PUSH MemOp takes 4 cycles, but

```
MOV     EAX,MemOp
PUSH    EAX
```

takes only 2 cycles.

Instruction Demonstration: The PUSH, PUSHA, POP, and POPA instructions are demonstrated together because of their logical interaction. See the demonstration under POP.

PUSHA   Push All General Registers
PUSHAD

INSTRUCTION	OPCODE	BINARY
PUSHA	60	01100000
PUSHAD	60	01100000

Purpose: PUSHA saves the contents of the eight general purpose registers on the stack. PUSHA eliminates the need for eight consecutive PUSH instructions. The order of the registers PUSHed is AX, CX, DX, BX, SP, BP, SI, and DI for word, or EAX, ECX, EDX, EBX, ESP, EBP, ESI, and EDI for dword. Note that the value PUSHed for SP or ESP is the original value. The order of the registers PUSHed is correct for a subsequent POPA.

Instruction Demonstration: The PUSH, PUSHA, POP, and POPA instructions are demonstrated together because of their logical interaction. See the demonstration under POP.

PUSHF   Push Flags Register EFLAGS onto the Stack
PUSHFD

INSTRUCTION	OPCODE	BINARY
PUSHF	9C	10011100
PUSHFD	9C	10011100

Purpose: PUSHF decrements ESP (stack pointer) by two and then transfers the low-order word of EFLAGS to the word at the top of stack pointed to by ESP. PUSHFD decrements ESP by four and then transfers both words of the EFLAGS to the top of stack pointed to by ESP. Note that the VM and RF flags are not moved.

PUSHF and POPF are useful for storing the flags in memory where they can be examined and modified. They also preserve the state of the flags register while executing a procedure.

Instruction Demonstration: PUSHF is demonstrated with the POPF instruction.

RCL   Rotate Left through Carry—Uses CF for Extension

RCR   Rotate Right through Carry—Uses CF for Extension

ROL   Rotate Left—Wrap bits around

ROR   Rotate Right—Wrap bits around

INSTRUCTION	OPCODE	BINARY
RCL r/m8,1	D0 /2	11010000 mm 010 r/m
RCL r/m8,CL	D2 /2	11010010 mm 010 r/m
RCL r/m8,imm8	C0 /2 ib	11000000 mm 010 r/m
RCL r/m16,1	D1 /2	11010001 mm 010 r/m
RCL r/m16,CL	D3 /2	11010011 mm 010 r/m
RCL r/m16,imm8	C1 /2 ib	11000001 mm 010 r/m
RCL r/m32,1	D1 /2	11010001 mm 010 r/m
RCL r/m32,CL	D3 /2	11010011 mm 010 r/m
RCL r/m32,imm8	C1 /2 ib	11000001 mm 010 r/m
RCR r/m8,1	D0 /3	11010000 mm 011 r/m
RCR r/m8,CL	D2 /3	11010010 mm 011 r/m
RCR r/m8,imm8	C0 /3 ib	11000000 mm 011 r/m
RCR r/m16,1	D1 /3	11010001 mm 011 r/m
RCR r/m16,CL	D3 /3	11010011 mm 011 r/m
RCR r/m16,imm8	C1 /3 ib	11000001 mm 011 r/m
RCR r/m32,1	D1 /3	11010001 mm 011 r/m
RCR r/m32,CL	D3 /3	11010011 mm 011 r/m
RCR r/m32,imm8	C1 /3 ib	11000001 mm 011 r/m
ROL r/m8,1	D0 /0	11010000 mm 000 r/m
ROL r/m8,CL	D2 /0	11010010 mm 000 r/m
ROL r/m8,imm8	C0 /0 ib	11000000 mm 000 r/m
ROL r/m16,1	D1 /0	11010001 mm 000 r/m
ROL r/m16,CL	D3 /0	11010011 mm 000 r/m
ROL r/m16,imm8	C1 /0 ib	11000001 mm 000 r/m
ROL r/m32,1	D1 /0	11010001 mm 000 r/m
ROL r/m32,CL	D3 /0	11010011 mm 000 r/m
ROL r/m32,imm8	C1 /0 ib	11000001 mm 000 r/m

ROR r/m8,1	C0 /1	11000000 mm 001 r/m
ROR r/m8,CL	D2 /1	11010010 mm 001 r/m
ROR r/m8,imm8	C0 /1 ib	11000000 mm 001 r/m
ROR r/m16,1	D1 /1	11010001 mm 001 r/m
ROR r/m16,CL	D3 /1	11010011 mm 001 r/m
ROR r/m16,imm8	C1 /1 ib	11000001 mm 001 r/m
ROR r/m32,1	D1 /1	11010001 mm 001 r/m
ROR r/m32,CL	D3 /1	11010011 mm 001 r/m
ROR r/m32,imm8	C1 /1 ib	11000001 mm 001 r/m

Purpose: Rotate refers to a process of moving each bit in a register in a circular manner, either to the right or left. Bits rotated out of an operand are not lost as in a shift, but are "circled back" into the other "end" of the operand. Rotate instructions affect only the carry and overflow flags. CF can act as an extension of the operand in two of the rotate instructions. This allows a bit to be isolated and then tested by a conditional jump instruction (JC or JNC). CF always contains the value of the last bit rotated out, even if the instruction does not use this bit as an extension of the rotated operand.

In single-bit rotates, OF is set if the operation changes the high-order (sign) bit of the destination operand. If the sign bit retains its original value, OF is cleared. On multi-bit rotates, the value of OF is *always* undefined.

RCL rotates bits in the byte, word, or doubleword destination operand *left* by one or by the number of bits specified in the count operand. RCL differs from ROL in that it treats CF as a high-order *one* bit extension of the destination operand. Each high-order bit that exits from the left side of the operand moves to CF before it returns to the operand as the low-order bit on the next rotation cycle.

RCR rotates bits in the byte, word, or doubleword destination *right* by one or by the number of bits specified in the count operand. RCR differs from ROR in that it treats CF as a low-order *one* bit extension of the destination operand. Each low- order bit that exits from the right side of the operand moves to CF before it returns to the operand as the high-order bit on the next rotation cycle.

ROL rotates the byte, word, or doubleword destination operand *left* by one or by the number of bits specified in the count operand, ECX. For each rotation specified, the high-order bit that exits from the left of the operand returns at the right to become the new low-order bit of the operand. If the ROL count is 1, the overflow flag (OF) is set to 0 if the carry flag (after the ROL) equals the high bit of the resultant operand. Otherwise, OF is set to 1. If ROL is not 1, OF is undefined. ROL with a 0 count does not affect OF or CF.

ROR rotates the byte, word, or doubleword destination operand *right* by one or by the number of bits specified in the count operand. For each rotation, the low-order bit that exits from the right of the operand returns at the left to become the new high-order bit of the operand. If the ROR count is 1, the overflow flag (OF) is set to 0 if the top two bits of the resultant operand are equal. Otherwise, OF = 1. If the ROR count is not 1, OF is undefined. Rotates with a zero count do not alter OF or CF.

Note: A rotate instruction with a count equal to 0 does not alter the carry flag. Also, RCL or RCR of 32 or 33 bits (for dwords) cannot be done, because only a count of 0 to 31 are valid.

Instruction Demonstration: This demonstrates the action of the rotate instructions. The rotate through-carry (RCx) that includes the carry as one of the bits rotated is demonstrated first. The rotate-only (ROx) is demonstrated and contrasted with the RCx. The instruction sequence is

```
14EB:0100 F8        CLC
14EB:0101 B081      MOV    AL,81
14EB:0103 B102      MOV    CL,02
14EB:0105 D0D0      RCL    AL,1
14EB:0107 D0D0      RCL    AL,1
14EB:0109 D0D8      RCR    AL,1
14EB:010B D0D8      RCR    AL,1
14EB:010D D2D0      RCL    AL,CL
14EB:010F D2D8      RCR    AL,CL
14EB:0111 90        NOP
14EB:0112 B081      MOV    AL,81
14EB:0114 D0C0      ROL    AL,1
14EB:0116 D0C0      ROL    AL,1
14EB:0118 D0C8      ROR    AL,1
14EB:011A D0C8      ROR    AL,1
14EB:011C D2C0      ROL    AL,CL
14EB:011E D2C8      ROR    AL,CL
```

The registers and flags at the start are

```
EAX=00000000 ECX=00000000   IP=0100   OV UP EI PL NZ NA PO NC
14EB:0100 F8                CLC
EAX=00000000 ECX=00000000   IP=0101   OV UP EI PL NZ NA PO NC
14EB:0101 B081              MOV       AL,81
EAX=00000081 ECX=00000000   IP=0103   OV UP EI PL NZ NA PO NC
14EB:0103 B102              MOV       CL,02
EAX=00000081 ECX=00000002   IP=0105   OV UP EI PL NZ NA PO NC
```

These commands forced the carry to zero, loaded a count of 2 into CL and a value of hex 81 into AL. The bits to be rotated are

```
1000 0001 0
14EB:0105 D0D0              RCL       AL,1
EAX=00000002 ECX=00000002   IP=0107   OV UP EI PL NZ NA PO CY
```

The first rotate has changed the bits to 0000 0010 1. Note that the carry has been set, as well as the overflow flag.

```
14EB:0107 D0D0                    RCL        AL,1
EAX=00000005 ECX=00000002  IP=0109  NV UP EI PL NZ NA PO NC
```

The second rotate changes the bits to 0000 0101 0. Note that the carry is zero, and the overflow flag is off.

```
14EB:0109 D0D8                    RCR        AL,1
EAX=00000002 ECX=00000002  IP=010B  NV UP EI PL NZ NA PO CY
```

The rotate right brings the bits back to 0000 0010 1. The carry is on, and the overflow flag is off.

```
14EB:010B D0D8                    RCR        AL,1
EAX=00000081 ECX=00000002  IP=010D  OV UP EI PL NZ NA PO NC
```

The bits are rotated back to their original values.

```
14EB:010D D2D0                    RCL        AL,CL
EAX=00000005 ECX=00000002  IP=010F  NV UP EI PL NZ NA PO NC
```

The two-bit rotate has included the carry flag. The overflow flag is changed but undefined. Therefore, it should not be used after a multiple bit rotate. Note that the bits are 0000 0101 0 after the two rotates. Also, the count is unchanged in CL.

```
14EB:010F D2D8                    RCR        AL,CL
EAX=00000081 ECX=00000002  IP=0111  OV UP EI PL NZ NA PO NC
```

The two-bit rotate right returns the value to

```
1000 0001 0
14EB:0111 90                      NOP
EAX=00000081 ECX=00000002  IP=0112  OV UP EI PL NZ NA PO NC
14EB:0112 B081                    MOV        AL,81
EAX=00000081 ECX=00000002  IP=0114  OV UP EI PL NZ NA PO NC
14EB:0114 D0C0                    ROL        AL,1
EAX=00000003 ECX=00000002  IP=0116  OV UP EI PL NZ NA PO CY
```

The rotate-only has rotated the bits to 0000 0011 1. Note that the carry and the overflow flags are set, but that the carry does not move into the rotated value.

```
14EB:0116 D0C0                    ROL        AL,1
EAX=00000006 ECX=00000002  IP=0118  NV UP EI PL NZ NA PO NC
```

Again, the rotate does not include the carry but does set it to zero, the value of the bit rotated out of the high order position. The result is

0000 0110 0

| 14EB:0118 D0C8 | | ROR | AL,1 |

EAX = 00000003 ECX = 00000002   IP = 011A   NV UP EI PL NZ NA PO NC

The right rotate returns the sequence to a value of

0000 0011 0

14EB:011A D0C8   ROR   AL,1

EAX = 00000081 ECX = 00000002   IP = 011C   **OV** UP EI PL NZ NA PO **CY**

The second right rotate brings the sequence back to the original value of 1000 0001 1. The carry flag is set on a right rotate when a bit is rotated into the high-order bit. The overflow is set on a single right rotate of 1 when the result shows the carry has changed.

14EB:011C D2C0   ROL   AL,CL

EAX = 00000006 ECX = 00000002   IP = 011E   **NV** UP EI PL NZ NA PO **NC**

The two-bit left rotate results in a value of 0000 0110 0. The carry is reset because the last bit rotated out of the high-order position was zero.

14EB:011E D2C8   ROR   AL,CL

EAX = 00000081 ECX = 00000002   IP = 0120   OV UP EI PL NZ NA PO **CY**

The two-bit right rotate returns the original value and sets the carry because the last bit rotated into the high-order position was a one.

REP	Repeat Following String Operation
REPE	Repeat while Equal
REPZ	Repeat while Zero
REPNE	Repeat while Not Equal
REPNZ	Repeat while Not Zero

INSTRUCTION	OPCODE	BINARY
REP INS r/m8,DX	F3 6C	11110011 01101100
REP INS r/m16,DX	F3 6D	11110011 01101101
REP INS r/m32,DX	F3 6D	11110011 01101101
REP MOVS m8,m8	F3 A4	11110011 10100100
REP MOVS m16,m16	F3 A5	11110011 10100101
REP MOVS m32,m32	F3 A5	11110011 10100101
REP OUTS DX,r/m8	F3 6E	11110011 01101110
REP OUTS DX,r/m16	F3 6F	11110011 01101111
REP OUTS DX,r/m32	F3 6F	11110011 01101111
REP STOS m8	F3 AA	11110011 10101010

REP STOS m16	F3 AB	11110011 10101011
REP STOS m32	F3 AB	11110011 10101011
REPE CMPS m8,m8	F3 A6	11110011 10100110
REPE CM PS m16,m16	F3 A7	11110011 10100111
REPE CMPS m32,m32	F3 A7	11110011 10100111
REPE SCAS m8	F3 AE	11110011 10101110
REPE SCAS m16	F3 AF	11110011 10101111
REPE SCAS m32	F3 AF	11110011 10101111
REPNE CMPS m8,m8	F2 A6	11110010 10100110
REPNE CMPS m16,m16	F2 A7	11110010 10100111
REPNE CMPS m32,m32	F2 A7	11110010 10100111
REPNE SCAS m8	F2 AE	11110010 10101110
REPNE SCAS m16	F2 AF	11110010 10101111
REPNE SCAS m32	F2 AF	11110010 10101111

Purpose: The REP prefixes specify repeated operation of a string that enables the 80486 to process strings much faster than with a regular software loop. When a string operation has one of these repeat prefixes, the operation is executed repeatedly for ECX times. Each time, the operation uses a different element of the string. The repetition ends when one of the conditions specified by the prefix is satisfied.

At the repetition of the instruction, the string operation can be suspended temporarily to handle an external interrupt or exception. After that interrupt has been handled, the string operation begins where it left off.

REPE repeats ECX times or until zero flag (ZF) becomes zero. REPZ is synonymous with REPE. REPNE repeats ECX times, or until ZF becomes one. REPNZ is synonymous with REPNE.

Instruction Demonstration: Demonstrated with MOVS.

RET   Return from Procedure

INSTRUCTION	OPCODE	BINARY
RET	C3	11000011
RET imm16	CA /w	11001010

Purpose: RET ends the execution of a CALLed procedure and transfers control through the back-link on the top of the stack, which is the extended instruction pointer (EIP) value. The back-link points to the program that originally invoked the procedure. RET restores the value of EIP (instruction pointer) that was saved on the stack by the previous CALL instruction.

RET can optionally specify an immediate operand. By adding this constant to the new top-of-stack pointer, RET removes any arguments that the CALLing program pushed onto the stack before the CALL executed.

Instruction Demonstration: The CALL instruction, ENTER instruction, LEAVE instruction, and RET instruction are demonstrated together because they logically "fit" with each other and complement each other. See the CALL instruction.

SAHF   Store AH into Flags Register

INSTRUCTION	OPCODE	BINARY
SAHF	9E	10011110

Purpose: Though specific instructions exist to alter CF and DF, no direct way exists of altering the other applications-oriented flags. The flag transfer instructions (LAHF and SAHF) allow a program to alter the other flag bits with the bit manipulation instructions after transferring these flags to the stack or the AH register. Then SAHF stores the contents of AH to the low byte of EFLAGS.

Instruction Demonstration: This demonstrates the movement of the AH register value into the flags register by SAHF. The instruction sequence is

```
14EB:0100 9E        SAHF
14EB:0101 F6D4       NOT        AH
14EB:0103 9E        SAHF
```

The registers and flags at the start are

```
EAX=00000000   IP=0100    OV UP EI PL NZ NA PO CY
```

First set the flags to zero (the value in AH).

```
14EB:0100 9E        SAHF
EAX=00000000   IP=0101    OV UP EI PL NZ NA PO NC
```

Invert all the bits of AH.

```
14EB:0101 F6D4       NOT        AH
EAX=0000FF00   IP=0103    OV UP EI PL NZ NA PO NC
```

Then set the flags to ones.

```
14EB:0103 9E        SAHF
EAX=0000FF00   IP=0104    OV UP EI NG ZR AC PE CY
```

SAL Shift Left through Carry
SAR Shift Right through Carry
SHL Shift Left
SHR Shift Right

INSTRUCTION	OPCODE	BINARY
SAL r/m8,1	D0 /4	11010000 mm 100 r/m
SAL r/m8,CL	D2 /4	11010010 mm 100 r/m
SAL r/m8,imm8	C0 /4 ib	11000000 mm 100 r/m
SAL r/m16,1	D1 /4	11010001 mm 100 r/m
SAL r/m16,CL	D3 /4	11010011 mm 100 r/m
SAL r/m16,imm8	C1 /4 ib	11000001 mm 100 r/m
SAL r/m32,1	D1 /4	11000001 mm 100 r/m
SAL r/m32,CL	D3 /4	11010011 mm 100 r/m
SAL r/m32,imm8	C1 /4 ib	11000001 mm 100 r/m
SAR r/m8,1	D0 /7	11010000 mm 111 r/m
SAR r/m8,CL	D2 /7	11000010 mm 111 r/m
SAR r/m8,imm8	C0 /7 ib	11000000 mm 111 r/m
SAR r/m16,1	C1 /7	11000001 mm 111 r/m
SAR r/m16,CL	D3 /7	11010011 mm 111 r/m
SAR r/m16,imm8	C1 /7 ib	11000001 mm 111 r/m
SAR r/m32,1	D1 /7	11010001 mm 111 r/m
SAR r/m32,CL	D3 /7	11010011 mm 111 r/m
SAR r/m32,imm8	C1 /7 ib	11000001 mm 111 r/m
SHR r/m8,1	D0 /5	11010000 mm 101 r/m
SHR r/m8,CL	C2 /5	11000010 mm 101 r/m
SHR r/m8,imm8	C0 /5 ib	11000000 mm 101 r/m
SHR r/m16,1	D1 /5	11010001 mm 101 r/m
SHR r/m16,CL	D3 /5	11010011 mm 101 r/m
SHR r/m16,imm8	C1 /5 ib	11000001 mm 101 r/m
SHR r/m32,1	D1 /5	11010001 mm 101 r/m
SHR r/m32,CL	D3 /5	11010011 mm 101 r/m
SHR r/m32,imm8	C1 /5 ib	11000001 mm 101 r/m

Note: SHL is an alternate assembler opcode for SAL.

Purpose: The bits in bytes, words, and doublewords can be shifted logically or arithmetically. Bits can be shifted up to 31 places, depending on a specified count in ECX. Shift instructions specify the count in one of three ways: implicitly, by specifying the count as a single shift; by specifying the count as an immediate value; or by specifying the count as the value contained in ECX. The result is stored back into the first operand.

The shift instructions provide a convenient way to multiply or divide by binary. The division of signed numbers by shifting right is *not* the same kind of division performed by IDIV.

CF always contains the value of the last bit shifted out of the destination operand. In a single-bit shift, OF is set if the value of the high-order (sign) bit was changed by the operation. If the sign bit was not changed, OF is cleared. After a multi-bit shift, the contents of OF is *always* undefined.

SAL shifts the destination byte, word, or doubleword operand left by one or by the number of bits specified in the count register. The processor shifts zeros in from the right (low-order) side of the operand as bits exit from the left (high-order) side. If the shift count is one, the overflow flag (OF) is set to zero if the carry flag (CF) after the shift equals the high bit of the first operand. Otherwise, OF is set to one. If the shift count is not one, OF is undefined.

SAR shifts the destination byte, word, or doubleword operand to the right by one or by the number of bits specified in the count operand. The processor preserves the sign of the operand by shifting in zeros on the left (high-order) side if the value is positive or by shifting in ones if the value is negative. If the shift count is one, OF is set to zero; otherwise it is unchanged. Another way to think of SAR is that operand one is being divided by two shift-count times. The divide rounds to negative infinity (which is different than IDIV) for negative numbers. Shifts of zero do not alter any flags.

SHL is a synonym for SAL.

SHR shifts the destination byte, word, or doubleword operand right by one or by the number of bits specified in the count operand. The processor shifts zeros in from the left (high-order) side of the operand as bits exit from the right (low-order) side.

Instruction Demonstration: This demonstrates the arithmetic and logical shift instructions SAL, SAR, SHL, and SHR. The instruction sequence is

```
14EB:0100 B88100        MOV    AX,0081
14EB:0103 F8            CLC
14EB:0104 B103          MOV    CL,03
14EB:0106 D0F8          SAR    AL,1
14EB:0108 D0F0          SAL    AL,1
14EB:010A D0E8          SHR    AL,1
14EB:010C D0E0          SHL    AL,1
14EB:010E B081          MOV    AL,81
14EB:0110 D2F8          SAR    AL,CL
14EB:0112 D2F0          SAL    AL,CL
14EB:0114 D2E8          SHR    AL,CL
14EB:0116 D2E0          SHL    AL,CL
```

The registers and flags at the start are

```
EAX=00000000 ECX=00000000    IP=0100    NV UP EI PL ZR AC PO CY
14EB:0100 B88100             MOV        AX,0081
EAX=00000081 ECX=00000000    IP=0103    NV UP EI PL ZR AC PO CY
14EB:0103 F8                 CLC
EAX=00000081 ECX=00000000    IP=0104    NV UP EI PL ZR AC PO NC
14EB:0104 B103               MOV        CL,03
EAX=00000081 ECX=00000003    IP=0106    NV UP EI PL ZR AC PO NC
14EB:0106 D0F8               AR         AL,1
EAX=000000C0 ECX=00000003    IP=0108    NV UP EI NG NZ AC PE CY
```

The arithmetic right shift extends the sign to the right and no rotation occurs. This can be considered a signed integer divide-by-two without rounding. Carry is set because of the bit shifted out to the right. The other flags reflect the result in the shifted register.

```
14EB:0108 D0F0               SAL        AL,1
EAX=00000080 ECX=00000003    IP=010A    NV UP EI NG NZ AC PO CY
```

The arithmetic left shift multiplies the shifted value by two. Carry is set because the high-order bit shifted out was a one.

```
14EB:010A D0E8               SHR        AL,1
EAX=00000040 ECX=00000003    IP=010C    OV UP EI PL NZ AC PO NC
```

The logical right shift fills zeros into the sign position. OV is set because the high bit of the original value of AL was one. The low-order bit was zero and was shifted into the carry.

```
14EB:010C D0E0               SHL        AL,1
EAX=00000080 ECX=00000003    IP=010E    OV UP EI NG NZ AC PO NC
```

The logical left shift performs an unsigned multiplication by two. The negative flag is set because the high bit of the operand is now set. OV remains set because the high bit of the result is different from the carry flag. OV records the factthat a left shift changed the sign bit.

```
14EB:010E B081               MOV        AL,81
EAX=00000081 ECX=00000003    IP=0110    OV UP EI NG NZ AC PO NC
14EB:0110 D2F8               SAR        AL,CL
EAX=000000F0 ECX=00000003    IP=0112    NV UP EI NG NZ AC PE NC
```

The shift of three bits (the value in CL is ANDed against hex 1F to limit the shift count to 31 bits maximum) caused the sign to be propagated into AL. The parity flag is set, as are other arithmetic flags. The OV flag is changed, but its value in multiple bit shifts is undefined.

14EB:0112 D2F0   SAL   AL,CL
EAX=00000080 ECX=00000003   IP=0114   NV UP EI NG NZ AC **PO CY**

The left shift of three bits sets the carry, because a *one* bit was shifted out of AL on the last shift of the count. Zeros are filled in from the right.

14EB:0114 D2E8   SHR   AL,CL
EAX=00000010 ECX=00000003   IP=0116   NV UP EI **PL** NZ AC PO **NC**

The logical shift right fills the left bits with zeros. Note that the sign bit has no special significance and is just another bit to be shifted. The carry flag reflects the state of the last bit shifted out of AL (0).

14EB:0116 D2E0   SHL   AL,CL
EAX=00000080 ECX=00000003   IP=0118   **OV** UP EI **NG** NZ AC PO NC

The left logical shift again fills zeros on the right. No carry is set because the last bit shifted out of the register was a zero. OV is changed but is undefined.

SBB   Subtract Integers with Borrow

INSTRUCTION	OPCODE	BINARY
SBB AL,imm8	1C ib	00011100
SBB AX,imm16	1D iw	00011101
SBB EAX,imm32	1D id	00011101
SBB r/m8,imm8	80 /3 ib	10000000 mm 011 r/m
SBB r/m16,imm16	81 /3 iw	10000001 mm 011 r/m
SBB r/m32,imm32	81 /3 id	10000001 mm 011 r/m
SBB r/m16,imm8	83 /3 ib	10000011 mm 011 r/m
SBB r/m32,imm8	83 /3 ib	10000011 mm 011 r/m
SBB r/m8,r8	18 /r	00011000 mm rrr r/m
SBB r/m16,r16	19 /r	00011001 mm rrr r/m
SBB r/m32,r32	19 /r	00011001 mm rrr r/m
SBB r8,r/m8	1A /r	00011010 mm rrr r/m
SBB r16,r/m16	1B /r	00011011 mm rrr r/m
SBB r32,r/m32	1B /r	00011011 mm rrr r/m

Purpose: SBB subtracts the source operand from the destination operand and then returns the results to the destination operand. It subtracts one if CF is set. If CF is cleared, SBB performs the same operation as SUB. SUB followed by multiple SBB instructions may be used to subtract numbers longer than 32 bits.

Instruction Demonstration: This demonstrates the action of the SBB instruction. The instruction sequence is

```
14EB:0100 F8          CLC
14EB:0101 B80100      MOV    AX,0001
14EB:0104 1D0100      SBB    AX,0001
14EB:0107 1D0100      SBB    AX,0001
14EB:010A 1D0100      SBB    AX,0001
```

The registers and flags at the start are

EAX = 00000000   IP = 0100   NV UP EI NG NZ NA PO NC

14EB:0100 F8   CLC

EAX = 00000000   IP = 0101   NV UP EI NG NZ NA PO NC

and force the carry flag off.

14EB:0101 B80100   MOV   AX,0001

EAX = 00000001   IP = 0104   NV UP EI NG NZ NA PO NC

Load a 1 into AX to prepare to demonstrate the instruction.

14EB:0104 1D0100   SBB   AX,0001

EAX = 00000000   IP = 0107   NV UP EI **PL ZR** NA **PE** NC

The result of the first SBB is to set the flags according to the result of the subtraction. $(1 - 1 = 0)$

14EB:0107 1D0100   SBB   AX,0001

EAX = 0000FFFF   IP = 010A   NV UP EI **NG NZ AC** PE **CY**

This subtraction causes a borrow (the result is as if a high-order bit were available just beyond the register). This sets the carry flag in addition to the sign and non-zero flags. $(0 - 1 = -1)$

14EB:010A 1D0100   SBB   AX,0001

EAX = 0000FFFD   IP = 010D   NV UP EI NG NZ **NA PO NC**

This SBB subtracts the immediate value from the register, but also subtracts one for the previous borrow as "remembered" in the carry flag. $(-1 - 1 - 1 = -3)$

SCAS   Compare String Data
SCASB   Compare Byte
SCASW   Compare Word
SCASD   Compare Doubleword

INSTRUCTION	OPCODE	BINARY
SCAS m8	AE	10101110

SCAS m16	AF	10101111
SCAS m32	AF	10101111

Note: SCASB is a common assembler mnemonic for SCAS m8

SCASW is a common assembler mnemonic for SCAS m16

SCASD is a common assembler mnemonic for SCAS m32

Purpose: These instructions operate on strings rather than on logical or numeric values. They operate on one element of a string, which could be a byte, a word, or a doubleword. SCAS subtracts ES:[EDI] from AL, AX, or EAX (for byte, word, or dword) operations. The result of the subtraction is not stored; only the flags are changed. After each string operation, EDI is updated to point to the next element of the string. If the direction flag (DF) is zero, the index register is incremented. If DF = one, it is decremented. The amount incremented or decremented is one, two, or four, depending on the size of the string element.

If the values are equal, the Zero Flag (ZF) is set to one; otherwise, ZF = zero. If DF = zero, the 80486 increments the memory pointer (EDI) for the string. The destination segment register (ES) cannot be overridden.

SCAS can be preceded by REPE (REPZ) or REPNE (REPNZ). If preceded by REPE, SCAS is repeated while ECX is not zero and the string elements are equal to AL, AX, or EAX (ZF = one). If preceded by REPNE, SCAS is repeated while ECX is not zero and the string element is not equal to AL, AX, or EAX (ZF = zero). In this way, SCAS is useful to find the first mismatch (REPE) or match (REPNE) to AL, AX, or EAX in the string if they exist.

The specification of mem is used by the assembler to determine the length of the operation only. The string is always taken from ES:EDI. No segment override is possible for SCAS.

Instruction Demonstration: This demonstrates the use of SCAS instruction in searching for a particular byte in a string. The instruction sequence is

```
14EB:0100 B90400     MOV      CX,0004
14EB:0103 BF0002     MOV      DI,0200
14EB:0106 B84300     MOV      AX,0043
14EB:0109 F2         REPNZ
14EB:010A AE         SCASB
```

The data to be scanned is

```
14EB:0200   41 42 43 44
```

The registers and flags at the start are

```
EAX = 00000000 ECX = 00000000 EDI = 00000000 IP = 0100
                              NV UP EI PL NZ NA PE NC
14EB:0100 B90400     MOV            CX,0004
```

EAX = 00000000 ECX = 00000004 EDI = 00000000 IP = 0103
                                      NV UP EI PL NZ NA PE NC

The count is in CX.

    14EB:0103 BF0002   MOV   DI,0200

EAX = 00000000 ECX = 00000004 EDI = 00000200 IP = 0106
                                      NV UP EI PL NZ NA PE NC

DI is now set to the string to be scanned.

    14EB:0106 B84300   MOV   AX,0043

EAX = 00000043 ECX = 00000004 EDI = 00000200 IP = 0109
                                      NV UP EI PL NZ NA PE NC

The value to be searched for is set in AL. Note that a REPNZ prefix is used to skip unmatching characters. If you want to skip matching characters such as spaces, use the REPZ prefix.

    14EB:0109 F2   REPNZ

    14EB:010A AE   SCASB

EAX = 00000043 ECX = 00000001 EDI = 00000203 IP = 010B
                                      NV UP EI PL **ZR** NA PE NC

Note that the zero flag is set. This indicates that a match was found in the string. Note that CX could be zero if it was matched on the last byte. DI points to the position following the position that matched.

SETcc   SET Byte on Condition Code

INSTRUCTION	OPCODE	BINARY
SETA r/m8	0F 97	00001111 10010111 mm rrr r/m
SETAE r/m8	0F 93	00001111 10010011 mm rrr r/m
SETB r/m8	0F 92	00001111 10010010 mm rrr r/m
SETBE r/m8	0F 96	00001111 10010110 mm rrr r/m
SETC r/m8	0F 92	00001111 10010010 mm rrr r/m
SETE r/m8	0F 94	00001111 10010100 mm rrr r/m
SETG r/m8	0F 9F	00001111 10011111 mm rrr r/m
SETGE r/m8	0F 9D	00001111 10011101 mm rrr r/m
SETL r/m8	0F 9C	00001111 10011100 mm rrr r/m
SETLE r/m8	0F 9E	00001111 10011110 mm rrr r/m
SETNA r/m8	0F 96	00001111 10010110 mm rrr r/m
SETNAE r/m8	0F 92	00001111 10010010 mm rrr r/m
SETNB r/m8	0F 93	00001111 10010011 mm rrr r/m
SETNBE r/m8	0F 97	00001111 10010111 mm rrr r/m

SETNC r/m8	0F 93	00001111 10010011 mm rrr r/m
SETNE r/m8	0F 95	00001111 10010101 mm rrr r/m
SETNG r/m8	0F 9E	00001111 10011110 mm rrr r/m
SETNGE r/m8	0F 9C	00001111 10011100 mm rrr r/m
SETNL r/m8	0F 9D	00001111 10011101 mm rrr r/m
SETNLE r/m8	0F 9F	00001111 10011111 mm rrr r/m
SETNO r/m8	0F 91	00001111 10010001 mm rrr r/m
SETNP r/m8	0F 9B	00001111 10011011 mm rrr r/m
SETNS r/m8	0F 99	00001111 10011001 mm rrr r/m
SETNZ r/m8	0F 95	00001111 10010101 mm rrr r/m
SETO r/m8	0F 90	00001111 10010000 mm rrr r/m
SETP r/m8	0F 9A	00001111 10011010 mm rrr r/m
SETPE r/m8	0F 9A	00001111 10011010 mm rrr r/m
SETPO r/m8	0F 9B	00001111 10011011 mm rrr r/m
SETS r/m8	0F 98	00001111 10011000 mm rrr r/m
SETZ r/m8	0F 94	00001111 10010100 mm rrr r/m

Purpose: Introduced with the 80386, SETcc sets a byte to zero or one depending on any of the conditions defined by the status flags and shown below. The byte can be in memory or could be a one-byte general register. SETcc sets the byte to one if the condition cc is true; otherwise, it sets the byte to zero.

The condition codes are

SETB/SETNAE/SETC	CF = 1
SETBE/SETNA	CF = 1, ZF = 1
SETE/SETZ	ZF = 1
SETL/SETNGE	SF = OF
SETLE/SETNG	SF = OF, ZF = 1
SETNB/SETAE/SETNC	CF = 0
SETNBE/SETA	CF = 0, ZF = 1
SETNE/SETNZ	ZF = 0
SETNL/SETGE	SF = OF
SETNLE/SETG	ZF = 0, SF = OF
SETNO	OF = 0
SETNP/SETPO	PF = 0
SETNS	SF = 0
SETO	OF = 1
SETP/SETPE	PF = 1
SETS	SF = 1

Instruction Demonstration: This demonstrates the action of the SETcc instruction.

The instruction sequence is

```
14EB:0100 0F95C0      SETNZ   AL
14EB:0103 0F94C0      SETZ    AL
14EB:0106 90          NOP
```

The registers and flags at the start are

        EAX = 00000001   IP = 0100   NV UP EI PL ZR NA PE NC
        14EB:0100 0F95C0   SETNZ   AL
        EAX = 00000000   IP = 0103   NV UP EI PL ZR NA PE NC

Because the zero flag is set, the SETcc instruction places a byte of zero into AL showing that the condition checked for was false.

        14EB:0103 0F94C0   SETZ   AL
        EAX = 00000001   IP = 0106   NV UP EI PL ZR NA PE NC

In this case, a byte of hex 01 is placed in AL because the condition tested checked for was true.

SGDT   Store Global Descriptor Table
SIDT   Store Interrupt Descriptor Table

INSTRUCTION	OPCODE	BINARY
SIDT m	0F 01 /1	00001111 00000001 mm 001 r/m

Purpose: These instructions copy the contents of the global descriptor table register (GDTR) or the interrupt descriptor table register (IDTR) to the six bytes (48 bits) indicated by the operand. The 16-bit forms of the SGDT/SIDT instructions are compatible with the 80286, but only if the value in the upper 8 bits is not referenced. The 80286 stores 1s in these bits while the 80386 and 80486 store 0s.

The 16-bit limit is stored in the low word and the 32-bit base is stored in the high doubleword.

Instruction Demonstration #1: This demonstrates the storing of the global descriptor table register.

        14EB:0100 660F0105   SGDT   [DI]
        14EB:0104 90   NOP

The data at ES:DI is

        14EB:0200   01 01 01 01 01 01 01 01   . . . .

The registers and flags at the start are

        AX = 0000   BX = 0000   CX = 0000   DX = 0000   SP = EA04   BP = 0000
        SI = 0000   EDI = 00000200   DS = 14EB   ES = 14EB   SS = 14EB   CS = 14EB
        IP = 0100   NV UP EI NG NZ NA PO NC

Note the operand width modifier.

14EB:0100 660F0105   SGDT   [DI]

AX=0000   BX=0000   CX=0000   DX=0000   SP=EA04   BP=0000
SI=0000   EDI=00000200   DS=14EB   ES=14EB   SS=14EB   CS=14EB
IP=0104   NV UP EI NG NZ NA PO NC

The resulting 48 bit register is

.0614EB:0200   FF FF 00 00 00 00 01 01 . . . .

Instruction Demonstration #2: This demonstrates the action of the SIDT instruction. The instruction sequence is

14EB:0100 660F010D   SIDT   [DI]

The data at ES:DI is

.0614EB:0200   01 01 01 01 01 01 01 01 . . . .

The registers and flags at the start are

EDI=00000200 ES=14EB   IP=0100   NV UP EI NG NZ NA PO NC

Note the operand width override prefix.

14EB:0100 660F010D   SIDT   [DI]

EDI=00000200 ES=14EB   IP=0104   NV UP EI NG NZ NA PO NC

The resulting 48-bit value is

.0614EB:0200   FF FF 00 00 00 00 01 01 . . . .

SHLD   Double Precision Shift Left
SHRD   Double Precision Shift Right

INSTRUCTION	OPCODE	BINARY
SHLD r/m16,r16,imm8	0F A4	00001111 10100100 mm rrr r/m
SHLD r/m32,r32,imm8	0F A4	00001111 10100100 mm rrr r/m
SHLD r/m16,r16,CL	0F A5	00001111 10100101 mm rrr r/m
SHLD r/m32,r32,CL	0F A5	00001111 10100101 mm rrr r/m
SHRD r/m16,r16,imm8	0F AC	00001111 10101100 mm rrr r/m
SHRD r/m32,r32,imm8	0F AC	00001111 10101100 mm rrr r/m
SHRD r/m16,r16,CL	0F AD	00001111 10101101 mm rrr r/m
SHRD r/m32,r32,CL	0F AD	00001111 10101101 mm rrr r/m

Purpose: Introduced with the 80386, SHLD and SHRD provide the basic operations needed to implement operations on long, unaligned bit strings. The double shifts either take two word operands as input and produce a one-word output, or take two doubleword operands as input and produce a doubleword output. The result is stored back in the first operand.

One of the two input operands can either be in a general register or in memory; the other might only be in a general register. The results replace the memory or register operand. The number of bits to be shifted is specified either in the CL register or in an immediate byte of the instruction. This count is masked to 5 bits; thus, shifts of zero to 31 bits are performed. CF is set to the value of the last bit shifted out of the destination operand. SF, ZF, and PF are set according to the value of the result. Of and AF are left undefined.

If the count in CL is zero, the instructions are equivalent to an NOP and do not alter the flags. If the shift count is greater than the operand length, the flags and the result in the first operand are undefined.

Instruction Demonstration #1: This demonstrates the effects of the SHLD instruction. The instruction sequence is

```
14EB:0100 B80000      MOV     AX,0000
14EB:0103 BB3412      MOV     BX,1234
14EB:0106 0FA4D808    SHLD    AX,BX,8
14EB:010A B10C        MOV     CL,0C
14EB:010C 0FA5D8      SHLD    AX,BX,CL
```

The registers and flags at the start are

```
EAX=00002123 EBX=00000000 ECX=00000000 IP=0100
                           OV UP EI PL NZ AC PO CY
14EB:0100 B80000        MOV             AX,0000
EAX=00000000 EBX=00000000 ECX=00000000 IP=0103
                           OV UP EI PL NZ AC PO CY
14EB:0103 BB3412        MOV             BX,1234
EAX=00000000 EBX=00001234 ECX=00000000 IP=0106
                           OV UP EI PL NZ AC PO CY
14EB:0106 0FA4D808    SHLD            AX,BX,8
EAX=00000012 EBX=00001234 ECX=00000000 IP=010A
                           NV UP EI PL NZ AC PE **NC**
```

The double shift uses the third operand for the count of bits to shift. The first operand is shifted in conjunction with a copy of the second operand the number of bits specified. The count might be immediate as in this example, or contained in CL. Note that the second operand is unchanged. The sign, zero, and parity flags are set according to the result in the first operand. Carry is set to the value of the last bit shifted out of operand one. The adjust and overflow flags are undefined.

Note that with an operand width of 16 bits, the upper half of EAX is undisturbed.

```
14EB:010A B10C        MOV                CL,0C
EAX=00000012 EBX=00001234 ECX=0000000C IP=010C
                                    NV UP EI PL NZ AC PE NC

14EB:010C 0FA5D8       SHLD               AX,BX,CL
EAX=00002123 EBX=00001234 ECX=0000000C IP=010F
                                    OV UP EI PL NZ AC PO CY
```

This 12-bit shift results in a carry because the last bit shifted out of the AX register was a one.

Instruction Demonstration #2: This demonstrates the action of the SHRD instruction. The instruction sequence is

```
14EB:0100 B80000       MOV       AX,0000
14EB:0103 BB3412       MOV       BX,1234
14EB:0106 0FACD808     SHRD      AX,BX,8
14EB:010A B10C         MOV       CL,0C
14EB:010C 0FADD8       SHRD      AX,BX,CL
```

The registers and flags at the start are

```
EAX=00000000 EBX=00000000 ECX=00000000 IP=0100
                                    OV UP EI PL NZ AC PO CY

14EB:0100 B80000       MOV                AX,0000
EAX=00000000 EBX=00000000 ECX=00000000       IP=0103
                                    OV UP EI PL NZ AC PO CY

14EB:0103 BB3412       MOV                BX,1234
EAX=00000000    EBX=00001234    ECX=00000000
IP=0106
                                    OV UP EI PL NZ AC PO CY

14EB:0106 0FACD808     SHRD               AX,BX,8
EAX=00003400 EBX=00001234 ECX=00000000       IP=010A
                                    NV UP EI PL NZ AC PE NC
```

The 8-bit right double shift has shifted the right 8 bits of the second operand's copy into the first operand. The carry flag is set to reflect the value of the last bit shifted out of the first operand. The sign, zero and parity flags are set according to the result in the first operand. Overflow and adjust are undefined. Note that the upper half of EAX is unchanged because of the 16-bit default width.

```
14EB:010C B10A         MOV                CL,0C
EAX=00003400    EBX=00001234    ECX=0000000C
IP=010C
                                    NV UP EI PL NZ AC PE NC

14EB:010E 0FADD8       SHRD               AX,BX,CL
```

EAX = 00002343   EBX = 00001234   ECX = 0000000C
IP = 010F

                                    NV UP EI PL NZ AC **PO** NC

The 12-bit right shift from the copy of BX into AX is now completed. Flags are set as indicated above.

SLDT   Store Local Descriptor Table Register (LDTR)

INSTRUCTION   OPCODE   BINARY

SLDT r/m16   0F 00 /0   00001111 00000000 mm 000 r/m

Purpose: The Local Descriptor Table is pointed to by a selector that resides in the LDTR. SLDT stores the LDTR in the register or memory location indicated by the effective address operand.

Note: The operand-size attribute has no effect on the operation of SLDT.

Instruction Demonstration: The SLDT instruction transfers the content of the local descriptor table selector register into memory or a 16-bit register. No flags are affected.

    0070:0100 0F00C0   SLDT   AX

The registers and flags at the start are

    EAX = 00000000   IP = 0100   NV UP EI PL NZ NA PO NC

Transfer the LDT selector to AX.

    0070:0100 0F00C0   SLDT   AX
    EAX = 00000010   IP = 0103   NV UP EI PL NZ NA PO NC

Note that the selector value is in AX.

SMSW   Store Machine Status Word

INSTRUCTION   OPCODE   BINARY

SMSW r/m16   0F 01 /4   00001111 00000001 mm 100 r/m

Purpose: The Machine Status Word is part of control register zero (CR0), as shown in FIG. 10-7. SMSW stores this word in the 2-byte register or memory location indicated by the effective address operand. SMSW provides compatibility with the 80286. 80386 and 80486 programs should use MOV CR0.

Instruction Demonstration: This demonstration shows how to store the Machine Status Word. The instruction sequence is

    14EB:0100 0F01E0   SMSW   AX

The registers and flags at the start are

EAX=00000000	EP=0100	NV UP EI PL NZ NA PO NC
14EB:0101 0F01E0	SMSW	AX
EAX=0000FFE0	IP=0103	NV UP EI PL NZ NA PO NC

The machine status word part of CR0 is stored in the destination.

STC   SET Carry Flag (CF)

INSTRUCTION	OPCODE	BINARY
STC	F9	11111001

Purpose: STC sets the carry flag (CF) to one. CF is bit zero of the EFLAGS register.

Instruction Demonstration: The STC instruction is demonstrated with the CLC instruction.

STD   SET Direction Flag (DF)

INSTRUCTION	OPCODE	BINARY
STD	FD	11111101

Purpose: STD sets the direction flag (DF) to one; DF is bit 10 of EFLAGS. This causes all subsequent string operations to decrement the index register(s) SI (or ESI), DI (or EDI).

Instruction Demonstration: The STD instruction is demonstrated with the CLD instruction.

STI   SET Interrupt Flag (IF)

INSTRUCTION	OPCODE	BINARY
STI	FB	11111011

Purpose: STI sets the interrupt flag (IF) to one; IF is bit nine of the EFLAGS register. After executing the next operation, the 80486 responds to external interrupts, but only if the next instruction allows the interrupt flag to remain enabled. However, if external interrupts are disabled, code STI, RET (such as at the end of a subroutine) and RET is allowed to execute before external interrupts are recognized. Also, if external interrupts are disabled, and STI, CLI are coded, the interrupts *are not* recognized because CLI clears the interrupt flag during its execution.

If the current task has insufficient privilege to alter IF, an undefined opcode fault is generated.

Instruction Demonstration: The STI instruction is demonstrated with the CLI instruction.

STOS	Store String Data
STOSB	Store Byte
STOSW	Store Word
STOSD	Store Doubleword

INSTRUCTION	OPCODE	BINARY
STOS m8	AA	10101010
STOS m16	AB	10101011
STOS m32	AB	10101011

Purpose: These instructions operate on strings rather than on logical or numeric values. They operate on one element of a string, which could be a byte, a word, or a doubleword. The string elements are transferred from AL, AX, or EAX into ES:EDI. After each string operation, EDI is automatically updated to point to the next element of the string. If DF = zero, the index registers are incremented. If DF = one, they are decremented. The amount incremented or decremented is one, two, or four, depending on the size of the string element.

STOS can be preceded by a REP prefix, which allows a string to be filled with the contents of the accumulator register (AL, AX or EAX).

Instruction Demonstration: This demonstrates the STOS instruction as used to initialize a memory area to a fixed value. The instruction sequence is

```
14EB:0100 BF0002      MOV     DI,0200
14EB:0103 B8FF00      MOV     AX,00FF
14EB:0106 B90800      MOV     CX,0008
14EB:0109 F3          REP
14EB:010A AB          STOSW
```

The original value in memory is

```
14EB:0200   00 00 00 00 00 00 00 00-00 00 00 00 00 00 00 00
```

The registers and flags at the start are

EAX = 00000000 ECX = 00000000 EDI = 00000000   IP = 0100
                                                NV UP EI NG NZ NA PO NC

14EB:0100 BF0002   MOV   DI,0200
EAX = 00000000 ECX = 00000000 EDI = 00000200   IP = 0103
                                                NV UP EI NG NZ NA PO NC

14EB:0103 B8FF00   MOV   AX,00FF
EAX = 000000FF ECX = 00000000 EDI = 00000200   IP = 0106
                                                NV UP EI NG NZ NA PO NC

14EB:0106 B90800   MOV   CX,0008
EAX = 000000FF ECX = 00000008 EDI = 00000200   IP = 0109
                                                NV UP EI NG NZ NA PO NC

The REP prefix continues the store process until the count of items in CX has been stored. In this case, the default bus width is 16 bits, so the AF register is stored in eight sequential locations.

14EB:0109 F3   REP
14EB:010A AB   STOSW
EAX = 000000FF ECX = 00000000 EDI = 00000210   IP = 010B
                                                NV UP EI NG NZ NA PO NC

The results in memory are

14EB:0200   FF 00 FF 00 FF 00 FF 00-FF 00 FF 00 FF 00 FF 00

STR   Store Task Register

INSTRUCTION	OPCODE	BINARY
STR r/m16	0F 00 /1	00001111 00000000 mm 001 r/m

Purpose: STR copies the contents of the task register to the 2-byte register or memory location specified in the first operand. The operand-size attribute has no effect on STR.

Instruction Demonstration: This instruction transfers the content of the task register into memory or a 16-bit register. No flags are affected. The operand size attribute has no effect on the operation of STR.

    0070:0100 0F00C8   STR   AX

The registers and flags at the start are

    EAX = 00000000   IP = 0100   NV UP EI PL NZ NA PO NC

Transfer the TSS selector to AX.

```
0070:0100 0F00C8   STR        AX
EAX=00000040       IP=0103    NV UP EI PL NZ NA PO NC
```

Note that the only change is the selector value in AX.

SUB   Subtract Integers

INSTRUCTION	OPCODE	BINARY
SUB AL,imm8	2C ib	00101100
SUB AX,imm16	2D iw	00101101
SUB EAX,imm32	2D id	00101101
SUB r/m8,imm8	80 /5 ib	10000000 mm 101 r/m
SUB r/m16,imm16	81 /5 iw	10000001 mm 101 r/m
SUB r/m32,imm32	81 /5 id	10000001 mm 101 r/m
SUB r/m16,imm8	83 /5 ib	10000011 mm 101 r/m
SUB r/m32,imm8	83 /5 ib	10000011 mm 101 r/m
SUB r/m8,r8	28 /r	00101000 mm rrr r/m
SUB r/m16,r16	29 /r	00101001 mm rrr r/m
SUB r/m32,r32	29 /r	00101001 mm rrr r/m
SUB r8,r/m8	2A /r	00101010 mm rrr r/m
SUB r16,r/m16	2B /r	00101011 mm rrr r/m
SUB r32,r/m32	2B /r	00101011 mm rrr r/m

Purpose: SUB subtracts the source operand from the destination operand and then replaces the destination operand with the result. If a borrow is required, the carry flag (CF) is set; CF is bit 0 of EFLAGS. They might be signed or unsigned bytes, words, or doublewords.

Instruction Demonstration: This demonstrates the action of the integer subtract instruction. The SUB instruction is to the SBB instruction as ADD is to ADC. It ignores the value of the borrow. The instruction sequence is

```
14EB:0100 B80100   MOV    AX,0001
14EB:0103 89C3     MOV    BX,AX
14EB:0105 29D8     SUB    AX,BX
14EB:0107 29D8     SUB    AX,BX
14EB:0109 29D8     SUB    AX,BX
14EB:010B 29D8     SUB    AX,BX
```

The registers and flags at the start are

```
EAX=0000FFFF EBX=00000001   IP=0100   NV UP EI NG NZ AC PE CY
14EB:0100 B80100                       MOV        AX,0001
EAX=00000001 EBX=00000001   IP=0103   NV UP EI NG NZ AC PE CY
```

14EB:0103 89C3   MOV BX,AX

EAX = 00000001 EBX = 00000001 IP = 0105 NV UP EI NG NZ AC PE CY

 Start with a one in AX and in BX.

14EB:0105 29D8   SUB AX,BX

EAX = 00000000 EBX = 00000001 IP = 0107 NV UP EI **PL ZR NA** PE **NC**

  The first subtract results in a zero in AX. The flags are set according to the result.

14EB:0107 29D8   SUB AX,BX

EAX = 0000FFFF EBX = 00000001 IP = 0109 NV UP EI **NG NZ AC** PE **CY**

  The result is − 1. The carry flag is set because a borrow was needed. The other flags are set according to the result. AC is set because a borrow was taken from the high four bits of AL to the low four.

14EB:0109 29D8   SUB AX,BX

EAX = 0000FFFE EBX = 00000001 IP = 010B NV UP EI NG NZ **NA PO NC**

  The result is − 2. The carry flag was not included in the operation. No borrow was required so the carry flag is reset.

TEST Logical Compare

INSTRUCTION	OPCODE	BINARY
TEST AL,imm8	A8 ib	10101000
TEST AX,imm16	A9 iw	10101001
TEST EAX,imm32	A9 id	10101001
TEST r/m8,imm8	F6 /0 ib	11110110 mm 000 r/m
TEST r/m16,imm16	F7 /0 iw	11110111 mm 000 r/m
TEST r/m32,imm32	F7 /0 id	11110111 mm 000 r/m
TEST r/m8,r8	84 /r	10000100 mm rrr r/m
TEST r/m16,r16	85 /r	10000101 mm rrr r/m
TEST r/m32,r32	85 /r	10000101 mm rrr r/m

Purpose: TEST "ANDs" two operands. It then clears the overflow flag (OF) and carry flag (CF), leaves auxiliary carry (AF) undefined, and updates the sign flag (SF), zero flag (ZF), and parity flag (PF). These flags are all contained in the EFLAGS register. The flags can be tested by conditional control transfer instructions or by the byte-set-on-condition instructions.

  The difference between TEST and AND is that TEST does *not* store the result in the first operand. TEST differs from BT (bit test) in that TEST tests the value of multiple bits in one operation, while BT tests a single bit.

Instruction Demonstration: This demonstrates the TEST instruction. The instruction sequence is

```
14EB:0100 B80F0F     MOV    AX,0F0F
14EB:0103 BE0002     MOV    SI,0200
14EB:0106 29DB       SUB    BX,BX
14EB:0108 A90F00     TEST   AX,000F
14EB:010B 8504       TEST   [SI],AX
14EB:010D F7C71000   TEST   DI,0010
```

The data at SI is

```
1114EB:0200          F0 F0
```

The registers and flags at the start are

```
EAX=00000000  EBX=00000000  ESI=00000000  EDI=00000210  IP=0100
                                           NV UP EI PL NZ NA PO NC

14EB:0100 B80F0F   MOV   AX,0F0F

EAX=00000F0F  EBX=00000000  ESI=00000000  EDI=00000210  IP=0103
                                           NV UP EI PL NZ NA PO NC

14EB:0103 BE0002   MOV   SI,0200

EAX=00000F0F  EBX=00000000  ESI=00000200  EDI=00000210  IP=0106
                                           NV UP EI PL NZ NA PO NC

14EB:0106 29DB   SUB   BX,BX

EAX=00000F0F  EBX=00000000  ESI=00000200  EDI=00000210  IP=0108
                                           NV UP EI PL **ZR** NA **PE** NC

14EB:0108 A90F00   TEST   AX,000F

EAX=00000F0F  EBX=00000000  ESI=00000200  EDI=00000210  IP=010B
                                           NV UP EI PL **NZ** NA PE NC
```

This TEST "ANDs" the immediate 000F against the value in the AX register (0F0F) to get a result of 000F that is non-zero. The flags are set according to the temporary result that is then discarded. The result is positive, non-zero, and its lowbyte has even parity. In all cases, the carry and overflow flags are forced to zero.

```
14EB:010B 8504   TEST   [S1],AX DS:0200=F0F0

EAX=00000F0F  EBX=00000000  ESI=00000200  EDI=00000210  IP=010D
                                           NV UP EI PL **ZR** NA PE NC
```

This TEST "ANDs" the value at [SI] (F0F0) against the value in AX (0F0F) to get a zero result. The flags are set accordingly.

14EB:010D F7C71000   TEST   DI,0010
EAX=00000F0F EBX=00000000 ESI=00000200 EDI=00000210 IP=0111
                                         NV UP EI PL **NZ** NA **PO** NC

This TEST "ANDs" the value in DI (0210) against the immediate value (0010) to get a result of 0010. The flags are set according to the temporary result.

VERR   Verify a Segment for Reading
VERW   Verify a Segment for Writing

INSTRUCTION   OPCODE   BINARY
VERR r/m16   0F 00 /4   00001111 00000000 mm 100 r/m
VERW r/m16   0F 00 /5   00001111 00000000 mm 101 r/m

Purpose: These instructions verify whether a segment noted by the selector can be reached with the current privilege level (CPL) and if the segment is readable. If the segment is accessible, the zero flag (ZF) is set to one. If not, ZF is set to zero. The validation done is the same as if the segment were loaded into DS, ES, FS, or GS and the indicated read was performed.

Because ZF receives the result of the validation, the selector's value does not result in a protection exception. Thus, software can anticipate possible segment access problems.

Instruction Demonstration: The VERR and VERW instructions test whether the issuing program can use the descriptor for the indicated selector for reading or writing data respectively. If the tested access is valid, the zero flag is set; otherwise it is reset.

```
0070:0100 B87000   MOV    AX,0070
0070:0103 09C0     OR     AX,AX
0070:0105 0F00E0   VERR   AX
0070:0108 0F00E8   VERW   AX
EAX=00000000 CS=0070   IP=0100   NV UP EI PL NZ NA PO NC
```

Load a selector into AX for testing. (The selector could also reside in memory.)

```
0070:0100 B87000        MOV    AX,0070
EAX=00000070 CS=0070    IP=0103   NV UP EI PL NZ NA PO NC
0070:0103 09C0          OR     AX,AX
```

The OR ensures that the zero flag is not set.

    EAX=00000070 CS=0070   IP=0105   NV UP EI PL NZ NA PO NC

Use the VERR to check if you have the authority to read the segment.

    0070:0105 0F00E0   VERR   AX
    EAX=00000070 CS=0070   IP=0108   NV UP EI PL **ZR** NA PO NC

The resulting setting of the zero flag indicates that you can read the segment (the code segment). Use the VERW to check if you have authority to write the segment.

    0070:0108 0F00E8   VERW   AX
    EAX=00000070 CS=0070   IP=010B   NV UP EI PL **NZ** NA PO NC

The resulting setting of the zero flag (NZ) indicates that you cannot write the segment (the code segment).

    xx (access flag)
    Descriptor 0070 = FF FF 00 AB 01 9B 0F 00

The access flag indicates present, code, readable, non-conforming, and accessed.

WAIT   Wait

INSTRUCTION	OPCODE	BINARY
WBINVD	9B	10011011

Purpose: WAIT causes the 80486 to check for pending unmasked numeric exceptions before proceeding. Coding WAIT after an ESC instruction ensures that any unmasked floating-point exceptions the instruction may cause are handled before the processor has a chance to modify the instruction's results.

FWAIT is an alternate mnemonic for WAIT.

Instruction Demonstration: Not demonstrated.

WBINVD   Write-Back and Invalidate Cache

INSTRUCTION	OPCODE	BINARY
WBINVD	0F 09	00001111 00001001

Purpose: WBINVD flushes the internal cache of the 80486 and issues a special-function bus cycle to indicate that external cache should write-back its contents to main memory. It then issues another special-function bus cycle, directing the external cache to flush itself. WBINVD affects no flags.

This instruction is new with the 80486.

Note: See also the INVD (Invalidate Data Cache) instruction.

Instruction Demonstration: Not demonstrated.

XADD   Exchange and Add

INSTRUCTION	OPCODE	BINARY
XADD r/m8,r8	OF C0 /r	00001111 11000000 mm rrr r/m
XADD r/m16,r16	OF C1 /r	00001111 11000001 mm rrr r/m
XADD r/m32,r32	OF C1 /r	00001111 11000001 mm rrr r/m

Purpose: XADD loads the destination operand into the source and then adds the destination operand and the original source, putting the sum into the destination. XADD sets the carry flag (CF—bit 0 of EFLAGS) if there is an overflow.

This instruction is new with the 80486.

Instruction Demonstration: Not demonstrated.

XCHG   Exchange Register/Memory with Register

INSTRUCTION	OPCODE	BINARY
XCHG AX,r16	90 + r	10010rrr
XCHG r16,AX	90 + r	10010rrr
XCHG EAX,r32	90 + r	10010rrr
XCHG r32,EAX	90 + r	10010rrr
XCHG r/m8,r8	86 /r	10000110 mm rrr r/m
XCHG r8,r/m8	86 /r	10000110 mm rrr r/m
XCHG r/m16,r16	87 /r	10000111 mm rrr r/m
XCHG r16,r/m16	87 /r	10000111 mm rrr r/m
XCHG r/m32,r32	87 /r	10000111 mm rrr r/m
XCHG r32,r/m32	87 /r	10000111 mm rrr r/m

Note:"XCHG, AX,AX" is a NOP.

Purpose: XCHG swaps the contents of two operands and takes the place of three MOV instructions. It does not require a temporary location to save the contents of one operand while loading the other. XCHG is useful for implementing semaphores or similar data structures for process synchronization.

If one of the operands is memory, the bus transfer is always performed as if a LOCK prefix is given, even if LOCK was not specified.

Instruction Demonstration: This demonstrates the exchange instruction XCHG. The instruction sequence is

```
14EB:0100 93            XCHG   AX,BX
14EB:0101 87F0          XCHG   SI,AX
14EB:0103 871E0002      XCHG   BX,[0200]
14EB:0107 871E0002      XCHG   BX,[0200]
```

The registers and flags at the start are

EAX=00000200 EBX=00000F0F ESI=00000000 IP=0100
                              NV UP EI PL NZ NA PO NC

```
14EB:0100 93            XCHG            AX,BX
```
EAX=00000F0F EBX=00000200 ESI=00000000 IP=0101
                              NV UP EI PL NZ NA PO NC

The values in AX and BX have been exchanged.

```
14EB:0101 87F0          XCHG            SI,AX
```
EAX=00000000 EBX=00000200 ESI=00000F0F IP=0103
                              NV UP EI PL NZ NA PO NC

The values in SI and AX are exchanged.

```
14EB:0103 871E0002      XCHG            BX,[0200] DS:0200=0000
```
EAX=00000000 EBX=00000000 ESI=00000F0F IP=0107
                              NV UP EI PL NZ NA PO NC

The value in BX is exchanged with the value at DS:0200.

```
14EB:0107 871E0002      XCHG            BX,[0200] DS:0200=0200
```
EAX=00000000 EBX=00000200 ESI=00000F0F IP=010B
                              NV UP EI PL NZ NA PO NC

Exchange again and the BX value is restored. Note that the exchange instruction does not affect the flags.

XLAT   Table Lookup-Translation
XLATB

INSTRUCTION	OPCODE	BINARY
XLAT m8	D7	11010111

Purpose: XLAT is useful for translating from one coding system to another, such as from EBCDIC to ASCII. The translate table can be up to 256 bytes long. The value placed in AL serves as an index to the location of the corresponding translation value.

XLAT replaces a byte in AL with a byte from a user-coded translation table at [EBX + AL]. AL is always an unsigned value. When XLAT is executed, AL should have the unsigned index to the table addressed by EBX. XLAT changes the contents of AL from the table index to the table entry. EBX is unchanged.

The table is always based at EBX, regardless of the m8. However, m8 does allow a segment override to be specified rather than the default DS:EBX.

Instruction Demonstration: This demonstrates the XLAT instruction. The instruction sequence is

```
14EB:0100 BB0002        MOV     BX,0200
14EB:0103 B80500        MOV     AX,0005
14EB:0106 D7            XLAT
14EB:0107 D7            XLAT
```

The data at DS:0200 is

14EB:0200   FF FF FF 0F 04 03 02 01-00 00 FF 00 FF 00 FF 00

The registers and flags at the start are

EAX = 000000FF EBX = 00000000   IP = 0100   NV UP EI PL NZ NA PO NC

You must set the address displacement of the translate table into BX.

14EB:0100 BB0002   MOV   BX,0200

EAX = 000000FF EBX = 00000200   IP = 0103   NV UP EI PL NZ NA PO NC

The byte to translate must be in AL.

14EB:0103 B80500   MOV   AX,0005

EAX = 00000005 EBX = 00000200   IP = 0106   NV UP EI PL NZ NA PO NC

14EB:0106 D7   XLAT

EAX = 00000003 EBX = 00000200   IP = 0107   NV UP EI PL NZ NA PO NC

The XLAT instruction replaces the byte in AL with the byte fetched from DS:BX + AL. In this case, the byte at DS:0205 was 03.

14EB:0107 D7   XLAT

EAX = 0000000F EBX = 00000200   IP = 0108   NV UP EI PL NZ NA PO NC

In this case, the byte at DS:0203 is fetched (DS:BX + AL). Note that no flags are affected.

XOR — Logical, Exclusive OR

INSTRUCTION	OPCODE	BINARY
XOR AL,imm8	34 ib	00110100
XOR AX,imm16	35 iw	00110101
XOR EAX,imm32	35 id	00110101
XOR r/m8,imm8	80 /6 ib	10000000 mm 110 r/m
XOR r/m16,imm16	81 /6 iw	10000001 mm 110 r/m
XOR r/m32,imm32	81 /6 id	10000001 mm 110 r/m
XOR r/m16,imm8	83 /6 ib	10000011 mm 110 r/m
XOR r/m32,imm8	83 /6 ib	10000011 mm 110 r/m
XOR r/m8,r8	30 /r	00110000 mm rrr r/m
XOR r/m16,r16	31 /r	00110001 mm rrr r/m
XOR r/m32,r32	31 /r	00110001 mm rrr r/m
XOR r8,r/m8	32 /r	00110010 mm rrr r/m
XOR r16,r/m16	33 /r	00110011 mm rrr r/m
XOR r32,r/m32	33 /r	00110011 mm rrr r/m

Purpose: XOR compares the bits in its two operands and stores the result into the first operand. Each bit of the result is one if the corresponding bits in the operands are *different*. Each bit is zero if the corresponding bits are the same. The result replaces the first operand.

    Operand 1   110001
    Operand 2   001101
    Result   111100

Instruction Demonstration: This demonstrates the XOR instruction. The XOR instruction computes the exclusive OR of the two operands. On a bit-by-bit basis, the result is computed as R = (A or B) and not (A and B). The instruction sequence is

    14EB:0100 B8FF0F   MOV   AX,0FFF
    14EB:0103 350FF0   XOR   AX,F00F

The registers and flags at the start are

    EAX=0000000F   IP=0100   NV UP EI PL NZ NA PO NC
    14EB:0100 B8FF0F   MOV   AX,0FFF
    EAX=00000FFF   IP=0103   NV UP EI PL NZ NA PO NC
    14EB:0103 350FF0   XOR   AX,F00F
    EAX=0000FFF0   IP=0106   NV UP EI **NG** NZ NA **PE** NC

The XOR produces the exclusive or in the destination. The flags are set according to the result for the sign, zero, and parity. Carry and overflow are forced to zeros. The adjust flag is undefined.

11

Introduction to Integrated Circuits (IC)

The electronics industry created another major evolution with the introduction of a 32-bit chip that enables desktop computers to enter the virtual system world. And in no other industry is the maxim "the future depends on the past" as much a keystone as in the data processing and electronics industries. To understand where it's all going, let's first take a look at what's already been done in the general electronics and integrated circuit technology.

To make a useful system, microprocessors interconnect with the various components that make up a microcomputer. This interconnection has to take into account the nature and timing of the signals generated and expected by each component. There are three classes of signals: data, address, and control. Obviously, those signals must travel from one component to another. That process is called *interfacing*. Chapter 12 overviews the processes of interfacing.

Information can be saved in various ways, but think of memory as the channel that allows data to be retained for future use. Thousands of 1-bit registers can be incorporated into a single integrated circuit (an IC), and share a common set of inputs, a common set of outputs, and a single clock line. This entity is referred to as a *memory* chip. Chapter 13 details memory and its management, and Chapter 4 discusses how the 80486 handles memory.

Computer speeds are determined by three basic limitations. One concerns hardware—that is, how fast gates switch, and how many inches of wire or board must a signal traverse. The second limitation concerns the logic of the interaction of machine design and organization. The third looks at how effectively the operating system uses the hardware design. Chapter 14 addresses these last two.

To better understand the current generation of Intel chips, take a look at Appendix A, which discusses the previous Intel chips—in the same family—to determine what design decisions and directions influenced the basic design of the 80486.

In the beginning

The leap-forward progress in electronics was made possible when early researchers built upon Thomas Edison's discoveries. Edison noticed that when he placed an isolated metal plate in his evacuated light bulb, he got a shock when he then touched a wire lead that was attached to it. This shock occurred because the metal plate was collecting electrons being emitted by the lamp filament. Edison's discovery was important for the later development of vacuum tubes.

Around 1904, J. Ambrose Flemming expanded on Edison's concept and discovered the two-element vacuum tube: the *diode*. The vacuum tubes were about 6 inches long and 1.5 inches in diameter. These high-cost tubes were inefficient glass bottles and were used in early radio receivers to introduce the age of radio.

In 1948, J. Bardeen and W.H. Brattain of the Bell Telephone Laboratories invented the transistor. The name *transistor* is derived from *trans*fer *resistor*. That first transistor came to life when two sharply-pointed metal needles were placed in contact with the surface of a piece of germanium. When one of these needles was forward biased with respect to the germanium n-type *base* wafer, holes were injected into the wafer. The name *base* remains for this transistor lead. The second needle was spaced close to the first and was reverse biased with respect to the base wafer. This second needle collected a large portion of the injected holes: this is transistor action.

These original needles were too fragile for high-quantity commercial manufacture and use. In 1949, William Shockley, also of Bell Laboratories, introduced the idea for the completely solid structure of the junction transistor. This breakthrough began the transistor era, in the 1950s.

The transistor is small and energy efficient. Nothing has to be heated to provide a source of current carriers. In addition, high voltages that were once required to drive the huge vacuum tubes are no longer needed. Relatively small voltages can be used because of the short travel distance due to the extremely small spacings between the different regions of a transistor. The continued reduction in spacing is the reason that the industry is expected to reduce the value of the present, standard, logic 5-volt power supply voltage. Even 5V is too high for the small transistors in the upcoming VLSIs.

As a historical note: to emphasize the low power requirements of the early transistors, a couple of wires were stuck into a lemon to demonstrate the simplest germanium transistor circuits. The electrolysis taking place created enough electrical power for the circuit to operate.

The early transistors were the point-contact type, with two thin wires or "whiskers" welded on a semiconductor block to form two junctions. This construction had good response for high frequencies but was limited in power dissipation. Practical consumer usage came next.

The first electronic calculator was introduced in 1963 by a British firm, the Bell Punch Company. That calculator was made of discrete transistors and was about the size of a cash register. Four years later, Texas Instruments came out with their first *Integrated Circuits* (IC) calculator, and the rush to miniaturization was on.

What is an IC made of?

All the materials we know contain two basic particles of electric charge, the *electron* and the *proton*. An electron is the smallest amount of electrical charge having the characteristic called *negative polarity*. The proton has a *positive polarity*. It is the arrangement of electrons and protons as basic particles that determines the electrical characteristics of a substance.

When electrons move easily from atom to atom within a substance, that substance is called a *conductor*. In general, metals are good conductors, with silver the best and copper second, because metal's atomic structure allows free movement of the electrons.

An IC is a small piece of silicon engineered (by a process like contact printing) to manipulate the positive and negative electrical signals. The IC generally looks like a dull fleck of aluminum, and is about the size of a baby's fingernail.

The major physical ingredient of an IC is silicon, the second most abundant substance on earth. As another historical note, the element *Si* (silicon) was discovered in 1823. Silicon is a *semiconductor*; it is a type of solid whose ability to conduct electricity is reasonably good, somewhere between copper (good) and rubber (poor). A semiconductor's ability to conduct electricity can be increased by adding impurity elements, a process called *doping*.

The purpose of doping is to inject free charges that can be moved easily by an applied voltage. These added charge carriers can be either negative or positive, depending on the doping. When electrons are added, the doped semiconductor is negative, or *N-Type*. A lack of electrons makes the material positive, or *P-Type*. Doping increases the conductance of the material by a factor of 10 to 50 times. Pure semiconductor without doping is *intrinsic*. The doping results in *extrinsic* semiconductor.

The IC is fabricated by extending previous semiconductor manufacturing processes to include a large number of transistors, diodes, and resistors on a common substrate. The circuit elements are formed on a single substrate of silicon by a technique that involves a combination of photo lithography, diffusion, heating and baking, vaporizing and depositing, and ion implantation. On each silicon slice, the same circuits may be repeated a large number of times, a definite savings in manufacturing costs and processing. For instance, a silicon-substrate chip less than a quarter of an inch on an edge can contain well over 250,000 semiconductor components. See FIG. 11-1.

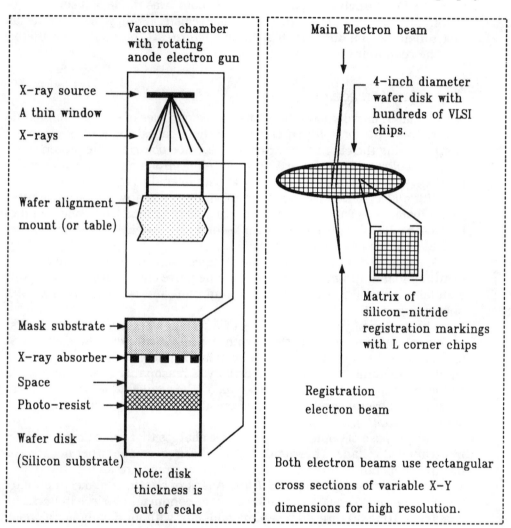

X–ray Lithography

Vacuum chamber with rotating anode electron gun

X-ray source
A thin window
X-rays

Wafer alignment mount (or table)

Mask substrate
X-ray absorber
Space
Photo-resist
Wafer disk
(Silicon substrate)

Note: disk thickness is out of scale

Electron–beam Lithography

Main Electron beam

4–inch diameter wafer disk with hundreds of VLSI chips.

Matrix of silicon–nitride registration markings with L corner chips

Registration electron beam

Both electron beams use rectangular cross sections of variable X–Y dimensions for high resolution.

11-1 Forming a silicon chip.

To reduce the handling costs of each IC chip, the original 3/4 inch (19 mm) diameter wafers that were used for the early ICs were quickly increased to 1.5 inches (38 mm). In 1971, 3 inch (76 mm) wafers were introduced to the IC fabrication lines. The 3 inch wafers continued in high volume production until the first part of 1980, when 4 inch (100 mm) wafers took over. Then, late 1982, 5 inch (125 mm) wafers went into production.

By the end of 1983, 6 inch wafers (150 mm) were rolling off the production lines and 8 inch were coming fast. The 8 inch wafers are so large that holes had to be drilled in the center to relieve film stresses created during fabrication. The consumption of silicon wafers in the United States alone exceeds 70 million per year. Piled on top of each other, they'd make a stack some 15 miles high.

An integrated circuit is made up of transistors. In general, transistors have two different applications. The first is in analog devices such as radios, televisions, and the like. In this application, the transistor serves primarily as an amplifier. The second application is in digital usages, such as computers, calculators, and such units. The transistors function here as switches, turning on and off millions of times a second.

A *Field-Effect Transistor* (FET) is a semiconductor device in which the resistance between two terminals is controlled by the voltage on a third terminal. One form of FET, referred to as a *Metal Oxide Semiconductor Field-Effect Transistor* (MOSFET), is constructed from a piece of lightly doped semiconductor material (called a substrate) upon which are formed two regions of the opposite type of semiconductor material. One of these regions is called a *source* because charge carriers originate from it. The other region is called a *drain* because charge carriers terminate at it.

The region of semiconductor material lying between the source and the drain is called the *channel*. Above the channel is a metal electrode called the *gate*, lying along the entire length of the channel and separated from it by a layer of insulation. The name for this type of FET comes from the metal gate, oxide insulation, and semiconductor substrate.

PMOS and NMOS

Several logic families are based on the field-effect transistor. Two well-known ones are NMOS, which designates that the N-channel MOSFETs are used, and PMOS, which says that P-channel MOSFETs are used. MOS material is doped so that it is either N-type or P-type. To obtain the N-type, the doping elements of arsenic, antimony, and phosphorous are used. For the P-type, aluminum, gallium, boron, and iridium are used.

A bipolar device is a semiconductor in which there are both minority and majority carriers present (i.e., it is a current-driven device). Bipolar fabrication generally requires 12 masking steps and 4 diffusion steps. The early PMOS wafers required fewer processing steps than were needed for bipolar fabrication. This simplicity allowed acceptable yields for more complex logic chips. Thus, it was PMOS that allowed the LSI circuit chips to be brought to the marketplace in the early to mid-1970s. Today, PMOS is essentially obsolete and few products are kept in production.

During this time, the technologists learned more about the physics of the silicon surface, and there was now strong motivation to develop the NMOS process to take advantage of the 3:1 performance benefits of the N-channel transistor over the P-channel transistor.

The NMOS circuits are faster than the PMOS, in addition to containing more transistors. Both PMOS and NMOS operate in enhancement mode. Enhancement mode simply means that an applied voltage enhances the number of charge carriers in the channel between the source and drain.

CMOS

A third, well known MOSFET is *Complementary Metal Oxide Semiconductor*, CMOS. The CMOS has both P-channel and N-channel MOSFETs in the same circuit. A CMOS logic gate consists of two portions: one pulls down the gate output for the correct input conditions, and the other pulls up the gate output for other input conditions.

CMOS logic is more complex than either NMOS or PMOS, and is, therefore, not capable of achieving gate densities as high as the other two. Its structure, however, does offer an advantage over all other common forms of logic. There is never a conductive path in the steady state between ground and power-supply voltage. Therefore, no discernible power is consumed during times in which the inputs are constant.

This different handling of power consumption is of great importance for applications that involve power supplied from batteries. Power is consumed during switching for two major reasons. The first is that there are capacitances throughout the circuit, primarily between the electrodes of the MOSFETs. A capacitance is the property that allows the storage of electrically separate charges when a potential difference exists between conductors. This capacitance must be charged each time a gate is switched. The second reason is that both the pull-up and pull-down portions of a logic gate are partially on during the transition from input signals. As a result, current momentarily flows from the power-supply voltage to ground.

The added processing steps that were required for a CMOS IC raised the fabricating cost of the CMOS wafer; this cost was passed along to users.

See FIG. 11-2 for a comparison of PMOS, NMOS, and CMOS.

Very Large-Scale Integration (VLSI)

When looking at gates on a chip, the number of gates fall into four categories: *Small-Scale Integration* (SSI), *Medium-Scale Integration* (MSI), *Large-Scale Integration* (LSI), and *Very Large-Scale Integration* (VLSI). From one to four gates, the IC is called an SSI. From four to 100 gates, it's called an MSI. At the 100-gate threshold, the chip is called LSI. Once the number of gates soars past 20,000, it's called a VLSI chip. Some VLSI chips hold as many as 250,000 gates.

Advanced high-density N-channel silicon-gate MOS technology (HMOS) has a potential of getting more and more gates onto a single chip. This

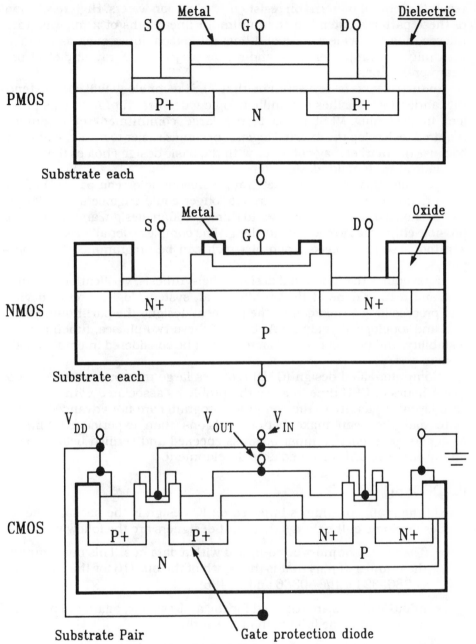

11-2 Comparison of PMOS, NMOS, and CMOS.

shrinking of IC patterns brings forward the possibility of increasing switching speeds and reducing the chip's power consumption.

VLSI technology became established because of the capability of IC manufacturers to make uncontaminated and accurate exposures of high-resolution circuit patterns on resist-covered silicon wafers. High resolution of these patterns extend to the minimum line-widths of 2 microns to 1 micron, due to a wide variety of lithographic techniques such as contact, proximity, 1:1 projection, step-and-repeat projection, X-ray, and electron-beam projections.

Industry experts now estimate that VLSI technology will soon extend the fabrication densities to a million logic gates per chip. A serious problem in designing VLSI chips is the large commitment of resources required to develop the internal logic. It becomes easier to miss the market because the market may not agree with the basic design choices that must be made at each major design step.

To avoid this missed-market trap, semiconductor companies had to learn to do business in a new way. No longer could engineers and design technicians use manual processes to think through, design, and then test a possible chip—that would take too long. The complex over-all design is broken into a series of tasks, each of which can be programmed into computers.

First comes the functional design—the synthesis, verification, simulation and testing done at the architectural, system, logic, circuit, device and process levels. Next comes the physical design—the partitioning, layout, and topological analysis. At both of these two phases, functionality, testability, and physical design factors must be considered in parallel with design.

Computer-aided design (CAD) requires large memory resources and many hours of CPU time to solve the problems associated with complex chip layout. In addition, the computer programs are not advanced to the state that they can make better decisions than experienced human designers, so each step must be cross-checked and verified before going on. Regardless, CAD has sped chip development.

IC packaging

One of the main constraints imposed on IC design is the package the IC resides in. Some of the things that limit designers are the following:

- The processor must be equipped with a data bus. This bus requires the number of pins that is the width of the bus (16 for the 8086 and 80286, 32 for the 80386 and 80486).

- Additional pins are required for the address bus, again the number of bits that is the full width of the address.

- Two pins are needed for power and ground.

- Tradeoff the number of pins for complexity like memory chips RAS /CAS.

- Finally, it requires at least two pins, sometimes four, for connection to an external clock.

In addition to those five points, some number of pins are an absolute minimum for synchronization with external events. In practice, this means that 32-bit microprocessors *cannot* be implemented in 40-pin packages. Note the pin layout of the 80486 as shown in Chapter 7.

Another constraint is due to the technological limitation of the amount of chip area (or real estate as it's often called) that can be economically implemented at any time. Designers realize they want to implement as many functions as possible.

The new gate array products have forced the IC industry to find ways to package high lead count—68 and greater. A combination of both insertion and surface mount packages are appearing, and both are available in ceramic for military applications and plastic for industrial and consumer applications.

A high density package is the *pin grid array* (PGA). The PGA looks like a square bed of nails (see FIG. 11-3). It uses a ceramic substrate, has 0.09 inch pin spacings, excellent thermal characteristics, and provides for very high density.

Traditional silicon processing is racing to its final, physical limits. Practical re-considerations are needed, for instance, in the reduced reliability that results from extensive device size reduction. There's also the limited economic resources that are made available to provide the necessary computer-based tools; only an extremely limited number of program-

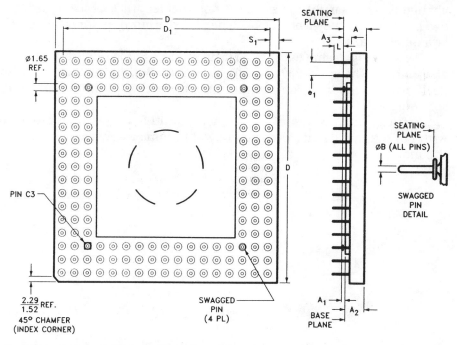

11-3 168 lead ceramic PGA package dimensions. Reprinted by permission of Intel Corporation, © Intel Corporation 1990.

Family: Ceramic Pin Grid Array Package						
Symbol	Millimeters			Inches		
	Min	Max	Notes	Min	Max	Notes
A	3.56	4.57		0.140	0.180	
A_1	0.64	1.14	SOLID LID	0.025	0.045	SOLID LID
A_2	23	0.30	SOLID LID	0.110	0.140	SOLID LID
A_3	1.14	1.40		0.045	0.055	
B	0.43	0.51		0.017	0.020	
D	44.07	44.83		1.735	1.765	
D_1	40.51	40.77		1.595	1.605	
e_1	2.29	2.79		0.090	0.110	
L	2.54	3.30		0.100	0.130	
N	168			168		
S_1	1.52	2.54		0.060	0.100	
ISSUE	IWS REV X 7/15/88					

11-3 Continued.

mers understand the CAD requirements thoroughly enough to program solutions. Also, there's the increased cost and reduced throughput of the new VLSI fabrication equipment.

Many observers are concerned that a move away from the 5V standard power supply voltage will meet with stiff opposition—even though this change is necessary if the smallest channel-length transistors are to be used. Too much, they feel, has been designed around 5V for either an easy or a quick change.

We are progressing to the SLSI (Super Large-Scale Integration). We are also entering the era of distributed processing. Within the microprocessor itself, each of the input/output and peripheral chips will become processor-equipped.

From a human and social standpoint, multi-function microprocessors with built-in intelligence predictably will become as common as the electric motor is today.

12
Interfacing concepts

To be a useful system, a microprocessor must connect with the various components that make up a microcomputer. This interconnection has to take into account the nature and timing of signals generated and expected by each component.

There are three classes of signals: data, address, and control. From the viewpoint of the CPU, the signals are bidirectional (both input and output) for data and control, and output only for addresses. Obviously, those signals must travel from one component to another and exchange information and data. That process is called *interfacing*.

To get signals from one component to another, supplementary circuits must be designed and choose appropriate components chosen.

Interfacing

Computers have two basic methods of interfacing: hardware and software. In practice, most designers use a combination of the two. A software interface has two major parameters: the time required for its execution, and the memory required to store it. Take care to avoid creating software bottlenecks. For instance, if a software interface spends too much time executing a complex I/O routine, the I/O routine may leave too little time for another necessary computation.

Hardware is suited to interface those signals sent and received for control of time-critical, fixed-logic operations such as collecting bit strings from serial devices. Instead of looping to collect and shift each bit to form a byte, the system program can handle interrupt requests which come from hardware signals to read a byte at a time. However, remember that hardware is more difficult to design and check than software. Figure 12-1 shows

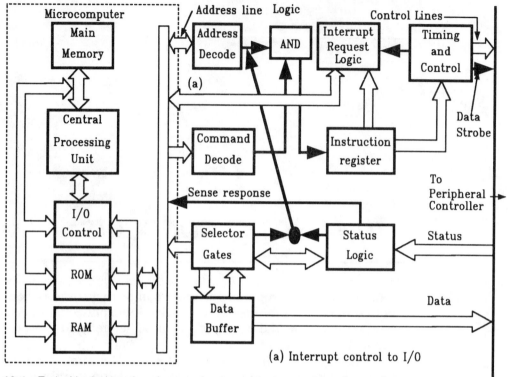

12-1 Typical logical interface from a microprocessor to a peripheral controller.

a block diagram of a typical interface between a processor and a peripheral controller.

Levels

Interfacing can be described at several levels: mechanical, electrical, functional (processor to peripheral), and user (peripheral to processor).

The mechanical interface concerns the physical characteristics of the connection between two devices or subsystems, which may take the form of a connector plug having a certain size and shape with a given number of pins. Electrical interfacing refers to the definition of the electrical signals on each of the pins, which includes the voltage level and the specific function of the electrical signal on the pins.

Functional interfacing refers to the rules or protocol for sending signals over the connection, including the specific sequence of signals generated by both devices that define the purpose of the communication.

The user interface level involves the meaning of the information or data being conveyed from one device to another. This meaning may be defined within the context of a particular operating system or application program. An example is a series of bits that is interpreted as "job is finished." The meaning may be defined by the device, such as a bit pattern indicating I/O error types.

Register

An essential component of any processor/device interface is a register to store data being transmitted to or from the processor. The register acts as temporary or buffer store so that information can be interchanged efficiently between the processor and devices which may have very different rates of information flow. Without this temporary storage, the faster of the two (usually the processor) would spend most of its time waiting until the slow one finishes.

Information may be stored as a byte, a word, a doubleword, or a number of words. The largest amount is probably that incorporated in some visual display units. Because the picture must be "refreshed" or re-presented on the Video Display Unit (VDU) 10 to 20 times each second, the entire body of information presented must be read out at the same rate. Often, to avoid monopolizing the processor, display units incorporate a store holding several thousand bytes that contain the display information.

A frequent requirement in interfacing design is a register with interstage connections arranged so that an external pulse can increase or decrease the register contents by one—in other words, a *counter*. A typical application for a counter is in the interface for a block data transfer where it checks the progress of the transfer. The counter is first loaded with the number of words to be transferred. A pulse is fed to it for each word transferred, thus decreasing the contents by one. The transfer operation is complete when the number stored in the counter falls to zero.

Another use for a counter is as an interval timer. The counter is decremented by the system clock, which allows a program to load an interval to be counted down.

Buffer

An issue in buffer interfacing is optimizing buffer space to keep the system coordinated. In essence, the CPU and the rest of the circuitry must be balanced so that the best throughput is achieved. For example, interrupts should be trapped and prioritized before being allowed to stop CPU processing; then the CPU should turn to interrupt handling software that needs to be quickly available.

To eliminate interface problems, many manufacturers developed special interfacing chips that correspond to individual devices. These interface chips provide all necessary logic circuits for a general-purpose interface and are identified to the processor by use of address select lines externally wired to specify the address of the subject chip.

Peripherals

Special instructions and control signals are provided for testing the status of peripheral devices and for transferring data to and from these devices. Three basic forms of communication handle this testing and transfer between processors and their outside world: programmed data transfers, direct memory access (DMA), and interrupts.

Peripherals may be wired to the computer's buses using the same control signals used to control memory. By using these signals, the peripheral is interfaced to the processor using *memory-mapped I/O* techniques. To communicate with the peripheral, the processor executes a memory-reference instruction so that the memory control signals are generated.

If the processor needs the data, the peripheral places information onto the data bus so that the processor can read it. If the processor is writing data, the peripheral takes the information off the bus. Peripherals may also be addressed using an address space set aside for that purpose. The addresses in this I/O space are known as I/O ports. There are special IN and OUT instructions for communicating with I/O ports.

Memory

Memory in a microcomputer is an array of storage locations for data and program instructions. There are many possible memory devices. There is a mixture of random-access memory (RAM), or certain memory-mapped devices such as I/O ports, digital-to-analog (D/A) devices, analog-to-digital (A/D) converters, and so on. The basic control signals that apply to memory operations are some form of memory request, memory write, and memory read.

The simplest arrangement is a single digital output that switches some device on or off. This consists of a single-digit store set or cleared by programs. Because how one of these stores settles when the power is first switched on is usually random, the computer normally sets all such circuits—internal and external—to a known state before starting computation.

A slightly more complex interface is used for a digital-to-analog converter. In its simplest form, this arrangement produces an output that varies in voltage, depending on what number is sent to it. Each output voltage remains until a different number is received by the device. For this interface, data is gated from the data lines into an interface register under program control. The register holds the number until the next one overwrites it. If several analog outputs are required, a multiplexer may be connected to the converter output, enabling it to energize several different circuits.

Often, a computer requires an analog-to-digital process. In other words, the computer samples an analog voltage occurring outside the computer and converts its value to a digital representation. Some care is required when doing this. The time taken to do the conversion with an accuracy of 10-12 binary digits may be many machine cycles, say 30 to 50 microseconds. Thus, once having started the process of conversion, the computer must wait before trying to transfer the contents of the converter buffer register into the accumulator.

Some analog-to-digital converters can be switched to provide a range of different output word sizes, the smaller sizes giving a less accurate but quicker result. Thus, it is possible to program or manually select the most suitable combination of speed and accuracy for each application. In such cases, no advantage is obtained unless the program delay is adjusted automatically to be just in excess of the conversion time. Generally, some single-digit flag bit is set to signal the end of the conversion.

Buses

A *bus* is a data path shared by the units of a system. It may be a number of lines etched on a printed circuit board, soldered wires between connectors into which circuit board modules are placed, or ribbon cable. The components of the computer system are physically packaged on one or more printed circuit boards, the number and type of functions supplied vary with the system, the manufacturer, and often by the generation of the chip.

Information travels over the bus in the form of groups of bits. A bus may have a separate line to accommodate each bit of a word (a parallel bus), or it may have a single line that is shared in time by all bits of a word (a serial bus). Figure 12-2 shows a typical data bus arrangement.

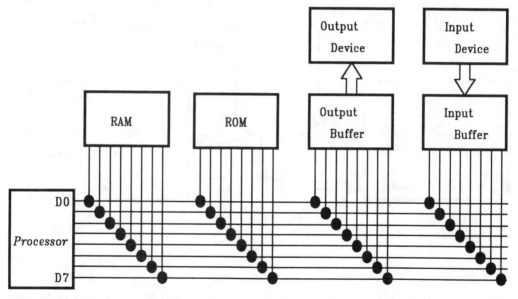

12-2 Typical data bus arrangement.

Three-state bus

A three-state bus is like a telephone party line, with many callers connected. The three states are High, Low, and High Impedance, which prevents the device/chip from affecting the state being presented by other devices/chips connected to the bus. Thus, only one device drives the bus. The control logic chooses only one driver (talker) to be active at any one time. When the driver is enabled, its data is placed on the bus and all other drivers are disabled.

There can be many listeners on the bus. In general, data on the bus is intended for only one of them, identified by a combination of control and address signals. The control logic generates signals (data strobes) to tell the listener when to receive the data. The talkers/listeners can be either unidirectional (able to be talker only *or* listener only) or bi-directional (able to be both). Figure 12-3 shows bi-directional talkers/listeners connected to bus lines.

The bus structure approach to design is popular because it uses a standard interfacing discipline for all devices. In general, standard architecture design calls for connecting the CPU modules and I/O through a set of three buses.

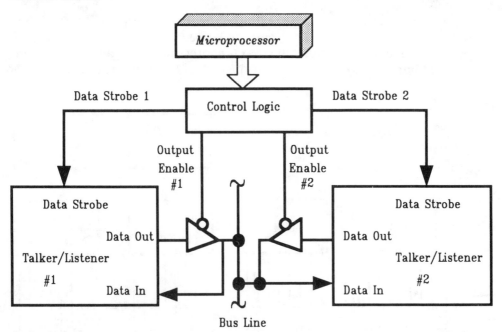

12-3 Bi-directional talker/listener connected to bus lines.

Bus types

The three buses that interface to the CPU are the *data bus*, the *address bus*, and the *control bus*. Data travels over the data bus between either the

CPU and memory or the CPU and I/O devices. This data can be either instructions for the CPU or information that the CPU is passing to or from I/O ports. In the 8088, the data bus is 8 bits wide. In the 8086, 80186, and 80286, it is 16 bits wide. In the 80386 and 80486, it is 32 bits wide.

The CPU uses the address bus to select the desired memory or I/O device by providing a unique address corresponding to one of the memory locations or I/O elements of the system. Finally, the control bus carries control signals to the memory and I/O devices, specifying whether data is to go into or out of the CPU, and exactly when the data is being transferred.

Most buses have a control module that acts as traffic director in the data exchange. The main purpose of the control module is to cause a word to be transferred between two other modules.

General operation

A bus system begins operating when the control module places a sending module's code word onto the bus and activates the Sender strobe line. This causes the module whose code word is on the bus to realize that it is the sender. The control module then places the receiving module's code word onto the bus and activates the Receiver strobe line, which causes the module whose code word is now on the bus to realize that it is the receiver.

The control module then activates the data strobe line, causing the contents of the sender's register to be transferred to the receiver's register. This step can be repeated for any additional data words to be transferred between the two modules.

Data is transferred between the sender and receiver in response to a pulse on the appropriate strobe line from the control module. Transference requires that, at the time of the strobe pulse, the sender module has data available and the receiver module is ready to accept the data. This is called *synchronous* (synchronized) transfer of data.

What happens if one or both the sender and receiver modules sends /accepts data only under certain conditions? The bus can be operated in asynchronous (unsynchronized) fashion. The transfer of data between a sender and receiver module could be coordinated with the use of status lines that reflect the condition of the two modules. Once a sender is designated, it controls the Sender Ready line, indicating when it is ready to send. The designated receiver controls the Receiver Ready line, indicating when it will accept data.

Two objectives must be met to coordinate data transfers. First, the transfer should occur as soon as both the sender and receiver are ready. Second, each data word should be transferred only once. To ensure that these objectives are met, a sequence referred to as *protocol* is prescribed for data transfer.

With protocols, the receiver is informed when a new word is available at the sender, and the sender is informed when a data word has been accepted by the receiver. The state of the ready lines at any point in time determines the appropriate action to be taken by each of the two modules.

Each instant of data transfer from one part of the system to another is called a *bus cycle* (or often, a *machine cycle*). The timing of these cycles depends on the CPU clock signal. The length of bus cycles is based on the frequency of a clock signal. Typical clock rates are 5, 8, 10, and 16 MHz (megahertz or millions of cycles per second). The newer clocks send up to 33 MHz.

Input/Output ports

Computer input/output (I/O) address space is organized into ports. A *port* is a group of I/O lines that are read or written in parallel between the CPU and the I/O unit, generally one line per bit. The number of lines in a port is usually the same as in the word-size of the processor. For inputs, ports are usually sets of logic gates that route input signals to the system's data bus. For outputs, ports are sets of latches into which signals from the data bus are stored.

By use and convention, the direction of input and output information flow that involves the microprocessor is regarded relative to the processor itself. An *input port* is any source of data (such as a register) that connects in a selectable manner to the processor data bus and that sends a data word *to* the processor. Conversely, an *output port* is a receptacle of data (such as a register) that connects in a selectable manner to the processor data bus. When selected, it receives a data word *from* the microprocessor.

A processor needs a means of coordinating its timing to that of an external device with which it wants to exchange information. Otherwise, a data transfer from a given input port might be performed before it was required, thus stepping on some process within the CPU. As noted above, this coordination of timing is called *handshaking*.

I/O port techniques

A processor can communicate through three types of I/O techniques: programmed I/O, interrupt I/O, and direct memory access (DMA).

Programmed I/O is a processor-initiated I/O transfer where the processor executes a program to accomplish the I/O. Interrupt I/O is a device-initiated technique. Generally, an external device connected to the processor interrupt pin raises the signal of the interrupt pin (or lowers the signal, depending on the processor). In response, the processor completes the execution of the current instruction, saves the program counter onto the correct stack, and executes a program called the Interrupt Service Routine to complete the transfer.

Direct memory access is also device-initiated. Data transfer between memory and the I/O device occurs without processor involvement. Typically, DMA controller chips are required to complete the transfer.

Universal Synchronous/Asynchronous Receiver/Transmitter (USART)

A microprocessor communicates with peripheral devices that receive and transmit data serially. The processor must go through a parallel-to-serial and then a serial-to-parallel conversion during this communication.

Most serial data transfers between the processor and peripheral devices are carried out asynchronously. In other words, the device may transmit at any point in time. When no data is being sent, the device sends a simple mark bit, generally a high signal value so that any break in the transmission circuit will be known immediately. When the device is ready to transmit data, the transmitter sends a zero bit to show the start of transmission. This start bit is followed by the data, then a parity bit, and one or two stop bits. At the end of transmission, the sender continues to send the high signal value as the "no data coming" mark.

To simplify interface design between processors and both synchronous and asynchronous serial devices, universal synchronous/asynchronous receiver/transmitter chips, called USARTs, are designed. USARTs consist of a receiver and a transmitter, and each section can operate independently. Figure 12-4A shows a typical transmitter of a USART, and FIG. 12-4B shows a typical receiver.

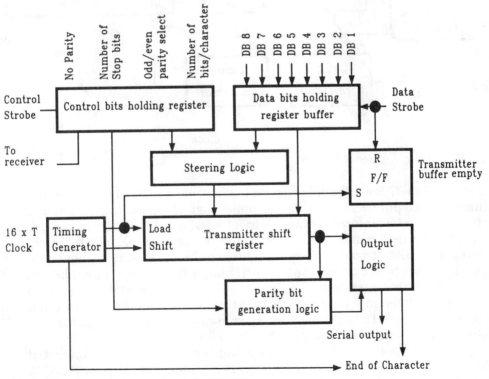

12-4A   Typical transmitter sections of a USART.

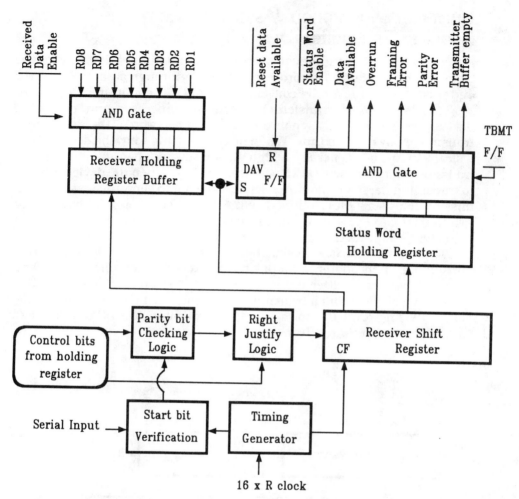

12-4B Receiver sections of a USART.

The USART is a full-duplex device (it can send and receive at the same time) in a 40-pin package. It also supplies logical formatting. Additional circuitry may be required for the electrical interface, but no common clock signal is required between the USART and the device with which it communicates. USART transmitters are double-buffered, so that the next data byte can be accepted as soon as the current byte is ready for transmission.

USARTs that operate at rates up to 200K baud are available. The baud rate can be different for the receiver and transmitter and is set by external clocks running at 16 times the desired baud rate and connected to the separate receiver and transmitter clock signals.

Typically, both the microprocessor and the I/O devices are connected in parallel to their USART with a serial connection (e.g., RS-232C) between them.

MULTIBUS

The bus structure that supplies the interface for all the hardware connections is one of the most important elements in a computer system. This structure allows the various system components to interact with each other. In addition, it allows generation of interrupts, direct memory access, memory and I/O data transfers, and so on.

As one sample of a general bus, the Intel MULTIBUS architecture provides a communications channel that can be used to coordinate a wide variety of computing modules. (For more information on 80486 and MULTIBUS I and II, see Appendix D.) To do this, the various modules in a MULTIBUS system are designated as *masters* or *slaves*.

Masters

A master is any module that has the ability to control the bus. It obtains control of the bus through bus exchange logic and initiates data transfers on it using either built-in processors or dedicated logic. Masters generate command signals, address signals, and memory or I/O addresses.

A master operates in one of two modes: Mode 1 or Mode 2. In Mode 1, masters are limited to a single bus transfer per bus connect. If all masters in the system are operating in Mode 1, then system timing is limited by a maximum bus busy period. This mode allows system designers to predict the overall performance of their system.

In Mode 2, masters are not limited in bus control and can invoke bus override. In this mode, bus time-outs are allowed, and masters are not required to operate within the maximum busy period. This mode allows a broad class of operations, which gives users flexibility in meeting their applications' needs.

Slaves

Slaves, on the other hand, are recipients of data transfer requests only. They decode the address lines and act on the command signals of masters. Figure 12-5 shows a block diagram of a MULTIBUS Master and Slave examples.

Bus operation

MULTIBUS accommodates several bus masters on the same system, each taking control as it needs to transfer data. The masters request bus control through a bus exchange sequence. This sequence uses a set of six signals that test whether the bus is currently in use, check that no other master with a higher priority is requesting the bus, request the bus, and release it.

Priority techniques There are two bus priority techniques: serial and parallel. In the serial scheme, master priority is resolved via a daisy-chain

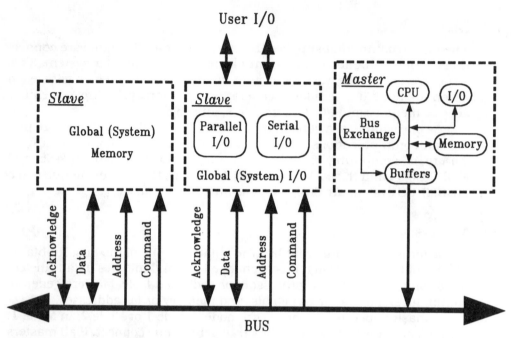

12-5 MULTIBUS master and slave examples.

technique. In essence, the bus priority of one master is connected to the bus priority of the next lower master. The highest priority is on one end of the chain and the lowest on the other end.

Serial priority is determined as each master requests the bus. If no other master of higher or equal priority is controlling the bus, then the requesting master takes control. The number of masters that can be linked in a serial chain is limited by the fact that the priority signal must propagate through the entire chain within one bus cycle. If 10 MHz is used, then the number of masters in a serial chain is limited to three. Figure 12-6 shows a serial priority technique.

In a parallel scheme, a Bus Arbiter determines allocation. This may be done with a priority scheme that determines the next master by a fixed priority list or other method as defined by the system. Figure 12-7 shows one parallel priority scheme.

Bus design

MULTIBUS has 16 data lines, 20 address lines, 8 multilevel interrupt lines, and control and arbitration lines. Because of these many lines, both 8-bit and 16-bit masters can be intermixed in a system.

MULTIBUS maintains its own clock that is independent of the clocks of the modules it links together. This clock allows masters of different speeds to share the bus and allows the masters to operate asynchronously

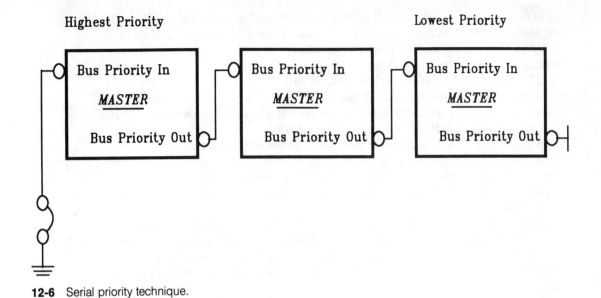

12-6 Serial priority technique.

12-7 Parallel priority technique.

with respect to each other. MULTIBUS arbitration logic permits slow masters to compete equitably for use of the bus. However, once a module has obtained the bus, transfer speeds depend on the capabilities of the transmitting and receiving modules.

The primary MULTIBUS function is to provide a data transfer path between modules on the bus. It allows systems to be constructed with boards of varying capability and allows for variations in data path width, I/O address path width, and interrupt attributes.

MULTIBUS II is designed to increase performance and multiprocessing capability of the 80486-based system. The new architecture includes message passing that makes higher multiprocessing performance possible. Message passing allows all transfers over the bus to occur at the fastest 32-bit data and burst-transfer rates available.

In addition to message passing, the MULTIBUS II board modules support virtual interrupts, geographic addressing, and distributed arbitration. Virtual interrupt allows one processor to write into a special memory location of another processor, which gives nearly unlimited interrupt signaling flexibility.

Geographic addressing provides interconnect space for software configuration of OEM systems by incorporating on-board interconnect registers. Distributed arbitration gives MULTIBUS II board products as many discrete arbitration levels as there are boards or slots in a system. Thus, each board in a system has the same priority for access time to the bus, which keeps high-performance master boards from locking out lower-priority boards. Discrete arbitration also allows multiprocessing with many potential bus masters.

The key concept when constructing a MULTIBUS system is that of *required* versus *supplied* capability. Each product provides some individual, basic set of capabilities. A transaction between two such products is restricted to that capability that is the intersection of the sets of capabilities of the two products. In some cases, the intersection could be null, implying fundamental incapability.

Power supply

The requirements of modern devices are for closely regulated direct current (DC) power. The regulation of the power may be done at the power supply or, as is the case in S-100 systems, on the individual circuit boards.

Most computer systems required a +5 volt DC power supply that delivers one to five amps. Typical requirements are 1, 3, 4, and 5 amps, depending on the system. Some systems require a current level of 10 amps at 5V. Power supplies often have a +12V supply at 2A to support diskette drives or hard disk drives.

Summary

Interfacing means connecting the microprocessor with the external world and its own internal units. The more intelligent the device, the more important it is to pay close attention to the interconnecting capabilities.

Interfacing is one of the more difficult aspects of hardware development. It is here that more savings and tradeoffs can be made. In most applications, the signals that must be detected by the processor are seldom, if ever, compatible. In the simplest case, this may be just voltage conversion to compatible 5V transistor-to-transistor logic (TTL). Incompatible voltages can easily corrupt the processing signals. In other instances, analog-to-digital converters may be required.

13
Memory organization overview

Memory transfers information through time and always in the same direction: forward. The information can be saved in various ways in a computer system, but think of memory as the channel that allows data to be retained for future use.

The smallest unit of information that a digital system stores is the binary digit or "bit": a binary one (1) or zero (0). This bit is first stored in a 1-bit *flip-flop* register. Flip-flop is a general term for a memory cell that has only two stable *states* in which it can remain, as long as its power supply is not interrupted. Inputs to that memory cell can change its state. Figure 13-1 shows a general description of a static MOS flip-flop, or single register circuit.

Thousands of such 1-bit registers can be incorporated into a single integrated circuit (an IC) and share common sets of inputs and outputs and a single clock line. This entity is referred to as a *memory* chip. Memory capacity is usually specified in terms of the maximum number of bytes the memory stores.

A microcomputer is a system of modules that include a processor along with memory and I/O units. The processor can be broken down further into subunits in order to achieve greater flexibility. One such approach involves separating the processor's data-handling portion from that which handles instructions and their sequencing. The data-handling portion consists of the arithmetic-logic unit (ALU) and various data registers. This data handling is formed by cascading several identical data units, each one referred to as a *microprocessor slice* and consisting of as an Arithmetic-Logic Unit and registers.

To form a complete microprocessor from microprocessor slices, additional components (such as a program counter, an instruction register, an instruction decoder, and a timing and control unit) are needed to handle instruction sequencing and decoding. These components fetch instruc-

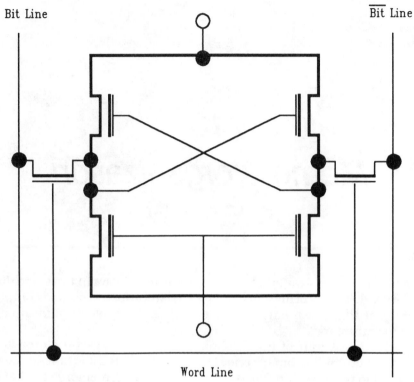

Bit Line $\overline{\text{Bit Line}}$

Word Line

13-1   Static MOS flip-flop circuit diagram.

tions from main memory according to the program counter and transfer them to the instruction register.

Real memory

Memory is now normally implemented in CMOS, VLSI technology (see Chapter 11 for more information on the physical composition of CMOS). Some manufacturers include a limited amount of memory directly on the CPU chip itself. Most, however, don't waste the CPU "real estate" and keep memory (other than cache memory) on separate chips.

ROM and RAM

Semiconductor memories come in two fundamentally different types: program changeable (Random-Access Memory, or RAM) and unchangeable (Read-Only Memory, or ROM).

Random Access Memory (RAM)   RAMs are memory cells that can be changed under program control. There are two types of RAM: *Static* (SRAM) and *Dynamic* (DRAM). SRAMs use a flip-flop for each memory element; each flip-flop can be set or reset to store a binary one (1) or zero (0).

The state of the flip-flop does not change unless new data is stored in it or power to the RAM is interrupted.

Dynamic RAMS (DRAMs) on the other hand, use an on-chip capacitor for each storage element. A charge on the capacitor indicates a 1; no charge indicates a 0. While this technique simplifies the storage cell and permits denser memory chips, it also causes a problem: the charge leaks off the capacitor in a few milliseconds (thousandths of a second). To correct this, the charge on the DRAMs must be *refreshed*.

DRAM refreshing consists of reading a sequence of memory locations within a specified time. While reading data, the RAM chip automatically rewrites the data back into the location just read. As a result, all the 1 bits are restored to full charge, and the 0 bits to a no-charge. DRAMs are typically refreshed at least every 2 milliseconds.

Read-Only Memory (ROM)   ROMs provide a means of permanently storing programs and data, because ROMs retain their contents even when power is off. MOS technology is ideal for fabricating ROMs because of the very dense geometrical layouts that are possible in ROM. Figure 13-2 shows a simplified model of a ROM.

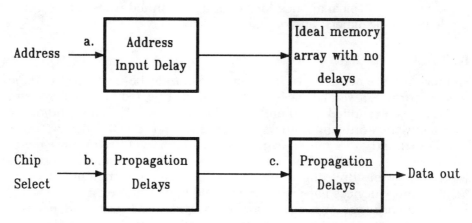

a.   Includes all propagation delays associated with address input buffers, row and column decoders, and the memory array.

b.   Includes all propagation delays associated with chip select logic.

c.   Includes all delays associated with the output buffers.

13-2   Simplified model of a ROM.

There are four types of ROMs: Mask-programmed, Programmable (PROM), Erasable-Programmable (EPROM), and Electrically Erasable (EEPROM).

Mask-programmable ROMs are programmed by the manufacturer who customizes the chip, based either on the manufacturer's or the customer's specifications. These ROMs are often used in high-volume products because they are the least expensive and the highest in bit density.

The user programs the PROM by electrically using a special device called a PROM programmer. Once the ROM is programmed, it cannot be changed. These ROMs are useful for special purposes when users require alterable environments that, once set, will continue.

The EPROM is similar to the PROM except that it can be erased and reprogrammed. Programmed bits are stored as a charge on a near-zero-leakage capacitor. Erasing is done by shining ultraviolet light through a clear window in the IC package. EPROMs are useful for prototypes or small-volume production runs.

The fourth type, the EEPROM, can be erased electrically while it is still in the circuit. A major advantage of the EEPROM over EPROM is that small sections of the EEPROM can be erased, while EPROMs must be completely erased. Typical applications include calibrated transducers, automatic telephone dialers, and digital TV tuners.

Memory systems

Memory requirements of a typical system cannot be met with a single memory device; several devices must be interconnected to form a system. Capacity is expanded by increasing the number of words and/or by increasing the word length above that attainable by a single device.

Word length is increased by placing the outputs of two or more memory devices in parallel. The number of words in a memory system is increased by multiplexing outputs from two or more memory devices. Most memory devices have features that aid this multiplexing.

A memory system requires a way to expand addresses; it needs a method to expand the number of memory address bits to which the memory system responds. The number of address bits that a processor provides dictates its physical *memory address space*.

Memory organization

Memory is designed so that a single device meets all the fundamental component requirements: an array of memory cells, each of which can store a single bit; logic to address any location in memory; circuitry to allow the reading of the contents of any memory location; and for writeable memory, circuitry to allow any memory location to be written.

Memories contain input drivers, output buffers, and circuitry for address expansion to provide easy interconnection between that device and other memory or logic circuits. The memory is organized internally several ways in an effort to obtain high speed, a large bit capacity, and low peripheral circuit and memory array costs.

Word organized and linear selection   The simplest organization is a *word organized* array with *linear selection*. In other words, the memory array has a column length equal to the number of words and a row length equal to the number of bits per word. Word selection requires a decoder with a mutually exclusive output for each word in memory. The address inputs to this decoder select one and only one word in the memory array. Although conceptually simple, the linear selection method requires a large decoder for a large number of words.

Two-level decoding   The address decoder size is reduced by organizing the memory array and word selection logic to allow *two-level* decoding. In a memory array using this method, one level corresponds to a physical word and one to a logical word. A physical word consists of the number of bits in a row of the array. A logical word is the number of bits of a physical word that are sensed and gated to the output device at one time.

Two-level decoding requires a row decoder that selects a physical word and a column decoder that selects one logical word from the selected physical word.

Bit organized   A common method of memory organization is when the number of segments in a physical word is equal to the number of bits in the physical word. That is, each logical word is a single bit in length. The bit organized memory has a single output, a square memory array, and row and column decoders of equal complexity.

Memory protection

A major problem in any system that has overlapping uses for memory is protecting the contents of that memory from unauthorized access or modification. Generally, the operating system must devise some scheme to keep each process from interfering from another while at the same time protecting itself.

In a simple system, the user application is placed in one particular location and the operating system in another, each able to access its own space. Generally, in this type of system, any addresses issued by the operating system are assumed to be "good" ones and, thus, are not checked. Any addresses issued by any other application must be assumed to be "suspect" and are checked to ensure that those addresses fall within the allowed area. Often, the hardware does the checking.

In order for the hardware to do this checking, it must know where the operating system starts and stops, and whether the user program or the operating system is running at any instant in time. The most common way to implement these requirements is by providing two modes of execution: a *user mode* and a *privilege mode*.

In the user mode, only a limited range of addresses are allowed—the addresses limited to the user area. In the privileged mode, all addresses in the memory area are valid. Transition between the two modes occurs when an interrupt occurs or when a special "enter operating system" instruction is issued.

Memory addressing

In a random access memory system, any word location is directly accessible. Each word location is assigned an identifier and consists of a fixed number of memory elements. The word identifier is known as the *address* of the word location. This address allows each word location to be distinguished from others for the purpose of either a read or a write operation.

Direct addressing combines the instruction code and the effective address into one word that permits a memory reference instruction to be executed in two machine phases: fetch and execute. The location of the instruction's operand, which specifies the operation to be performed, indicates the source or destination register. For direct addressing, generally only two memory pages (zero and one) of static or dynamic RAM are allocated.

Quite often, applications and operating systems must use the same real memory and must be protected from each other. Using a limit register is one method of protection. However, this has limitations when several applications must share and re-use space. The most satisfactory solution is to provide some relocation mechanism within the store accessing hardware itself. Each application or internal process now sees a *virtual store* that extends from a base address up to some limit.

The translation between real addresses and virtual addresses must be done for every store access in user mode; it can be done well, however, only if the design provides suitable hardware between the CPU and memory. The most effective hardware has a base and limit register that does the translation and limit checking. Figure 13-3 shows a generic arrangement.

Before doing a memory access, the base register is set to the start of

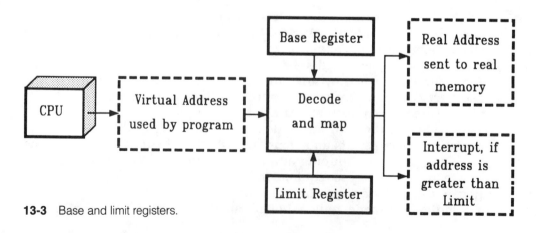

13-3　Base and limit registers.

the memory allocated to this process and the limit register is set to its size. These registers are set as part of the register reloading normally done when starting a process. In the user mode, all addresses are translated by adding the base register to the virtual address generated by the program, which produces a real address used for the memory access.

Memory management unit

Most computer systems have some kind of memory management unit (MMU) that helps the multitasking operating system allocate memory for each task and provide protection from user programs. For example, a common problem is when an application program makes an error in computing an address, perhaps using an array subscript that is too large or too small. If the system is not protected, this kind of problem can change operating system code, modify device tables, or actually cause a device to perform an undesired and unrequested function such as overwriting a data file.

Besides protecting the operating system from inadvertent tampering, the MMU provides automatic program relocation. Through the MMU, memory accesses by user programs are translated from a logical or program address to a physical or hardware address. These physical addresses may be located at a completely different place in memory than the logical address would imply. By doing the translating, the operating system and protected I/O are removed completely from the user address. Any attempt to read or write to memory outside the user's assigned address space causes the processor to abort the user's program.

Information generally is transferred in units of a fixed number of bits; the 80486 uses 32 bits when not specifically having been signaled to use 8 or 16 bits. These fixed bits are called *words*. When it goes into the memory system, the process is called a *memory write*. When the word is obtained from a memory position, the process is called a *memory read*.

There are two types of memory access methods: random and sequential. *Sequential access* refers to a type of memory system in which the word positions become available for access in some predefined order. *Random access,* on the other hand, refers to a type of memory system in which every word position may be directly selected and accessed in any order, and in approximately the same time.

No matter how good the memory, there will be propagation delays when the signal travels between devices. Propagation delay is the time required for a logic pulse signal to travel through a device or series of devices forming a logic string. This delay also includes all the interconnecting signal pulse lead paths between the IC chips.

Direct Memory Access (DMA)

Direct Memory Access (DMA) is the ability to transfer data directly between memory and external devices without the intervention of a program. DMA facilitates maximum I/O data rate and maximum concurrency. While interrupt I/O and programmed I/O route data through the processor, DMA directly transfers data between the I/O device and memory.

To keep the number of data pathways to a minimum, a special provision allows the normal bus system to be used for DMA. To do this, the processor must release control of the buses so that the external device can then use and control them.

During the DMA process, program execution is usually suspended. The buses are released whenever a special DMA request control line is activated. The processor finishes the current execution, releases the Address and Data bus, and keeps one line on the Control bus so that unintentional events do not arise from undefined control signals.

The I/O interface transfers data directly to the memory unit by means of a special register. When a transfer must be made, the interface requests a memory cycle-time from the processor. After acknowledgment, the interface causes data to be transferred directly to memory as the processor halts for the cycle-time. The logic that does this transfer is called a *channel*.

The channel contains a memory address register to control the location in the memory to and from which the data is transferred. In most cases, it also contains a word counter that keeps track of the number of direct memory-transfers made. Additional circuitry must be provided for all the related operations in this transfer, such as control signals and timing. Figure 13-4 shows the logical connections between a CPU and a DMA controller.

DMA components   The major components in a DMA are a request flip-flop, an address register, a counter, and a data register for the use of the peripheral device. DMA transfers involve the following:

- Initializing the DMA logic to start the DMA during repeated cycle-stealing steps.

- DMA occurs asynchronous to program operations.

- Signals end (the counter runs out or the device status changes).

- A routine "cleans up" the end of transfer.

- DMA terminates through a program interrupt routine that switches back to the main program.

Data block transfer   DMA schemes for high-speed data devices involve the transfer of data words in blocks. Under program control, the processor often initiates the transfer of a block of data and might specify the number of words that comprises the block. Actual transfer of the individual data words is, however, controlled by separate circuitry: the DMA Controller. The maximum rate of a DMA block transfer is limited only by the read or write cycle time of the memory and the speed of the DMA Controller.

13-4 Logical connections between a DMA controller and CPU.

Cycle stealing DMA A program initiates a block transfer by outputting the starting address to the address counters; then it outputs a count of words to the word counter and finally issues a start command. This type of DMA is often referred to as *cycle stealing* because it suspends the execution of a program for about one machine cycle at a time.

In cycle-stealing DMA, data is transferred concurrently with other processes being carried out by the processor. The steps in executing a cycle-stealing DMA are similar to those for the block transfer, except that the DMA Controller steals cycles from the processor during which it transfers data and thereby slows it.

Memory segmentation

Segmentation is the act of dividing memory into segments, with a segment simply being one small piece of a larger whole. To software designers, segmentation offers a convenient way of sharing information between processes. Individual segments can be shared without reducing the protection that each segment requires.

Segmentation also suggests the natural separation of code from data and module from module.

To hardware designers, segmentation can also mean a specific division of memory by the physical units called ROM and RAM. For example, if each RAM is 64K, then each segment is a 64K segment. The allied circuitry, the physical registers, latches, and so on, all are built around that specific division.

In the Intel world, when the 8080 came out and addresses could be built up to the 65,536 bytes (64K), that number became the maximum memory size. For a relatively long time, 64K became the design base of the microcomputer world. The 8086 expanded this by implementing programmable segmentation that mapped 64K segments over a 1 megabyte address space.

Today with the 80386 and 80486 physical address segments can vary from 1 byte to 4 gigabytes (4 billion). In virtual memory, the 80486 can address up to 64 terabytes (64 trillion bytes), with each segment given a different protection or priority level.

Virtual memory

A simple memory system is one where the logical and physical address space are the same. Little memory management is needed for individual programs in this scheme. For a virtual memory system, on the other hand, the logical address space (the total needed for all programs and processes) is mapped onto the primary physical memory (that memory physically present in a system).

For instance, at any instant in time and using 4096 bytes of memory for this example, all 4096 bytes can be physically and directly addressed. However, those 4096 bytes need not relate on a one-to-one basis with physical memory. The operating system can tell the physical system that from now on, whenever the address 4096 is referenced, memory word 0 is used, and so on. In other words, the operating system defined a mapping from the address space onto the actual memory addresses. Figure 13-5 shows a mapping of 4K of memory onto memory addresses.

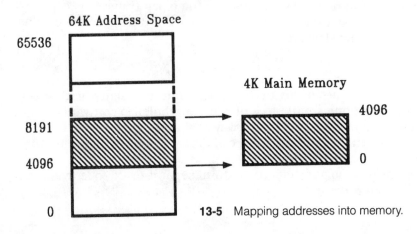

13-5 Mapping addresses into memory.

At each point in time, the entire logical address space may or may not reside entirely in the primary physical memory. Those portions that are not in main memory usually are stored in a memory hierarchy made up of auxiliary devices such as disk space. When a logical address not in the primary area is needed, it is brought into primary memory from the stored area and some mapping between physical and logical addresses is done.

Virtual memory management Memory management is the application of strategy and algorithms to the problems of allocating the memory resource among competing processes. Virtual memory management involves a relocation technique, mapping an address space used by a process onto a physical address space. The major allocation technique, *dynamic relocation*, is that act of mapping: taking a program's logical information onto physical memory. This mapping occurs immediately before any instruction of the program is executed.

In a *segmented virtual memory* system, the entire logical address space is divided into smaller logical segments of any size. To point to a particular element within a segment, the segment name as well as a symbolic element name or its address within the segment must be addressed.

When any segment is brought into primary memory, it is placed into a space equal to or greater than the segment size. Because a segment and its physical location are unrelated, a segment table is built containing the base address of each segment in memory. A reference to a segment name is then mapped by the system into a segment number representing an offset into the segment table. Additional mapping indexes into the segment for references to a particular element.

Paged virtual memory In a *paged virtual memory* system, the primary address space is divided into equal-sized blocks, each known as a *page*. The page represents a block of code and/or data with consecutive addresses. Because the logical address space is also divided into the same size pages, when information is transferred into physical memory, the basic unit of transfer is the page and fills the page frame.

If memory is not allocated well or is allocated in variable size units, it can fragment into pieces too small to be easily used. Then throughput slows because the CPU is forced to delay dispatching and reorganize physical memory by moving or swapping other tasks until a large enough place opens to continue processing.

To solve this fragmentation, the concept arose of allocating memory in fixed size units and then automatically overlaying the units into real memory. The process is called paging and the chunks of program read in from secondary memory are called pages, much the same as in the virtual paging system described above. The main memory into which the pages go are called *page frames*.

Paging is a practical division of the virtual space within a system and intended primarily to avoid the many problems of memory fragmentation. The main disadvantage of paging is that space may be wasted if only very small areas are required, as the smallest unit that can be allocated is a page.

Programs are written as though there were enough space in real memory for the entire required space. The hardware's internal logic devices and the operating system interact so that the programmer ignores the fact that pages will be loaded over previously used pages. This is contrasted to segmentation, where the programmer must remember how each segment is used and how to address it.

To find which page is required for the next instruction, a word table called the *page table* is used. The table holds the beginning addresses for each page along with bits that show if the page is currently in memory. If so, hardware points to the page and continues. If not, the hardware interrupts so the operating system can find the page in auxiliary storage, load it into real memory, and then continue.

When a reference is made to a page that is not in main memory, an error called a *page fault* occurs. After a page fault, the operating system reads in the required page from secondary memory, enters its new physical memory location in the page table, and then repeats the instruction that caused the fault.

Cache memory

A cache is a buffer type of high-speed memory filled at medium speed from main memory, often with instructions and programs. In a computer system that uses cache memory, instructions and data are stored in main memory, and some selected pieces of the instructions and data is copied in the cache. Figure 13-6 shows a block diagram of the 80386 cache memory. (The 80486 has a built-in cache.)

Cache was designed when processors became much faster than RAM and had to wait because data items were not ready for processing. Information flows from secondary storage to main memory to cache memory. To get to cache, the following process occurs:

When a program tries to reference its address space, it presents a virtual address to the hardware or the microprogram. If the page or segment containing that address is in main memory, the virtual address is translated into a main memory address. Otherwise, a fault occurs and the page/segment is brought into main memory.

The cache hardware then checks to see if the block is already in cache memory. If so, the contents of the addressed location are fetched from cache or the result is stored in cache. If not there, a cache block fault occurs (similar to a page fault) and the information is copied from main memory to the cache. After the block is loaded into cache, the instruction is executed again. Due to the short time involved, the cache-main memory paging system is handled by the logic external to the CPU without assistance from the operating system.

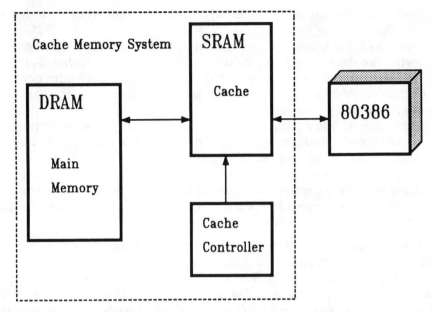

13-6 Block diagram of a cache memory system.

Cache information selection The selection process is the key to making best use of the processor. Predicting the address of the next memory location to be accessed is highly uncertain if all memory accesses were truly random. In actuality, they rarely are. Most programs access memory in the neighborhood of the location accessed most recently. This is called *program locality*, and this locality makes cache systems as efficient as they are.

For instance, in reading data variables, they are generally organized in some (often ascending) logical sequence that makes the next read immediately after the previous one. Character strings are most often scanned in sequence. Stacks change from one end so that the next few accesses are all near the top of the stack.

When the processor needs the next instruction or the next piece of data, it is programmed to search the cache first before requesting it from more distant and slower memory. If the requested data is found in the cache, the memory access is called a *cache hit*. If it is not, it is called a *cache miss*. The hit rate is the percentage of accesses that are hits. This percentage is affected by the size and the physical organization of the cache, the cache algorithm, and the program being run.

Block fetch A cache memory has a controller whose purpose is to maximize its efficiency and to manage its resources. The controller partitions the main memory into blocks of typically 2, 4, 8 or 16 bytes. A 32-bit processor usually uses two or four words per block. When there is a cache miss, the cache controller moves both the needed word from the main memory into the cache along with the entire block that contains the needed word.

The block fetch can get the data in one of three ways: *lookbehind*—retrieving the data located before the requested byte; *lookahead*—retrieving the data that follows the requested byte; or both. Blocks are generally aligned on doubleword boundaries. An access to any byte in the block copies the entire block into cache.

Block size is a key parameter in a cache memory system. If the lookahead and lookbehind are too small, the hit rate is reduced. Too large a block size reduces the number of blocks that fit into a cache. In addition, as the block becomes larger, each new word is further from the requested word and less likely (because of program locality) to be needed by the processor. Finally, too large a block size requires a wider bus between main memory and the cache memory, which results in increased cost.

Cache organizations   Cache is high-speed memory used similar to a scratch pad. If a telephone number is needed soon, the digits are jotted down. When the need is satisfied, the digits are then crossed out and the space used for something else. The organization of this scratch pad determines how a system will use it. The three general types of cache organization are fully associative, direct mapped, and set associative.

Fully associative cache   In a fully associative cache, the cache holds the blocks most likely to be used by the processor (normal process). However, there would be no single relationship between all the addresses of these blocks, so the cache would also have to store the entire address of each block as well as the block itself.

When the processor asks for data, the cache controller compares the address of the requested data with *each* of the addresses in the cache. If a match is found, the data for that address is sent to the processor. Either a hit or a miss occurs. If a miss happens, because the addresses have no relationship to each other, a tradeoff is made: a slow sequential search begins, or the hardware does a parallel search, expensive in its need for comparators and controllers.

Direct mapped cache   The direct mapped cache allows each block from main memory only one possible location in cache, reducing the number of searches and comparing to one before a hit or miss is determined.

Each direct mapped address has two parts. One part is the cache index field, containing enough bits to specify a block location within the cache. The other, the tag field, contains bits to distinguish a block from other blocks possibly stored at a particular cache location.

The major limitation of a direct mapped cache is that the cache controller allows only one location in the cache from a particular piece of main memory. If the program makes frequent requests from two conflicting locations, the cache must be swapped each time. This sort of program behavior is infrequent, so the direct mapped cache organization offers acceptable performance at a lower cost than fully associative.

Set associative cache The set associative organization is a compromise between the fully associative and direct memory mapping cache. This type of cache has several sets of direct mapped blocks that operate as several direct mapped caches in parallel. For each cache index, several block locations are allowed, one in each set. When a block of data arrives from main memory, it goes into a particular block location of any set.

For the same amount of memory, the set associative cache contains half as many mapping blocks, but each block can take two addresses that would have conflicted in a 1-way cache. Two- and 4-way caches appear to be most efficient in terms of the speed and cost performance tradeoffs.

The cache controller must decide which block of the cache to overwrite when a block fetch is executed. The controller has three choices, any of which is adequate depending on the program behavior. Those choices are to overwrite at random, overwrite in sequential order, or overwrite the least recently accessed block. This last choice requires the controller to maintain an aging counter that indicates the block to overwrite. This counter must be updated on each cache transaction.

Cache updating When using cache, you should definitely remember that two copies of the data and information exist, one in main memory and one in cache. If one of the copies is updated and the other is not, two different sets of information become associated with one memory address, resulting in erroneous data being saved if the wrong set is saved.

The two copies require that the cache contain an updating method preventing old data (often called stale data) from being used. Several ways have been developed to store only "good" data: write-through, buffered write-through, write-back, and cache coherency.

In a *write-through* system, the cache controller writes data to the main memory immediately after it is written to the cache, thus making two writes for each updated piece of data. The results are that main memory always contains valid data and any block of cache can be overwritten without data loss. The major problem with this method is that a performance loss occurs due to the time required to write main memory. In addition, increased bus traffic causes a significant problem in multiprocessing systems.

In a *buffered write-through* system, write accesses to main memory are buffered, allowing the processor to begin a new cycle before the write cycle to the main memory is completed. A speed up occurs when the next read finds a cache hit so that the processor can continue. This allows a simultaneous write and read. In this system, only a single write to main memory is buffered. Therefore, if the processor needs a second write, the processor must go to a wait state until the first write completes. Additionally, a write followed by a cache miss also requires a wait for new data to be brought from main memory.

The next design is called a *write-back* system. The tag field of each block in the cache includes a bit that shows if the block has been altered. Before overwriting any block in cache, the cache controller checks the altered bit. If it's set, the controller writes the block to main memory before reading new data into the cache block. Write-back is faster than either the first two methods because the number of altered bits written to main memory is generally much smaller than the number read into cache.

There are a few drawbacks to the write-back system. Once the majority of block of cache have been altered, *all* the block must be written to memory before processing can go on. Second, this write-back controller logic is more complex than the first two cache updating methods. Finally, if there is a catastrophic error such as a power failure, cache data is lost, leaving no way to tell if main memory contains stale data.

The above three methods minimize stale data in main memory caused by cache write operations. However, another problem arises: *cache coherency.* This occurs when cache is used in a system where main memory is updated by more than one device. When memory can be updated from various devices, it's difficult to tell if data in cache is more stale than data in main memory. Three developed methods attack this problem.

The first method is called *cache flushing.* In the case of altered data, the data is written to main memory (most often through a write-through method), and then the contents of cache are flushed. If all the caches are flushed before a device writes to shared memory, stale data is eliminated from the caches.

Second, *hardware transparency* maintains cache coherency. In this case, the hardware guarantees non-stale data by ensuring that all accesses to memory mapped by a cache are seen by the cache. Two ways to do this have been created. All cache writes can be copied both to main memory and to all other caches that share the same memory, a technique called *broadcasting.* Also, the hardware can guarantee non-stale data by routing the accesses of all devices to main memory through the same cache.

Finally, cache coherency can be maintained by designating shared memory as *non-cacheable.* All accesses to the shared memory are cache misses because shared memory is never copied to cache. Software can help offset the reduction in hit rate by copying data between non-cacheable memory and cacheable memory and mapping shared memory accesses to the cacheable locations.

Buffers

Buffering is the process of storing results (outputs) of a process temporarily before forwarding them to the next process. Buffers are essential in smoothing out the flow of a system when the timing for each processing module involved is not fixed, and when that timing is vastly different (even in terms of milliseconds). For instance, the computer may have an extremely fast processor and much slower memory.

In addition to the memory array and decoding logic that make up a memory device structure, output buffers are used to buffer data from memory before it is output to the pins of the memory package. These buffers are useful in that they provide the desired output voltage levels and drive current and also allow easy multiplexing of the outputs of several IC packages.

Buffers are controlled by one or more chip selects, chip enables, or output enable inputs.

Timing

A programmable counter/timer monitors external events. The counter/timer can be addressed and accessed either as a memory location or an input/output port. The initial value of the counter can be set under program control. With each clock pulse, the contents of the counter can be either decremented or incremented.

Instructions have a different length of execution times, generally between one and six clock pulses. Total time is determined by how many clock pulses it takes for the instruction to do each step. In some cases, one or two clock pulses are automatically added to allow external logic to complete the requested operation. During this time, the CPU may go into wait state.

Timing constraints

Timing constraints exist on the sequencing of data, address, and control signals to a RAM device. These constraints ensure proper operation. The processor supplies the address and chip select signals to memory and must wait a period of time equal to the access time before it can use the output from memory.

Summary

In a professional or business environment, many programs are being executed all the time, and any one program may fill all the available microcomputer memory. Thus has grown the need for faster memory and multi-leaving of tasks.

Direct Memory Access allows the parallel transfer of data and continuation of CPU processing. DMA is a specialized transfer that temporarily isolates the CPU from the buses and manages the required transfer between memory and an I/O device.

14
Improving system performance

Early microcomputer design philosophy was based on the premise that, at any one time, only one person used one computer and ran one program. The typical user waited (perhaps) patiently for the program to complete before starting a second job. Today, users want to do several jobs (such as printing, editing, and sorting data) at the same time and expect the computer to perform efficiently while doing them. Essentially, users want "fast" computers.

Computer speeds are determined by three basic limitations. One concerns hardware—how fast do gates switch and how many inches of wire or board must a signal traverse. The second limitation concerns the logic of the interaction of machine design and organization. The third looks at how effectively the operating system uses the hardware design. This chapter addresses these last two limitations.

Early microcomputers executed one operation at a time. For example, they either computed, handled I/O, or scheduled interrupts. However, the designers always knew that if more than one operation could be performed, then program speedups would occur. As early as October 1842, Charles Babbage said in a lecture that ". . . when a long series of . . . computations is to be performed, such as those required for the formation of numerical tables, the machine can be brought into play so as to give several results at the same time, which will greatly abridge the whole amount of the processes."

Control units

In the 1950s, machine designs incorporated the concept of simultaneously executing several operations for solving differential equations. Today, many microcomputer manufacturers provide two-processor systems (for example, using a numeric coprocessor), and some have as many as four special-purpose processors. The processing speedups are due to parallelism between operations, as well as parallelism between memory and processor activities. To reach speed goals, many systems use some sort of control unit.

Control units for high-speed computers handle the traditional functions, including instruction fetch, I/O and interrupt handling, instruction sequencing, address mapping, and memory indexing. A well-designed control unit is one that does not get in the way of either the processor(s) or memory. It operates fast enough to supply instructions whenever they are needed by the processor.

An essential part of any computer system is the mechanism that allocates the system processor(s) among the various competitors for their services. This allocation occurs automatically in today's systems with methods such as the use of interrupts and interval timers.

Processor independence

At the base of any system performance improvement rests the independence of each process. The assumption is that certain sequences of actions follow naturally and are more or less independent of other sequences. For example, a disk-to-printer routine and a memory-to-memory move sequence are two very distinct processes that logically can execute independently of each other. In reality, it's realized that each may require one of the buses, but conceptually they're not otherwise interdependent.

An operating system aims to share the computer's resources as effectively as possible among many programs making unpredictable (asynchronous) demands on those resources. An efficient operating system that uses the hardware in an optimum manner speeds throughput enormously.

Now, let's look at some concepts that, when used efficiently, improve total computer throughput:

- prefetching data before it's required.
- pipelining instructions to get them into higher-speed work areas.
- using coprocessors to achieve parallel work.
- running a concurrent operation.
- using multitasking and multiprogramming.

Prefetching

As processor effective speeds increased, memory tried to keep up. However, it failed to do so for the following three major reasons: propagation delays, gate density, and slower technological advances. Those issues are under attack by today's designers. In the meantime, other approaches had to be taken.

To avoid the processor spending too much time waiting for memory to produce requested data, some parallel or pipeline process became mandatory. Generally, then, when the processor calls for the first pieces of information, a fetch goes out to memory for more. This fetching of information before it is required is called *prefetching*; the hardest task for prefetching is to determine which piece of memory is required next.

Prefetch effectiveness

Prefetch effectiveness is based on the idea of locality. In essence, it has been observed that the locus of reference of most programs varies (relatively) slowly over time and space. During certain periods of execution, the program accesses a subset of locations that lie in close spatial proximity. This subset changes over time. Simple prefetch algorithms then fetch information "next in line" from the previously fetched data.

Prefetching algorithms

In general, prefetch algorithms are divided into two classes: demand and anticipatory.

Demand algorithms are based on the concept that a processor runs through the information already in the system and then page faults. In other words, it sends a demand for the next portion of information.

Anticipatory algorithms, on the other hand, do not necessarily prefetch at the time of a fault; they do so at the first reference to a new page. Anticipatory prefetching generally saves transfer time because of the overlap between the time a page is requested and when the page is actually needed.

One Page Lookahead (OPLA)

One page lookahead (OPLA) assumes some behavior on the part of the program and prefetches accordingly. It assumes that the next sequential page will be the one required for continued execution.

Pipelining

Pipelining is where several distinct tasks are compacted in any certain time-frame for simultaneous processing. Pipelining is one form of embedding parallelism or concurrency in a computer system; it refers to dividing a computer's processes into several subprocesses executed by dedicated autonomous units. Successive processes can be carried out in an overlapped mode.

For instance, the CPU may be engaged in decoding and executing one instruction while additional registers on the data bus could be prefetching or looking ahead for the next instruction. Figure 14-1 shows the difference in instruction processing in a nonpipelined system versus a pipelined one.

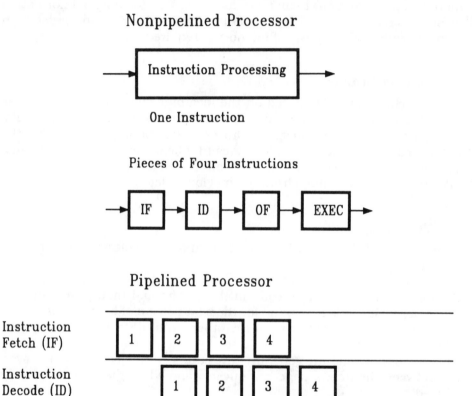

14-1   Pipelined versus nonpipelined instructions.

Methods

Three steps are taken to execute an instruction: fetching the instruction, decoding its operations, and fetching its operands. In Figure 14-1, four successive and independent instructions may be executed in parallel.

As you see, while the EXEC module executes the first instruction, the Operand Fetch (OF) module fetches the operand needed for the second instruction, the Instruction Decode (ID) module prepares the different operations for the third instruction, and the Instruction Fetch (IF) module fetches the fourth instruction. The overlapped execution among the four modules is shown in the space-time diagram.

Pipelining can be applied at more than one level. The first level usually chosen is at the processor, for instruction decoding as shown below. The next level is at the subsystem level, a typical example being the pipelined arithmetic units. Pipelined add, multiply, divide, and square-root functions are in existence in a number of contemporary computers.

Problems

Program branching is extremely damaging to pipeline performance. When a conditional branch is found, the system cannot tell which instruction sequence will follow until the deciding result is available at the output. Therefore, a conditional branch not only delays further execution but also affects the entire pipe, starting from the instruction fetch. An incorrect branch of instruction fetched must be flushed from the pipeline before the correct branch can be loaded.

One way to minimize branching effects is to have a branch target buffer or a lookahead mechanism. The fetching process actually gets *both* possibilities and decodes the operands. This way, no matter which way is finally determined as being correct, the next set of instructions is at hand.

An interrupt can disrupt the continuity of the instruction stream. To offset this, a recovery mechanism can be used to save the pipelined instructions and recover them after the interrupt has been serviced. This can be costly, however, so it is seldom implemented.

Control structure

Two major control structures are used in a pipelined system. The simpler one involves a streamlined (synchronized) flow of instructions through the system. One instruction or task follows another so that they begin and end in the same order. Simple interlocks in the system ensure that a simultaneous flow exists through modules of different speeds. When a bottleneck appears at any segment, input is halted until the segment is once again free.

The second control structure is somewhat more complex. In this more flexible and powerful method, flow through the system is totally asynchronous (i.e., each piece is allowed to go at its own speed). If a bottleneck occurs, the next instruction is allowed to go ahead. This scheme is useful whenever the system has multiple (either physical or virtual) execution units or facilities running in parallel.

Multitasking and multiprogramming

Performing two or more processing tasks by a single CPU is called *multiprogramming or multitasking*. The CPU rapidly switches back and forth between two or more programs, executing the instructions for each one in turn. This switching became practical when the CPU became faster than I/O processes.

Most operating system (OS) environments schedule applications programs using a time-slicing algorithm for program tasks not currently waiting on I/O. The OS uses the system clock to time just how long each application is allowed to use the major system resources. Each application receives equal time slices of execution time, on a round-robin basis.

The time-slice approach is simpler than many other and more complex scheduling algorithms. The conventional approach is that while one program waits for an I/O request to complete, another program runs. Because some I/O operations are massive and time-consuming to the CPU, some operating systems break large I/O requests into smaller requests so that scheduling can occur more often.

Memory management is a complex aspect of concurrency. Some operating systems require memory to be fixed-size partitions and that operating characteristics be assigned to each partition. Other operating systems allocate memory dynamically using PIFs (Program Information Files) to describe the characteristics and needs of an application package. PIFs describe the amount of memory required, which peripherals are directly accessed, which interrupts are processed, and so on.

Defining foreground and background tasks is one method for managing access to displays and keyboards. The foreground task is given control of the keyboard and the entire screen; all others are background tasks.

Windowing allows multiple applications to share the screen. The screen is divided into tiled or overlapped segments called *windows*, where each window displays a portion of an application's output. In some cases, one application can own multiple windows; for other applications, the user is responsible for sizing, moving, or hiding windows and that user scrolls within the windows.

A significant problem in multiprocessing is the proper execution of applications that perform direct video I/O. These applications write directly to the screen and bypass the operating system. When they do this, they can interfere with the operating system and are called *ill-behaved* applications.

If a system supports multitasking, mechanisms must be provided for the synchronization transfers of information to shared resources (i.e., a video buffer).

Ordering of events

The concept of time is fundamental in any ordering of system processes and events within those processes. Each computer system is composed of a collection of processes, with each process being subdivided into various events occurring in some sequence. The choice of what constitutes an event affects the ordering of the events within that process.

In a very basic sense, clock timing is just a way of assigning a number to an event, where the number is thought of as the time at which the event occurred.

Multitasking is a technique achieving concurrency by separating a single program or several programs into two or more interrelated tasks that share code, buffers, and files.

Multitasking involves providing a means for a program to interrelate referenced procedures and data manipulation, and to do this independently of their physical location in memory. In addition, multitasking provides a way for programs to use common procedures and data formatting. It expedites switching the actual computation hardware from one program/task to another.

Multiprogramming lets several people or programs use the system at the same time by allowing a second program to use the processor while the first program is waiting for some external process (such as a request for data) to complete. Instead of the processor going to a *wait* state, it stays busy processing. (A wait state is the internal pause the processor takes when a synchronizing signal is not present or when it has been halted under program control to await input from another device.) As soon as the second user needs an external process or finishes its task, the first program is brought back to continue running. This multi-use increases the productivity of the system by handling the processes effectively simultaneously instead of one at a time.

An increasing percentage of computation activity is carried out by multiprogrammed systems. Such systems are characterized by the application of computer resources (such as the processor, main memory, and peripherals) to many separate but interleaved operating computations. A *computation* is a set of processes that work together harmoniously on the same program or job.

Multiprogramming properties

Four important properties of multiprogrammed systems are the following:

- Computation processes may be concurrent operation for more than one user.

- Many computations share pools of resources, such as memory, in a flexible way.

- Individual computations vary widely in their demands for computing resources at any point in time.

- The multiprogrammed system evolves to meet the changing user requirements.

Concurrency in the micro world is normally confined to hardware-controlled concurrent processing of a main processor and a numeric coprocessor. Intel, with the 80386 and 80486 and the LOCK/XCHG instruction, provides the potential of multiprocessing on a mainframe scale.

Summary

One of the most important performance measures of a system is its throughput rate. *Throughput* is defined as the number of outputs or instructions processed per unit of time. It directly reflects the processing power of a system: the higher the throughput rate, the more powerful the system is.

The basic concept of parallelism in machine organization came into being as early as Charles Babbage's computing engines. It continues to be exploited, along with hardware speed improvements, to build and operate faster computers. It is expected that hardware costs will decrease faster than hardware speeds increase, thus forcing the increased use of parallelism and including the concepts discussed earlier.

A

Integrated Circuits and Intel

The semiconductor industry really began in New Jersey at the Bell Telephone Laboratories. It soon transplanted to the intellectually fertile region of California just south of San Francisco. The Santa Clara Valley, soon dubbed "Silicon Valley," now holds hundreds of companies whose products are descendants of the early days.

In the mid-1950s, a small group of scientists left Bell Labs to start a venture, backed by Fairchild Camera and Instrument Company. The scientists formed the Fairchild Semiconductor Company and settled in Santa Clara Valley, CA. Two of those scientists, Robert Noyce and Gordon Moore, left Fairchild Semiconductor in 1968 to form another company in Sunnyvale, CA; they named it Intel—for *Integrated Electronics*. Three years later, Intel introduced the first microprocessor with both high success and general industry acceptance.

The first IC calculators were limited in function and cost hundreds of dollars. Only slowly did engineers and manufacturers realize the potential of these first clunky machines. As more uses became apparent, engineers began to design chips for those special needs. Eventually the market for cheap pocket calculators became available, and technology was ready.

In mid-1969, Busicom, a Japanese calculator manufacturer, asked Intel Corporation to develop a set of chips for a new line of programmable calculators. Busicom's engineers had a design requiring twelve logic and memory chips with three to five thousand transistors each. Intel had recently developed a technique for manufacturing and fabricating 2,000-transistor chips. Busicom hoped that this technology would transfer easily into the calculator market.

New design concept

The industry-wide design strategy up until the early 1970s was for each chip to be designed to a particular customer's specifications. The processors were not powerful and were actually quite inadequate for general purpose computing.

While working on the Busicom project, an Intel engineer came up with a revolutionary design concept: why not have a general-purpose chip that could perform *any* logical task? The chip would have to be programmable, taking its instructions from some ROM and/or RAM chips. If customers wanted to have a specific product, they could program it and Intel would install that program into ROM. In essence, this meant that Intel would not design a new set of logic chips for each customer. The burden of design shifted from the manufacturer to the OEM people, and that concept formed the basis for Intel's now-popular family of chips.

Designed by three people in less than a year, the first multipurpose chip—the 4004—rolled off the production line in late 1970. Industry experts were divided. Some felt that a general-purpose chip was too general to find a useful home. Others wondered why the concept hadn't been used before.

See FIG. A-1 for the design steps of a microprocessor-based system.

The 4004 chip

The 4004 is a 4-bit (half-byte) microprocessor. Instead of distributing the arithmetic and logic functions of the calculator among several hardwired ICs, the 4004 included these functions on the chip itself.

The 4004 has 2,250 MOS transistors and can execute about 60,000 operations a second. It addresses 1,280 half-bytes of data and 4K (4096) of programmed instructions. It isn't powerful enough to serve as a processor, but certainly enough as a base for a calculator.

This chip can add two 4-bit numbers in about eleven millionths of a second (eleven microseconds) but can multiply only by repeated additions. It contains a 4-bit adder, an accumulator, and sixteen registers for temporary storage. The ROM contained the inner program and stored 2K bits of data, while the RAM that provided temporary storage held only 320 bits. Its size is 0.110 inches by 0.150 inches.

The 4004 contains a great deal of logic associated with computer central processing unit (CPU) implementation. One large-scale integration (LSI) chip replaced hundreds of circuits that were found in conventional minicomputers at that time. The 46-instruction set is not large by today's standard, but it is adequate for control applications that require decision making not easily implemented in programmable-logic arrays.

See FIG. A-2 for comparisons of the 4004 chip to the following two chips: the 8008 and the 8080.

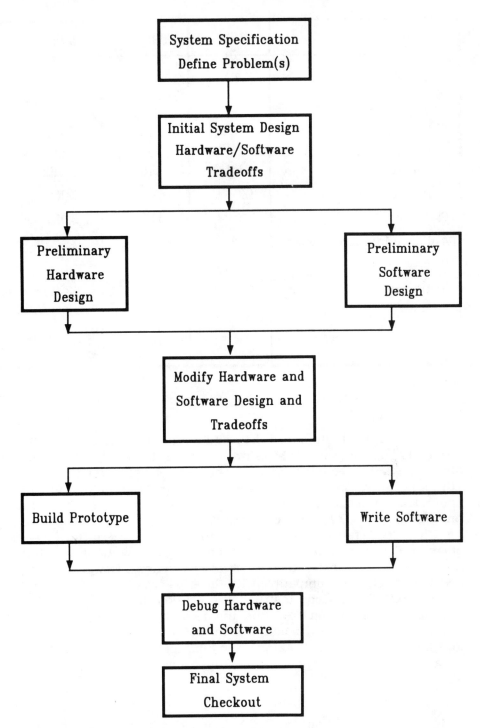

A-1 Steps in designing a microprocessor-based system.

	4004	8008	8080
Chip Class	4 bit	8 bit	8 bit
Technology	PMOS	PMOS	NMOS
Word Size:			
Data	4 bits	8 bits	8 bits
Instruction	8 bits	8 bits	8 bits
Address capacity	4K	16K	64K
Clock KHz	740	800	2,083
Add time in microseconds	10.8	20	2
Package size	16 pin	18 pin	40 pin
Instruction set size	45	48	72 (includes 8008 instructions)

A-2   Comparison of early chips.

The 8008 chip

In April 1972, Intel introduced their first 8-bit microprocessor, the 8008. The 8008 has about 3,300 MOS transistors, a thousand more than the 4004. The 8008 executes over 30,000 operations a second and addresses 16K of memory. The 8008 executes a single operation in 12.5 microseconds. However, it also multiplies by repeated addition, a time-consuming process. Its size is 0.125 inches by 0.170 inches.

The 8008 retains the PMOS fabrication techniques of the 4004 but offers an 8-bit wide *data bus* (the electronic pathway along which data flows) and a larger instruction set of 48 instructions. However, the 8008 instruction set is not compatible with the 4004 set.

The 8008 has a faster instruction execution time than the 4004, as data for both instruction execution and decoding and for operands could be handled in 8-bit slices. In addition, the 8008 addresses 16,384 memory locations of 8 bits each, contains seven 8-bit registers, has memory stack capability, and has a single-level interrupt capability.

The 8080 chip

In 1974, Intel brought out the 8080, designed to be useful in a great variety of applications. The 8080 chip is powerful enough to run a microcomputer but had some drawbacks that Intel wanted to overcome, mainly processing speed. With more than 4,500 transistors, the 8080 executes about 200,000 operations a second.

To achieve compatibility with the 8008 instruction set, the 8080 instruction set included the 8008 set and added 30 more instructions. The 79 instructions of the 8080 had decidedly moved away from one for primarily control applications to one that had more general purposes. For the first time, Intel chips were upwardly compatible. The 8008 users could now change to a faster, more versatile microprocessor while not discarding their current software.

The 8080 is an NMOS microprocessor that allows faster clock rates than its predecessors. Additions of two 8-bit operands could now be carried out at rates of 500,000 per second. In addition, all other instruction times were shorter because the 8080 was built around a 40-pin chip, requiring the CPU to do much less time-sharing of the data bus between data transfers and instruction implementation.

Like its precursors, the 4004 and 8008, the 8080 has no multiply instruction and so must multiply by adding. The 8080 supplemented hardware features of the 8008. Instead of 16K, memory addresses went to 64K. Rather than a limited 7-level memory stack, the 8080 offers a memory stack in external memory itself instead of in the CPU. Its size is 0.165 inches by 0.191 inches.

The 8080 placed Intel as one of the largest IC companies in the United States, with 21,500 employees and over $1 billion in annual sales.

The 8080A chip

In 1976, Intel brought out a variation on the 8080, the 8080A. The 8080A is an 8-bit microprocessor on a single chip, an NMOS device. It has about 4,000 transistors on a chip that is about 0.165 inches by 0.191 inches in size. It is a 40-pin, *dual in-line package* (DIP). Sixteen of the pins (A0–A15) provide three-state outputs for addressing memory and input/output (I/O). Eight of the pins (D0–D7) provide bi-directional three-state data for data transfer and internal state information. Finally, ten of the pins provide timing and control signals.

Figure A-3 shows the functional block diagram of the 8080A, while FIG. A-4 shows the pin assignments.

The 8080A instruction set consists of 72 instructions supported by the next chip in the family, the 8085A.

The 8085A chip

The 8085A is an enhanced, upward-compatible version of the 8080A and the two are nearly functionally equivalent. Basically, the 8085A is a single-chip version of the three-chip combination of the 8080A microprocessor, the 8224 clock driver, and the 8228 system controller.

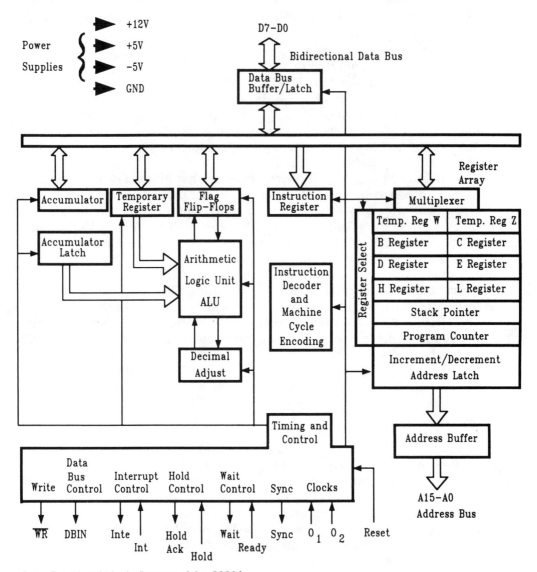

A-3 Functional block diagram of the 8080A.

The 8085A is an 8-bit microprocessor, NMOS device implemented with about 6,200 transistors. The chip is 0.164 inches by 0.222 inches, contained in a 40-pin DIP. The pins and their configuration are shown in FIG. A-5.

The 8085A operates on a single 5V power supply. This chip is capable of directly addressing up to 64K memory locations with its 16-bit address. The I/O ports are treated as external registers. They can be treated as memory and written to and read from by any instruction that references memory.

8080A Pin Assignments

Pin	Signal		Signal	Pin
1	A10	8080A	A11	40
2	GND		A14	39
3	D4		A13	38
4	D5		A12	37
5	D6		A15	36
6	D7		A9	35
7	D3		A8	34
8	D2		A7	33
9	D1		A6	32
10	D0		A5	31
11	$-5V$		A4	30
12	RESET		A3	29
13	HOLD		$+12V$	28
14	INT		A2	27
15	0_2		A1	26
16	INTE		A0	25
17	DBIN		WAIT	24
18	WR		READY	23
19	SYNC		0_1	22
20	$+5V$		HLDA	21

A0–A15	Address Lines
D0–D7	Data Bus Lines
SYNC	Machine Cycle Synch
DBIN	Data Input Strobe
READY	Data Input Stable
WAIT	CPU in Wait State
WR	Data Output Strobe
HOLD	Enter Hold State
INT	Interrupt Request
INTR	Interrupt Enable
0_1 0_2	Clock Signals
$-5V$	} Power and Ground
$+5V$	
$+12V$	

A-4 Pin assignments of the 8080A.

Also, the 8085A directly addresses up to 256 input and 256 output ports using special I/O instructions with an 8-bit address. The 8085A's internal data bus is 8 bits wide and transfers instructions and data among various internal registers or to external devices through the multiplexed address/data bus buffer latch.

Only two new instructions were added to the basic 8080 instruction set—to read and to write serial and interrupt data. Because the 74 instructions of the 8085A set include those of the 8080A, programs written for the 8080A run on the 8085A. The execution times for those programs are different, even when clock frequencies are chosen that provide identical state times for the two microprocessors. This difference is the result of the

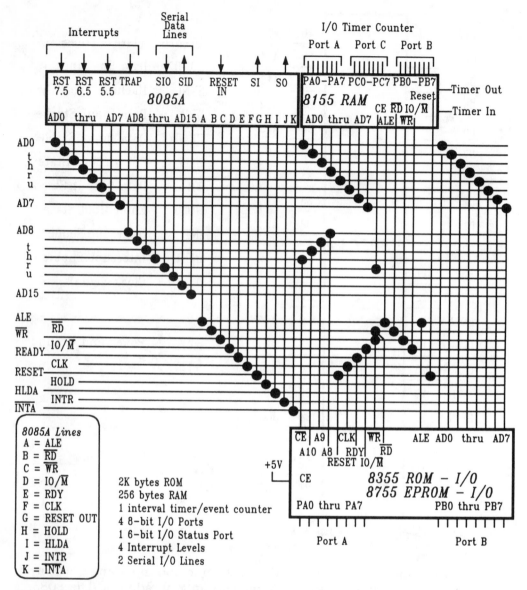

A-5 8085A microprocessor pin assignments.

differing number of states in the instruction cycles of identical instructions on the two machines.

The 8086 chip

Appearing in 1978, the 8086 was the first microprocessor capable of working with 16 bits of data at one time. Two key architectural concepts shaped the microprocessor designs, beginning with the 8086. These concepts are memory segmentation and an instruction encoding scheme.

The 8086 processor is divided into two separate units. The first is the *bus interface unit* (BIU), and the second is the *execution unit* (EU).

The BIU has two main functions: to fetch instructions from memory, and to pass data to and from the execution hardware and the outside world (outside from the view of the processor). The BIU contains the *instruction pointer* (IP), which holds the address of the next instruction to be fetched. The BIU also contains an instruction stream byte queue and the *segment registers.*

The 8086 segment registers are 16-bit registers and are called CS (Code Segment), DS (Data Segment), SS (Stack Segment), and ES (Extra Segment).

The BIU is independent from the Execution Unit (EU). While the BIU fetches additional instructions, the EU executes a previously fetched instruction. This is made possible by the instruction pipeline (or queue) between the BIU and the EU. The BIU fills this pipeline with instructions awaiting execution. Whenever the EU finishes a given instruction, the next instruction is usually ready for immediate execution without delays caused by instruction fetching. The 8086 BIU queue stores up to six bytes of the instruction stream.

The EU has no connection to the system bus, which it considers the outside world. The EU obtains instructions from the queue maintained by the BIU. When an instruction requires access to memory or to a peripheral bus, the EU requests the BIU to fetch or store the data. All addresses manipulated by the EU are 16 bits wide, but the address relocation facility provided by the BIU provides the EU with access to a full megabyte (one million bytes) of memory.

The EU contains the 16-bit *arithmetic logic unit* (ALU), the Operand and Flag File, and the General Register File containing registers AH, AL, BH, BL, CH, CL, DH, DL, BP, SP, SI, and DI. All register and data paths in the EU are 16 bits wide. The 8-bit registers combine to form 16-bit registers. For instance, AH and AL combine to form AX, the accumulator register. BH and BL form BX, the base register. CH and CL form CX, the count register. Finally, DH and DL form DX, the data register. See FIG. A-6 for a diagram of BIU and EU.

The general registers can be addressed either as 8-bit or 16-bit registers. This enables the 8086 to run 8080 instructions with only a code translation.

Depending on the number and complexity of the peripheral devices, the system designer can choose either a maximum and minimum system configuration mode. The two modes are defined by a pin (MN/MX) that is strapped either to ground (for maximum mode) or to the VCC potential (for minimum mode).

In the maximum mode configuration, a bus controller is used for generating the control signals to memory and I/O. This frees the minimum

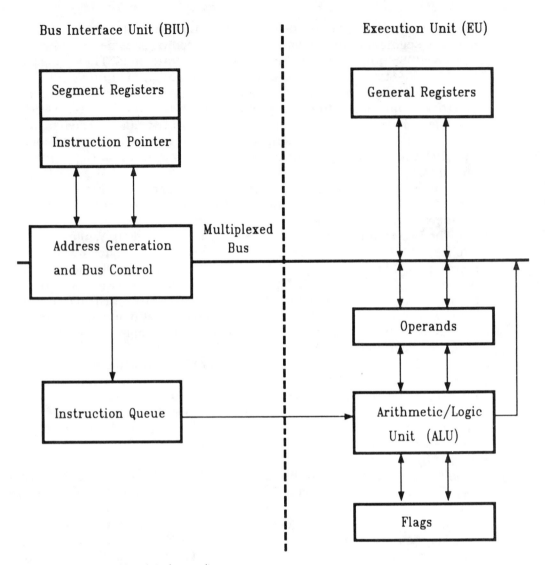

A-6 Execution and bus interface units.

control signal pins to take on other functions such as bus-locking capability and extra direct memory access (DMA) control. In the minimum mode configuration, the 8086 generates the control signals used by the memory and I/O devices.

The instruction set of the 8086 is divided into six categories: Data transfer, Arithmetic, Logic, String manipulation, Control transfer, and Processor control.

Memory in the 8086 is made up of 8-bit bytes with any two consecutive bytes forming a 16-bit word. For the first time, more than 64K of memory could be addressed. Memory itself is composed of an arbitrary number of segments, each consisting of 64K successive bytes. The concept of *segments* is important because memory addressing takes place through such segments.

Each memory segment begins at an address that is evenly divisible by 16. The segment of interest method is specified through the four segment registers. At any specific moment, the 8086 can directly address the contents of the four segments: code segment, data segment, stack segment, and extra data segment. Segments may overlap each other.

To address bytes or words inside a segment, a 16-bit offset address, often called the *effective address* (EA), is used with the contents of any segment registers. The programmer specifies which segment register is to be used, and the designation of that segment register is incorporated within the instruction itself.

The 8086 can address up to one megabyte of memory (actually 1,048,576 bytes). The physical address is constructed by using both the offset address and the content of the designated segment register. This begins by shifting the segment address left four places and appending four zeros (0000) to the low-order bit positions. The effective address is then added to this 20-bit number to form the actual physical address. See FIG. A-7 for a representation of the 8086 memory addressing.

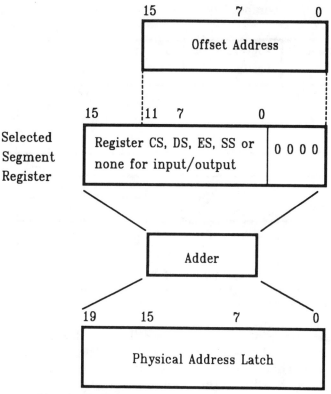

A-7   Memory addressing in the 8086.

The basic form of the 8086 instruction is shown in FIG. A-8. The first byte comprises an opcode, a 1-bit D field, and a 1-bit W field. The D means direction, and the W is width. If D=0, it is the direction "to"; if D=1, it is "from." The width field distinguishes between byte instructions (where W=0) and word instructions (where W=1).

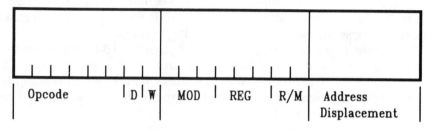

A-8   8086 instruction format.

The mode field, MOD, makes up the next two bits of the instruction format. MOD refers to the addressing mode being used. It specifies how the data in the R/M (register/memory) field is to be used in finding the operand. If MOD=11, the R/M field is treated as a register field.

The register field, REG, specifies either an 8-bit or 16-bit register, which is the location of the operand. The register fields are defined in FIG. A-9.

Instruction Prefix	Address–Size Prefix	Operand–Size Prefix	Segment Override
0 or 1	0 or 1	0 or 1	0 or 1
Number of Bytes			

Opcode	MOD R/M	SIB	Displacement	Immediate
1 or 2	0 or 1	0 or 1	0, 1, 2, or 4	0, 1, 2, or 4
Number of Bytes				

A-9   General instruction format.

The register/memory field specifies either the location in memory where the operand can be found or the location of the operand. One of two bytes can follow. They are the address displacement, if the R/M field requires it. Finally, the DISP is the displacement byte that follows the R/M field.

Certain memory locations in the 8086 (and later in the 8088 and the 80186) are reserved by Intel for use by future hardware and software products. The various locations are shown in FIG. A-10.

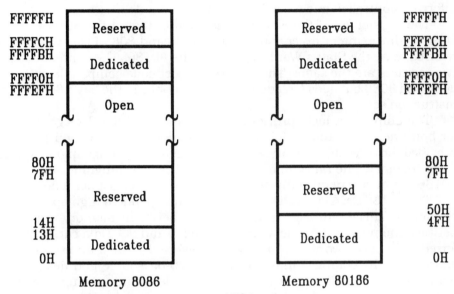

A-10   Reserved and dedicated memory and I/O locations.

8087 coprocessors   During the evolution of Intel's processors, a parallel evolution occurred: coprocessors. A *coprocessor* is a subordinate processor that performs a specialized function for a general-purpose processor. The first popular coprocessor was the 8087, which performs floating-point computations for both the 8086 and the 8088. It also served as the coprocessor for the 80186 when that processor was developed.

The 8088 chip

The 8088 is an 8-bit version of the 8086 and appeared in 1979. Memory handling in the 8088 is sequenced up to a million bytes, the same as with the 8086. The 8088 accesses memory in bytes, however. Word operands are accessed in two bus cycles regardless of their alignment. Instructions are also fetched one byte at a time.

As with the 8086, memory is made up of an arbitrary number of segments, each containing a maximum of 64K. The calculation of the address is done the same way, to result in the 20-bit word address automatically by adding the 16-bit offset address (also called the logical address) to the contents of a 16-bit segment register, with the four low-order zero appended. See the more complete description under the 8086 chip. IBM used the 8088 as the processor for their popular IBM PC.

The 80186 chip

In addition to the features of the 8086 and 8088 CPUs, the 80186 integrates a chip-select logic unit, two independent high-speed *direct memory address* (DMA) channels, three programmable timers, a programmable interrupt controller, and a clock generator.

The register set of the 80186 is identical to that of the 8086 and the 8088, with the minor exception that the 8086 and 8088 Flags Register is referred to as the Status Word Register in the 80186. The contents of the two registers are the same. The 80186 is object code compatible with the 8086 and 8088 but adds ten additional instructions to the basic 8086/8088 instruction set.

The chip-select logic provides programmable chip-select generation for both memories and peripherals. Six memory chip-select outputs are provided for three address areas: upper memory, midrange memory, and lower memory. The range of each chip-select is user programmable. The 80186 can also generate chip-selects for up to seven peripheral devices.

The 80186 DMA controller provides two independent high-speed DMA channels. This controller transfers data between memory and I/O, between memory and memory, or between I/O and I/O. Data can be transferred in bytes or words and may be transferred to or from even or odd addresses. The channels maintain both a 20-bit source and destination pointer that optionally can be incremented or decremented after each data transfer.

Three 16-bit internal programmable timers exist, two of them flexible, connected to external pins and able to count external events, time external events, generate nonrepetitive waveforms, and so on. Not connected to external pins, the third timer is useful for real-time coding and time delays.

The on-chip clock generator provides both internal and external clock generation. It includes a crystal oscillator, a divide-by-two counter, synchronous and asynchronous ready inputs, and reset circuitry.

The interrupt controller on the 80186 receives interrupts from a number of sources, both internal and external. The internal interrupt controller merges these two requests on a priority basis for individual service by the CPU. This controller has its own control registers that it uses to set the mode of operation for the controller.

The BIU (bus interface unit) of the 80186 is functionally identical with the 8088 but is implemented differently to match the data path size (which is 16 bits wide). Where the 8088 instruction queue held four bytes of the instruction stream, the 80186 stores up to six bytes. This queue size keeps the EU (execution unit) supplied with prefetched instructions under most conditions without monopolizing the system bus.

The 8086 and the 80186 access either 8 or 16 bits of memory at a time. If an instruction refers to a word variable and that variable is located at an even-numbered address, both the 8086 and the 80186 access the complete word in one bus cycle. If the word is located at an odd-numbered address, it is accessed one byte at a time in two consecutive bus cycles.

The 80186 instruction set includes all the instructions from as early as the 8080 chip. Ten new instruction types were added to streamline the existing code or to produce optimum 80186 code.

Figure A-11 shows a block diagram of the 80186.

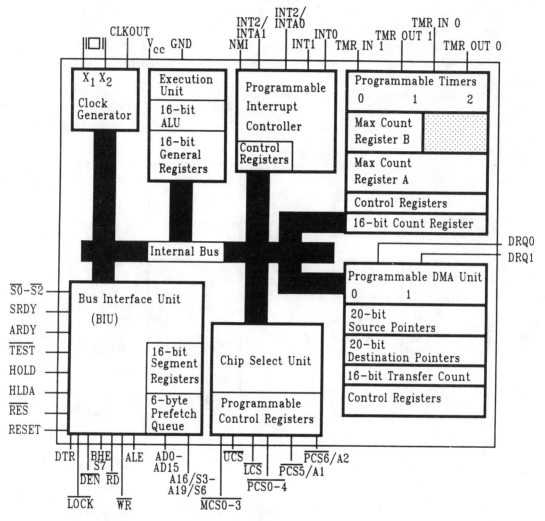

A-11 80186 block diagram.

The 80286 chip

In 1983, Intel came out with the 80286, a big leap beyond the 80186. A year later, IBM announced that the 80286 would be the processor for their IBM PC/AT (AT stands for Advanced Technology).

The 80286 has two modes of operation: *real* and *virtual*. In *real mode*, the 80286 operates much like a fast 8086. Think of the memory as a number of segments, each containing a maximum of 2^{16} bytes. Each segment begins at a byte address evenly divisible by 16. At any moment in time, the processor can access the contents of four segments. Those segments are the current code segment (CS), the current data segment (DS), the current stack segment (SS), and the current extra segment (ES). These segments may overlap and need not be unique. The addresses of these segments are stored in the segment registers.

Full addresses are computed by placing the 16 most significant bits of the address into the register, with four zeros appended to the end. This scheme is identical to the 8086.

Bytes within the segments are referred to by using a 16-bit offset within the segment. See FIG. A-12 for an example of how segments are established. Note that the stack segment and the data segment overlap in the example.

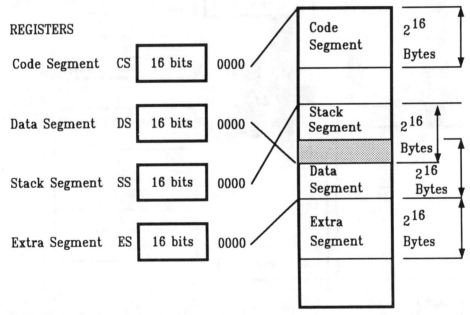

A-12 Example of memory segments.

Virtual mode still has segments and offsets. It differs from real in that the segment start addresses are not computed by appending four zeros to the contents of segment registers but are obtained from tables indexed by the segment registers. Additional information on address calculations is given in Chapter 8.

The 80286 is first brought up in real mode, and various necessary registers and flags are set. Then the processor switches from real to virtual mode by use of the LMSW (Load Machine Status Word) instruction. This instruction loads the Status Word with a word in which the protection enable bit is set. Once the 80286 is in virtual mode, only a hardware reset signal can return it to real mode.

This processor addresses up to two megabytes (mega = million) of real memory or four gigabytes (giga = billion) of virtual memory. However, because it was designed to perform 16-bit arithmetic, the addresses it manipulates can only be 16 bits in length. Virtual mode was the solution to this constraint.

The 80286 took the DMA controller off-chip. The purpose of a DMA channel is to produce a steady stream of memory references without involving the CPU. The off-chip controller allows overlap of execution with input or output to memory. The DMA controller contains four DMA channels, so up to four devices may be empowered to perform DMA.

The 80286 instruction set incorporates all the instructions sets, beginning with the 8086. In addition, new instructions exist for virtual and real modes. In real mode, the advanced 80286 features are suppressed, while in virtual mode, they are enabled.

80287 coprocessor The popular 8087 floating-point processor used with the 8086 and 8088 was modified for the 80286 to handle the new coprocessor interface that Intel developed for the 80286. The new coprocessor was named 80287.

The 80287 provides additional registers for the floating point computation. The floating point operands of the 80287 instructions reside either in memory or in one of the eight numeric registers. These registers hold numbers in extended precision format only.

It's possible for the 80286 and 80287 to both execute instructions simultaneously. When the 80286 finds an 80287 instruction (the first five bits are "11011"), it waits until the 80287 is idle and then allows the 80287 to begin that instruction. In the meantime, the 80286 doesn't remain in wait state; it moves to the next instruction in the queue. If the 80286 finds another 80287 instruction *before* the 80287 has finished with its first one, then the processor does go into a wait state. Otherwise, it executes that next instruction.

Privilege levels The 80286 initiated a scheme for protecting various parts of memory for its virtual mode. The smaller level number, the more privileged the level. These privilege levels are stored in three different places. The first is the *Descriptor Privilege Level* (DPL), which is the segment classification. The second is the *Requested Privilege Level* (RPL). The third is the *Current Privilege Level* (CPL). These are automatically maintained by the 80286.

In order to access a segment for reading or writing, a program must load a selector for that segment into a segment register. To keep the program from simply accessing any segment by creating a selector for it and loading that selector into a segment register, the 80286 produces a protection exception if the currently executing program has a level less than that associated with the segment.

Multitasking Another new feature the 80286 offers is the ability to support multiple tasks by switching from one task to another. With the task, the 80286 associates a memory segment containing all the information needed to start and stop the task. This special segment is called a *Task State Segment* (TSS). The main use for the TSS is to hold the contents of that task's registers when the 80286 is not executing the task.

The 80386 chip

The 80386 is a high-performance, 32-bit microprocessor that processes instructions at a quick rate of 3 to 4 million per second. It has a complete 32-bit architecture with a 4 gigabyte physical address space and on-chip support for paged virtual memory. The 80386 can address up to 2^{64} bytes of virtual memory—or 64 terabytes (tera = trillion). Shown in FIG. A-13 is a block diagram of the functional blocks of the 80386.

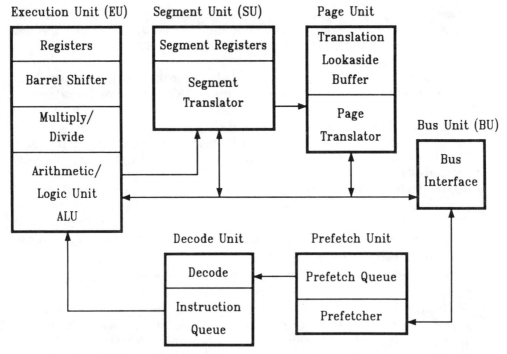

A-13 Functional blocks within the 80386.

The 80386 package is a 132-pin ceramic *pin grid array* (PGA). Pins in this package are arranged 0.100 inch (2.54 mm) center-to-center in a 14 × 14 matrix, three rows around. From the pin side of the package, pin number one is in the upper left corner. See FIG. A-14.

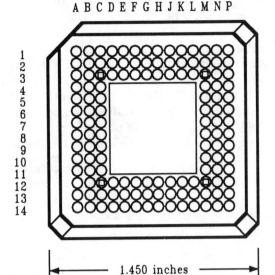

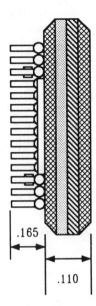

⬛ = Swedge pin standoff, 4 places

A B C D E F G H J K L M N P

1 2 3 4 5 6 7 8 9 10 11 12 13 14

1.450 inches

.165

.110

A-14 132-pin ceramic PGA package.

With this processor, for the first time, true virtual machine capability is offered. Virtual memory allows very large programs, or groups of programs, to run in much smaller amounts of physical memory without overlays. A virtual memory operating system stores all segments or pages in a large disk area, often called the *swap area*. The much smaller real memory holds only the most frequently used segments or pages.

The 80386 can switch between programs running under different operating systems such as MS-DOS and UNIX. This allows software designers to incorporate standard 16-bit applications software directly onto the new 32-bit system.

The 80386 instruction set is divided into nine categories of operations: Data transfer, Arithmetic, Shift/Rotate, String Manipulation, Bit Manipulation, Control Transfer, High Level Language Support, Operating System Support and Processor Control. The average instruction is 3.2 bytes long. Because the 80386 has a 16-byte instruction queue, that means an average of 5 instructions will be prefetched.

Operands in the 80386 instruction set can be 8, 16, or 32 bits long. When executing existing 80286 or 8086 code (both 16-bit codes), operands are 8 or 16 bits.

The two generations of processors (8086 and 80286) are compatible with the 80386 at the binary level. The 80386s most innovative step is its compatibility feature of Virtual 8086 capability. This capability establishes a protected 8086 environment within the 80386 multitasking framework.

Segments   The 80386 logical address space can be defined as one or more segments any size from 1 byte to 4 gigabytes. The segments can be individually protected by privilege level and thus selectively shared between tasks.

An 80386 program can potentially refer to multiple segments. Therefore, the logical address must identify the segment. The logical address consists of 16-bit *segment selector* and a 32-bit *offset* into the selected segment. The 80386 determines the segment's address by using the selector as an index into a *descriptor table* which it maintains. The processor then adds the offset part of the logical address to the base address it just obtained from the segment's descriptor to produce the operand address.

Coprocessor   The 80386 can use either the 80287 numeric coprocessor or the newer 80387 coprocessor. Both numeric coprocessors contain registers that improve the 80386s performance. By connecting either the 80287 or the 80387 to an 80386, the coprocessor's registers are effectively added to the 80386s.

Privilege levels   The 80386 provides an array of protection mechanisms that operating systems can employ selectively to fit their needs. Many of the 80386 protection facilities are based on the notion of a *privilege hierarchy*. On other words, various tasks or programs can be assigned various levels used on an exclusive basis to other tasks operating within the system.

An unprotected system can be implemented by simply placing all procedures in a segment (or segments) where the privilege level is 0 (zero). In a slightly more protected environment, the operating system can be placed in level zero while application programs can run in level 1 (one), and so on.

In a protected system, a task's privilege level determines what instructions it may execute and what subset of segments in its address space it may reference. An attempt by a task to use a more restricted segment results in a general protection exception.

In addition to defining which segments it can use, a task's privilege level defines the instructions it can execute. The 80386 was designed with a number of instructions whose execution must be tightly controlled to prevent serious system disruption. Those instructions are called *privileged instructions.*

Multitasking   Multitasking is the technique that manages the system's work when that work consists of multiple activities. Three examples of that work are editing one file, compiling another, and transmitting a third to another computer system. In the multitasking system, each activity that can proceed in parallel with other activities is called a *task* or process.

The operating system simulates multiple processors by providing each task with a *virtual processor.* At any point in time, the operating system assigns the real processor to one of the virtual processors that runs its associated task. The operating system frequently switches the real processor to a different virtual processor, thus maintaining the illusion of one processor per task.

The operating system interleaves task execution according to a scheduling policy that sets the order in which tasks run. The 80386 keeps a selector and a descriptor for the running task's TSS in its *task register*.

Each task can have a system-wide logical address space that it stores in a *Global Descriptor Table* (GDT) as well as a logical address space that it stores in the *Local Descriptor Table* (LDT). These descriptor tables can contain up to 8,192 descriptors each. Together, they define the task's logical address space.

The 80486 chip

The 80486 is essentially an enhanced version of the 80386. In fact, from the application programmer's viewpoint, it may appear to be unchanged from the 80386. After all, the addressing range, virtual machine capability, operand sizes, and instruction set (with a few system-related extensions) of the 80486 are the same as on as the 80386.

However, the 80486 is a much faster processor, due to an on-chip cache that allows many instructions to execute much faster on the 80486 than they can on the 80386. In fact, on the 80486, many instructions execute in a single clock cycle!

The 80486 also has an on-chip numeric processor, called the Floating-point Unit, that is functionally the same as the 80387 coprocessor. With the FPU on the chip, we can consider the 80486 as having an additional category of instructions: those that do floating-point math operations.

Comparison of chips

The 8086/88 processors are the foundation of industry-standard personal computing. They provide the base from which the Intel microprocessor family continued to evolve in both function and performance. However, hardware innovation outgrew the 8086/88 architecture. TABLE A-1 shows the growth in functional aspects of the Intel microprocessor chips.

Table A-1   Comparison of Intel microprocessor chips.

Features	8086/88	80286	80386	80486
Maximum physical memory	1 MB	16 MB	4 GB	4 GB
Maximum virtual memory	1 MB	1 GB	64 TB	64 TB
Maximum segment size	64 KB	64 KB	64 KB/4 GB	64 KB/4 GB
Prefetch queue (bytes)	4/6	6	12	32
Operand sizes (bits)	8, 16	8, 16	8, 16, 32	8, 16, 32
Register sizes (bits)	8, 16	8, 16	8, 16, 32	8, 16, 32
Paging hardware?	No	No	Yes	Yes
Memory-I/O protection?	No	Yes	Yes	Yes
Coprocessor support	8087	80287	80287/387	On-chip

B
Register, bits, and flags listings

The following is an alphabetic list of all the registers used with the 80486 processor.

AH	High-order byte of AX register
AL	Low-order byte of AX register
AX	16-bit register, part of EAX
BH	High-order byte of BX register
BL	Low-order byte of BX register
BP	16-bit register, part of EBP
BX	16-bit register, part of EBX
CH	High-order byte of CX register
CL	Low-order byte of CX register
CR0	Control register, low order 16 bits is MSW
CR1	Control register, Reserved
CR2	Page fault linear address register
CR3	Page directory base address
CX	16-bit register, part of ECX
DH	High-order byte of DX register
DI	16-bit register, part of EDI
DL	Low-order byte of DX register
DR0	Debug register, linear breakpoint address 0
DR1	Debug register, linear breakpoint address 1
DR2	Debug register, linear breakpoint address 2
DR3	Debug register, linear breakpoint address 3
DR4	Debug register, Intel reserved
DR5	Debug register, Intel reserved
DR6	Debug register, breakpoint status
DR7	Debug register, breakpoint control

DS	Data segment register	
DX	16-bit register, part of EDX	
EAX	General 32-bit register	
EBP	General 32-bit register, stack-frame base pointer	
EBX	General 32-bit register	
ECX	General 32-bit register	
EDI	General 32-bit register	
EDX	General 32-bit register	
EFLAGS	Flags register	
EIP	Instruction pointer	
ES	Data segment register	
ESI	General 32-bit register	
ESP	Stack pointer register	
FLAGS	The low-order 16 bits of EFLAGS	
FS	Data segment register	
GDT	Global Descriptor Table	
GS	Data segment register	
IDT	Interrupt Descriptor Table	
IP	Instruction pointer, low-order 16 bits of EIP	
LDT	Local descriptor table	
SI	16-bit register, part of ESI	
SP	16-bit register, part of ESP	
SS	Stack segment register	
TR3	Test register for cache, test data	
TR4	Test register for cache, test status	
TR5	Test register for cache, test control	
TR6	Test register for translation lookaside buffer, test command	
TR7	Test register for translation lookaside buffer, test data	
TSS	Task State Segment	

The following is a list of the flags used in the 80486 and its environs, along with which register they're in. Note that if the bit is in the EFLAGS register, it is commonly called a "flag"; otherwise, it's called a "bit."

Bit/Flag	Location	Description
A	Bit 5 of page table entry	Accessed
AC	Bit 18 of EFLAGS	Alignment check
AF	Bit 4 of EFLAGS	Auxiliary carry
AM	Bit 18 of CR0	Alignment mask
B	Bit 15 of FPU status register	Busy
C0	Bit 8 of FPU status register	Condition code 0
C1	Bit 9 of FPU status register	Condition code 1
C2	Bit 10 of FPU status register	Condition code 2
C3	Bit 14 of FPU status register	Condition code 3
CD	Bit 30 of CR0	Cache disable
CF	Bit 0 of EFLAGS	Carry flag

D	Bit 6 of page table entry	Dirty
DE	Bit 1 of FPU status register	Denormalized operand exception
DF	Bit 10 of EFLAGS	Direction flag
DM	Bit 1 of FPU control register	Denormalized operand exception mask
EM	Bit 2 of CR0	Emulation coprocessor
ES	Bit 7 of FPU status register	Error summary
IE	Bit 0 of FPU status register	Invalid operation exception
IF	Bit 9 of EFLAGS	Interrupt enable
IM	Bit 0 of FPU control register	Invalid operation exception mask
IOPL	Bit 13/12 of EFLAGS	I/O privilege level
MP	Bit 1 of CR0	Math present
NE	Bit 5 of CR0	Numeric error
NT	Bit 14 of EFLAGS	Nested task flag
NW	Bit 29 of CR0	Not write-through
OE	Bit 3 of FPU status register	Overflow exception
OF	Bit 11 of EFLAGS	Overflow
OM	Bit 3 of FPU control register	Overflow exception mask
P	Bit 0 of page table entry	Present
PCD	Bit 4 of CR3 and page table entry	Page cache disable
PE	Bit 5 of FPU status register	Precision exception
PE	Bit 0 of CR0	Protection enable
PF	Bit 2 of EFLAGS	Parity flag
PG	Bit 31 of CR0	Paging enable
PM	Bit 5 of FPU control register	Precision exception mask
PWT	Bit 3 of CR3 and page table entry	Page-level write-through
R/W	Bit 1 of page table entry	Read/write
RF	Bit 16 of EFLAGS	Resume flag
SF	Bit 6 of FPU status register	Stack flag
SF	Bit 7 of EFLAGS	Sign flag
TF	Bit 8 of EFLAGS	Trap flag
TS	Bit 3 of CR0	Task switched
UE	Bit 4 of FPU status register	Underflow exception
UM	Bit 4 of FPU control register	Underflow exception mask
U/S	Bit 2 of page table entry	User/supervisor
VM	Bit 17 of EFLAGS	Virtual 8086 mode
WP	Bit 16 of CR0	Write protect
ZE	Bit 2 of FPU status register	Zero divide exception
ZF	Bit 6 of EFLAGS	Zero flag
ZM	Bit 2 of FPU control register	Zero divide exception mask

C
Acronyms and letter groups

A20M#	Address bit 20 Mask pin on 80486
AC	Alternating Current
ACC	Accumulator
ACK	Acknowledge
ADMA	Advanced Direct Memory Access
ADS#	Address status pin on 80386
AHOLD	Address hold request pin on 80486
ALU	Arithmetic-Logic Unit
ASCII	American Standard Code for Information Interchange
ASR	Automatic Send and Receive
A0-A31	Address pins
BCD	Binary Coded Decimal
BCR	Byte Count Register
BEn#	Byte Enable pins on 80486, n = 0 to 3
BIU	Bus Interface Unit
BLAST#	Burst last pin on 80486
BOFF#	Backoff pin on 80486
BPS	Bits Per Second
BREQ	Bus request pin on 80486
BRDY#	Burst ready pin on 80486
BS16#,BS#8	Bus size pins of 80486
BSC	Binary Synchronous Communication
CAD	Computer-Aided Design
CAM	Computer-Aided Manufacturing, also Content-Addressable Memory
CAS	Column Address Select
CCD	Charge-Coupled Device
CE	Chip Enable

CLK	Clock
CML	Current Mode Logic
CMOS	Complementary Metal Oxide Semiconductor
CPG	Clock Pulse Generator
CPL	Current Privilege Level
CPS	Characters Per Second
CPU	Central Processing Unit
CRn	Control Registers, 0 to 3
CRT	Cathode Ray Tube
CRTC	CRT Controller
CS	Chip Select, also Code Segment Register
CU	Control Unit
D/C#	Data/Control Pin on 80486
DC	Direct Current
DCD	Data Carrier Detect
DIP	Dual In-line Pins or Package
DMA	Direct Memory Access (or Address)
DMAC	Direct Memory Access/Address Controller
DOS	Disk Operating System
DPL	Descriptor Privilege Level
DPn	Data Parity pins on 80486, n = 0 to 3
DRAM	Dynamic Random Access Memory
DS	Data Segment Register
DTL	Diode Transistor Logic
D0-D31	Data lines
E	Enable
EA	Effective Address
EADS#	Valid external address pin on 80486
EAROM	Electrically Alterable Read Only Memory
EBCDIC	Extended Binary-Coded-Decimal Interchange Code
ECL	Emitter Coupled Logic
EIP	Instruction Pointer, 32-bit implementation
EMI	ElectroMagnetic Interface
EOF	End of File
EOR	Exclusive OR
EOT	End of Tape, or End of Text
EPL	Effective Privilege Level
EPROM	Erasable Programmable Read-Only Memory
ES	Extra Segment Register
ESI	ElectroStatic Interface
ESP	Extended Stack Pointer
EU	Execution Unit
FDC	Floppy Disk Controller
FDM	Frequency-Division Multiplexing
FERR#	Floating-Point Error pin on 80486
FET	Field Effect Transistor

FF	Flip-Flop
FIFO	First-In/First-Out
FLUSH#	Cache flush pin on 80486
FPLA	Field Programmable Logic Array
FPU	Floating-Point Unit
FSK	Frequency Shift Keying
GDT	Global Descriptor Table
GDTR	Global Descriptor Table Register
GP	General Purpose
GPIB	General Purpose Interface Bus
GR	General Registers
HDLC	High-Level Data Link Control
HEX	Hexadecimal
HLDA	Hold Acknowledge Pin on 80486
HMOS	High-density Metal Oxide Semiconductor
HOLD	Bus hold request Pin on 80486
I	Interrupt, also Interrupt Mask
IC	Integrated Circuit
IDT	Interrupt Descriptor Table
IDTR	Interrupt Descriptor Table Register
IGNNE#	Ignore Numeric Error pin on 80486
INT	Interrupt
INTR	Maskable Interrupt
I/O	Input/Output
IOCS	Input/Output Control System
IOPL	Input/Output Privilege Level
IP	Instruction Pointer, 16-bit implementation
IRET	Interrupt Return
IRQ	Interrupt Request
JP	Jump
K	Kilo, also 1024
KEN#	Cache enable pin on 80486
KSR	Keyboard Send/Receive
LAN	Local Area Network
LCD	Liquid Crystal Display
LDT	Local Descriptor Table
LDTR	Local Descriptor Table Register
LED	Light-Emitting Diode
LIFO	Last-In/First-Out
LOCK#	Bus lock pin on 80486
LP	Line Printer
LPM	Lines per Minute
LSB	Least Significant Bit
LSI	Large Scale Integration
MHz	Mega-Hertz, millions of cycles per second
M/IO	Memory and Input/Output

MMU	Memory Management Unit
MOFFS	Memory offset
MOS	Metal Oxide Semiconductor
MOSFET	Metal Oxide Semiconductor Field Effect Transistor
MPSC	Multi-Protocol Serial Controller
MPU	Microprocessor Unit
MSB	Most Significant Bit
MSI	Medium Scale Integration
MSW	Machine Status Word (used on 80286)
MUX	Multiplexer
N	Negative
NDRO	Non-Destructive Read Out
NMI	Non-Maskable Interrupt
NMOS	N-Channel Metal Oxide Semiconductor
OEM	Original Equipment Manufacturer
OP	Operation
OPLA	One-Page Lookahead
OS	Operating System
P	Positive
PAL	Programmable Array Logic
PC	Printed Circuit, also Personal Computer
PCD	Page Cache Disable
PCHK#	Parity Check pin on 80486
PCI/O	Program Controlled Input/Output
PCM	Pulse Code Modulation
PDBR	Page Directory Base Register
PFR	Power Fail Restart
PGA	Pin Grid Array
PIC	Priority Interrupt Control
PIO	Programmable Input/Output Chip (Interface)
PIT	Programmable Interval-Timer
PL	Privilege Level
PLA	Programmable Logic-Array
PLL	Phase-Locked Loop
PLOCK#	Pseudo-lock pin on 80486
PMOS	P-channel Metal Oxide Semiconductor
PROM	Programmable Read-Only Memory
PSW	Programmable Status Word
PWT	Page Write-through
R	Read
R/W	Read/Write
RALU	Register Arithmetic-Logic Unit
RAM	Random Access Memory
RAS	Row Address Select
RDSR	Receiver Data Service Request
RDY#	Non-burst ready pin on 80486

RDY#	Ready pin on 80486
RESET	Reset pin on 80486
ROM	Read-Only Memory
RPL	Requestor's Privilege Level
RPT	Repeat
RS	Register Select
RST	Restart
RTC	Real-Time Clock
RTS	Request to Send
SDLC	Synchronous Data Link Control
Si	Silicon (element)
SIB	Scale Index Base
SIP	Single In-line Package
SLSI	Super Large Scale Integration
SOS	Silicon-On-Saphire
SP	Stack Pointer
SR	Service Request
SRAM	Static Random Access Memory
SS	Stack Segment Register
SSI	Small Scale Integration
STB	Strobe
STEN	Status Enable
SUB	Subroutine
TDM	Time Division Multiplexing
TLB	Translation Lookaside Buffer
TOS	Top of Stack
TSS	Task State Segment
TTL	Transistor-Transistor Logic
U/S	User/Supervisor
USART	Universal Synchronous/Asynchronous Receiver Transmitter
VLSI	Very Large Scale Integration
VM	Virtual Mode, also Virtual Machine
Vss	Ground
W	Write
WPM	Words per Minute
W/R#	Read/Write Pin on 80486
X	Index
XOR	Exclusive OR
Z	Zero Bit

D
MULTIBUS I/II
and the 80486

The system bus structure that supplies the interface for all the hardware connections is one of the most important elements in a computer system. This structure permits various system components to interact with each other and to share resources. Resource sharing results in a significant increase in throughput over a single-bus system. Among other actions, the system bus allows memory and I/O data transfers, direct memory accesses, and the generation of interrupts.

System buses are usually isolated from failures occurring in other parts of the system, which enhances the system's overall reliability. As samples of a general bus, the Intel MULTIBUS I and II architectures provide a communications channel that can be used to coordinate a wide variety of computing modules.

MULTIBUS I and II were introduced in Chapter 12. Some background is included here, but this appendix primarily addresses the bus and its relationship with the 80486.

Both MULTIBUS I and II are built on the master-slave concept. A *master* is any module that has the ability to control the bus. The master does this by acquiring the bus through bus exchange logic and then generating command signals, address signals, and I/O or memory addresses. To do these tasks, the master is equipped with either a central processing unit or logic dedicated to transferring data over to the bus to and from other destinations. A *slave* is a module that decodes the address lines and acts upon the command signals from the masters; a slave is *not* capable of controlling the bus. This handshake between the master and slave allows modules of different speeds to be interfaced via the bus. The bus master can override the bus control logic when it is necessary to guarantee itself back-to-back bus cycles. This is called "locking" the bus, which temporarily prevents other masters from using the bus.

Another important feature is the bus's ability to connect multiple master modules for multiprocessing systems.

MULTIBUS I allows for both 8- and 16-bit data paths and up to a 24-bit address path. MULTIBUS II can accept 8-, 16-, and 32-bit data and up to 32-bit addresses. MULTIBUS I and II protocols are described in detail in the Intel documentation, which should be studied in detail before implementing either MULTIBUS I or II on a system.

MULTIBUS I

Intel's MULTIBUS I is a 16-bit multiprocessing system bus that conforms to the IEEE 796 standard. Figure D-1 shows a block diagram of the MULTIBUS I interface. The figure does not include the 80486 local bus interface and local resources.

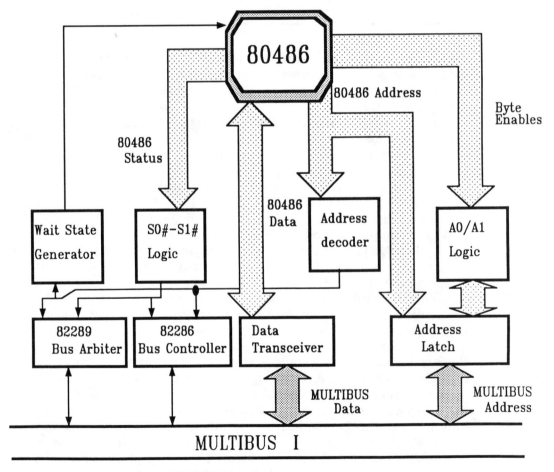

D-1 Block diagram of 80486-MULTIBUS I interface.

MULTIBUS I interface sample

One way to construct an interface between the 80386 and MULTIBUS I is to generate all the MULTIBUS I signals using only PAL and TTL devices. A simpler way is to use the 80286-compatible interface, outlines of which are shown below.

This MULTIBUS I interface consists of the 80286-compatible 82289 Bus Arbiter and the 82288 Bus Controller. The 82288 operates in either local-bus mode or MULTIBUS I mode; a pullup resistor on the 82288 MB input activates the MULTIBUS I mode. The MBEN output of the address decoder PAL selects both the 82288 and the 82289. The AEN# signal from the 82289 enables the 82288 outputs.

Communication between the 80486 processor and these two devices is done with PALs programmed to do the necessary signal generation and translation. Along with the bus arbiters of other processing subsystems, the 82289 coordinates control of MULTIBUS I by providing the control signals to perform MULTIBUS I accesses.

In a MULTIBUS I system, each processing subsystem contends for the use of shared resources. If a subsystem requests access to the bus while another is already using it, the second must wait. Bus arbitration logic controls all accesses to the bus by the subsystems. Each of the processing subsystems has its own 82289 Bus Arbiter. The 82289 directs its processor onto the bus and allows higher and lower priority bus masters to access the bus, based on pre-established priorities.

Two common techniques for resolving priority are serial priority and parallel priority. Serial priority is implemented by daisy-chaining the Bus Priority In (BPRN#) and Bus Priority Out (BPRO#) signals of all the bus arbiters in the system. There is some built-in delay in this scheme, which limits the number of bus arbiters that can be attached. Parallel priority requires external logic to recognize the BPRN# inputs from all bus arbiters and to return the BPRO# signal active to whichever requesting bus arbiter has the highest priority. The number of arbiters that can be attached with parallel priority is limited by the complexity of the decoding logic.

After a MULTIBUS I cycle, the controlling bus arbiter can either keep control or release it to another bus arbiter. To release control, the bus arbiter can release the bus at the end of each cycle, retain control of the bus until a higher priority bus master requests control, or retain control until another bus master of any priority requests control.

MULTIBUS I allows up to 24 address lines and 16 data lines. Its addresses are located in a 256-kilobyte range (between F00000H and F3FFFFH) and all 24 lines are used. The 16 data lines consist of the lower half (least significant 16 bits) of the 32-bit 80486 data bus. MULTIBUS I address bits are numbered in hexadecimal; A23-A0 on the 80486 bus becomes ADR17#-ADR0# on MULTIBUS I. Inverting addresses latches convert the 80486 address outputs to the active-low MULTIBUS I address bits.

Address decoder A MULTIBUS I system generally has both shared and local memory. In addition, I/O devices can also be located on either a local bus or on MULTIBUS I. In essence, the address space of the 80486 must be allocated between MULTIBUS I and the local bus, and address decoding logic must be used to select one bus or the other. Two signals are needed for MULTIBUS I selection:

- MULTIBUS Enable (MBEN) selects the 82288 Bus Controller and the 82289 Bus Arbiter on the MULTIBUS I interface. The decoder PAL has other outputs programmed to select memory and I/O devices on the local bus.

- Bus Size 16 (BS16#) must be returned active to the 80486 to ensure the 16-bit bus cycle. Other terms for other devices that require a 16-bit bus can be added to the BS16# PAL equation.

I/O resources residing on MULTIBUS I can be either I/O-mapped into the I/O address space independent of the physical location of the devices on MULTIBUS I or memory-mapped into the memory space of the 80486. The addresses of memory-mapped I/O devices must be decoded to generate the correct I/O read or I/O write commands for all the memory references that lie within the I/O-mapped region of the memory space.

Address latches/Data transceivers The address on all bus cycles is latched because MULTIBUS I requires address outputs to be valid for at least 50 nanoseconds after the MULTIBUS I command goes inactive. The 82289 Bus Arbiter Address Enable (AEN#) output goes active when the 82289 has control of MULTIBUS I. AEN# is an output enable for the MULTIBUS I latches. As shown in FIG. D-2, the 82288 Bus Controller ALE# output latches the 80486 address.

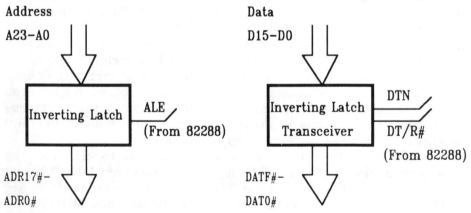

D-2 Example of MULTIBUS I address latches and data transceivers.

MULTIBUS I data bits are numbered in hexadecimal, so that D15-D0 converts to DATF#-DAT0#. Inverting latch/transceivers provide active-low

MULTIBUS I data bits. Data is latched only on write cycles. During *write* cycles, the 82288 ALE#, DEN, and DT/R# inputs control the address latches and the data latch/transceivers. For *read* cycles, the local bus RD# signal controls the latch/transceivers because, if DEN were used, data contention on the 80386 local bus would occur when a MULTIBUS I read cycle immediately followed a local write cycle.

iSBX expansion I/O bus

The iSBX Bus is independent of processor or board type. Each expansion interface supports up to 16 8-bit I/O ports directly. Enhanced addressing capability is available using slave processors or FIFO devices. Also, each expansion interface can optionally support a DMA channel capable of data rates up to 2 Mwords/second.

Two basic elements of the iSBX are the baseboard and the expansion module. The *baseboard* is any board that provides one or more I/O expansion interfaces (connectors) meeting the electrical and mechanical requirements of the Intel specification. Logically, the baseboard is always the master device, which makes it responsible for generating all addresses, chip selects and commands.

The iSBX *expansion module* is a small, specialized I/O board that attaches to a baseboard. Each module can be single wide and double wide. The expansion module converts the general bus interface into a specific I/O interface.

Increasing the number of functions residing on each system board attached to the MULTIBUS I interface increases system performance. The improved performance results because the resident functions are accessed without bus arbitration.

Multi-channel bus

The multi-channel bus is a specialized electrical and mechanical interfacing protocol operating within the overall MULTIBUS I interfacing system. This bus is designed for high speed block data transfers between the MULTIBUS I system and the interconnected peripheral devices. Where a series of bytes or words are moved to or from consecutive locations, the block data transfer protocol minimizes that transfer overhead. The transfers are asynchronous and use a positive handshake protocol along with transfer parity verification to assure accurate data transfer.

Reducing the impact of burst-type peripherals on MULTIBUS I provides a means of increasing system performance. The data transfers from a burst type peripheral can saturate a general purpose interface. The multi-channel bus protocol specifically accommodates burst-type data transfers. The full performance improvement requires use of dual port memory accessed over both the multi-channel bus and the MULTIBUS I interface.

iLBX execution bus

The iLBX bus is designed for direct high-speed master-slave data transfers and provides the following: two (maximum) masters that can share the bus, limiting the need for complex bus arbitration; bus arbitration that is asynchronous to the data transfers; a minimum of two and maximum of five devices that can be connected over the iLBX bus; slave devices that are defined as byte-addressed memory resources; and slave devices whose functions are directly controlled from iLBX bus signal lines.

Increasing the local (on-board) memory resources of a high performance processor provides a means of increasing system performance. As with other special functions, memory residing on the processor board improves performance because the processor directly addresses the memory without waiting for bus arbitration. However, because of physical limits, only a restricted amount of memory can reside on the processor board. The iLBX bus helps to reduce that physical space limitation.

Using the iLBX bus, additional memory no longer needs to be located on the processor board. The full number of megabytes of memory addressable by the processor can be accessed over the iLBX bus and appears to the processor as though it were resident on the processor's board. Dual porting the memory between the iLBX bus and the MULTIBUS I interface makes the same memory available to other system components.

Up to five devices can be attached to the iLBX bus. This set must include a *primary master* and one *slave* device. The remaining three devices are optional and may include additional slave devices and one *secondary master*. The primary master controls the iLBX bus and manages the secondary master access to the slave memory resources. The optional secondary master provides alternate access over the iLBX board to the slave resources.

MULTIBUS I design considerations

Some design considerations must be kept in mind when using MULTIBUS I with the 80486, such as interrupt handling, 8-bit transfers, timeout protection, and power failure handling. For complete details, a designer should obtain Intel's latest manuals on the MULTIBUS I architecture. A summary of those items follows.

Interrupt handling   When the 80486 receives an interrupt, it generates an interrupt-acknowledge cycle to fetch an 8-bit interrupt vector from a device such as the 8259A Programmable Interrupt Controller, which can be located on either MULTIBUS I or on a local bus. Multiple 8259As can be cascaded (one master and up to eight slaves) to process up to 64 interrupts.

The 80386 responds to an active INTR input by performing two bus cycles. During the first cycle, the master interrupt controller determines which of its slave controllers should return the interrupt vector. During the second cycle, the 80486 reads the vector from the selected interrupt controller and uses this vector to service the interrupt.

8-Bit transfers   All byte transfers on a MULTIBUS I must be performed on the lower eight data lines regardless of the address of the data. An 80486 system must swap data from eight of its upper 24 lines (D8-D15, D16-D23 or D24-D31) to its lower eight data lines (D0-D7) before transferring data to MULTIBUS I. It also must swap data from its lower data lines to the appropriate upper data lines when reading a byte from MULTIBUS I. This byte-swapping maintains compatibility between 8-bit, 16-bit, and 32-bit systems sharing the same MULTIBUS I.

BS16# is generated and returned to the 80486 for all MULTIBUS I cycles. The 80486 automatically swaps the data on its data bus and adds an extra bus cycle as necessary to complete the data transfer. Thus, only logic to swap from D8-D15 to D0-D7 needs to be added.

Bus timeouts   The MULTIBUS I XACK# (transfer acknowledgment) signal ends an 80486 bus cycle by driving the wait-state generator logic. If the 80486 addresses a nonexistent device on MULTIBUS I, the XACK# signal is never generated. If the system does not have a bus-timeout protection circuit, the 80486 could wait indefinitely for a never-arriving active READY# signal, which would prevent other processors from using MULTIBUS I.

Power failure handling   MULTIBUS I includes a Power Fail Interrupt (PFIN#) signal indicating an imminent system power failure. PFIN# is typically connected to the nonmaskable interrupt (NMI) request input of each 80486. The NMI service routine should direct the 80486 to save its environment immediately, before falling voltages and the MULTIBUS I Memory Protect (MPRO#) signal prevent further memory activity. In a system with memory backup power or nonvolatile memory, this saved environment can be recovered on power-up.

The 80486 power-up sequence should check the state of the MULTIBUS I Power Fail Sense Latch (PFSN#). If a previous power failure occurred, the 80486 can branch to a routine that resets the latch using the Power Fail Sense Reset signal (PFSR#) and then restore the previous 80486 environment to resume execution.

MULTIBUS II

The MULTIBUS II is a processor-independent bus architecture. It features a 32-bit parallel system bus with a maximum throughput of 40 megabytes per second. MULTIBUS II boards from every manufacturer are implemented with the same bus controller: a Message-Passing Coprocessor (MPC).

iPSB Parallel System Bus

The iPSB Parallel System Bus is used for interprocessor data transfers and communication. Its burst transfer capability provides a maximum sustained bandwidth of 40 megabytes per second.

A *bus agent* is a board encompassing a functional subsystem. Each bus agent must provide a means of transferring data between its 80486, its interconnect registers, and the iPSB bus. The iPSB supports four address spaces per bus agent: conventional I/O, conventional memory address space, a 255 address message space supporting message passing, and an interconnect space that allowing geographic addressing, which is the identification of any bus agent (board) by slot number. Because the 80386 accesses only memory space or I/O space, the message space and interconnect space can be mapped into either memory space or the I/O space.

Three types of bus cycles define the activity that passes over the iPSB. The first is an *arbitration cycle* that determines the next owner of the bus. This cycle is made up of decision phase (which determines priority for bus control) and an acquisition phase (where the agent with the highest priority starts a transfer cycle).

The second iPSB bus cycle is a *transfer cycle* that performs a data transfer between the bus owner and another bus agent. The third iPSB bus cycle is the *exception cycle*, which indicates that an exception has occurred during a transfer cycle.

Message-Passing Coprocessor (MPC)

Intel's 82389 Message-Passing Coprocessor (MPC) chip greatly simplifies the design of message-passing boards and reduces the software burden by assisting data movement. The 82389 MPC is a 70,000-transistor VLSI device that implements the MULTIBUS II Parallel System Bus (PSB) specification.

The MPC contains nearly all of the logic needed to interface any microprocessor to the Parallel System Bus. To assemble a complete MULTIBUS II interface, all you need is the MPC, some bus transceivers, and a microcontroller such as the Intel 8751. The external signals of the MPC support four major interfaces: PSB bus interface, processor (local) bus interface, interconnect bus space, and dual-port memory control interface.

The 82389 MPC makes the PSB bus interface very straightforward, which simplifies board design and enhances compatibility with other boards. The processor bus interface offers board designers more options, such as the option of using an 8-, 16-, 24-, or 32-bit local processor. It also offers signals to control DMA or assist in dual-port memory operations.

E
Instructions used
in protected mode
and a sample program

The program listed in this appendix first sets up an 80486 environment and then task switches to a virtual 8086 (V86) task. From the V86 task, a return and stay-resident exit is made to MS-DOS. Input/Output and I/O interrupt masking is left up to MS-DOS. Figure E-1 shows the overview flow chart. Following the chart is a word description of the logic flow to the program.

The program is included as a demonstration of use of 80486 instructions and is *not* meant as a model to learn the most effective or efficient way to program. It tries to use most of the instructions a "working" program would and has thorough internal documentation easily followed by programmers.

Logic flow

Most of the program interrupts are reflected to the MS-DOS interrupt handlers. IRET and INT nn instructions cause an interrupt 13.

STEP 1: Define the macros for the 80486 instructions, prefixes, and so on, which are used in the instruction examples.

- Convert an 8086 segment register value to a linear address.

- Set TSS linear address into a descriptor.

- Convert an 8086 segment into a linear address in a segment descriptor.

STEP 2: Describe the data structures used by the program. The TSS is described within the body of the data in order to allow use of data references for its initialization. This descriptor is "generic" because descriptors define

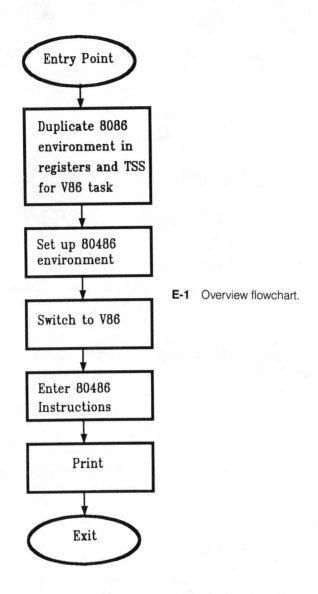

E-1 Overview flowchart.

segments, such as code segments, data segments, stacks, and so on.

DESCRIPTION	STRUCTURE	EXPLANATION
LIMIT	Word	Offset of last byte of TSS or (if not a TSS), the low 16 bits that limit the descriptor
BASE_L	Word	Bits 0-15 of 32-bit address
BASE_M	Byte	Bits 16-23 of address
ACCESS	Byte	Access Privilege

DESCRIPTION	STRUCTURE	EXPLANATION
GRAN	Byte	Granularity and LIMIT
BASE_H	Byte	Bits 24-31 of BASE

- Describe the stack of the Level 0 interrupt handler for the V86 (Virtual 8086) mode task. Note that, in the program, the description is "upside down" because it is used as a data area that addresses from low to high, not a stack.

STEP 3: Define the segmented structure of the program. A simple model with a single real segment was chosen because it is easily converted to a .COM file.

STEP 4: Declare the Stack Segments and the Data Segments.

STEP 5: Define the Global Descriptor Table (GDT) space.

- Level 3 empty LDT.

- Level 0 empty LDT.

- Dynamic data reference used in Interrupt Handler.

- Reference to real location zero for MS-DOS interrupt vectors.

- Descriptors for use by Interrupt Handlers.

- Descriptors for use by instruction execution task.

STEP 6: Define the Interrupt Descriptor Table (IDT) space. The addresses are initialized as part of the setup. The selector is that of the supervisor code descriptor.

STEP 7: This section describes a Task State Segment (TSS). On some of the field names, a "t" is prefixed to keep from using the standard 80486 system name.

STEP 8: This section defines various TSSs and Work Areas.

TSS Definitions

- The first TSS gets control on an INT 00 from the V86 mode task. It runs as a Level 0 protected mode task.

- The second TSS is an 80386 task switched out of, to start the V86 task.

- V86 Task, under which MS-DOS will execute. All 8K of the I/O Bit Map bits are set to zero, to allow I/O to devices 0000-FFFF. A byte of all 1's ends the I/O map.

Local data and work areas

- Debug dump controls.

- "1" in a byte enables trace entries.

- "2" causes a normal dump to be taken.

- "3" causes a disaster dump to be taken.

- "0" means no output.

- Define displacement into stack for Interrupt Handler.

- Set segment descriptors.

STEP 9: Build and set up Segment Descriptors for use by 80486 task.

- Convert the real mode segment registers into linear addresses in 80486 descriptors

- Set interrupt handler displacements in their descriptors. We count on the fact that the descriptors and handlers are each generated in a group so they are adjacent within their group.

- Convert linear address of data areas for segment descriptors, such as TSS descriptors and LDT descriptors.

STEP 10: Convert the segment selectors in the 80486 TSS for Interrupt Handlers

STEP 11: Set the Code, Stack, and EFLAGS Registers

- An EFLAGS register of 0002 is fine, so it's left as it is initialized in the TSS.

STEP 12: Set up the V86 TSS. Set descriptor values into the V86 TSS. In this case, we duplicate the environment of the real mode 8086 that would be actually running.

- Set the Level 0 interrupt handler stack segment selector and pointer. We really only need Level 0 but set Level 1 and Level 2 for completeness. We also set only the low 16 bits of ESP because we know that the upper 16 bits will always be zero.

- Set register values needed to continue in 8086 mode (IP and SP).

- Set the EFLAGS in the TSS so it will execute in the V86 mode.

- VM = 1, IOPL = 3, and Interrupts are enabled.

- Set the LDT value in the V86 TSS.

STEP 13: Set up the 80486 registers to run in protected mode.

- Set the GDT and IDT registers in the 80486 CPU.

- We compute the linear address for the descriptor table and store it in memory. We store the size of the table and then load the Descriptor Table Register with these values.

STEP 14: The 80486 environment is set. Now transfer into protected mode. Set the protected mode bit in CR0 and do an intrasegment jump to flush the instruction pipeline.

- Now executing in protected mode.

- Debug aid will optionally dump the data areas just built.

STEP 15: Set the 80486-form descriptor, the Task Register, and do an intersegment jump to load CS. At this point, all descriptors are of 80486 form, even CS.

- Now set the Nested Task (NT) flag and go to the V86 task.

- We transfer to the V86 mode using an IRET. The back chain in the current TSS and the NT flag cause the transfer. The end result is that, from here on, MS-DOS runs as a virtual 8086 task. Entry to protected mode can be done by an INT 00.

Note: This transfer to MS-DOS leaves the user in memory. This is both fortuitous and planned because real control of the CPU is in the hands of the rest of the program. The code to this point could be overlaid; its purpose is complete.

Additional support code for protected mode

- Generate the initial entry points for the interrupt handlers. These entries have a correspondence with the 8086 interrupt vector table. They are the same length (4 bytes) and the return address from the call is used to generate the proper displacement into that table.

- Handle all interrupts and traps. The handler here reflects the interrupt to MS-DOS. This initial code provides a known stack format for later use. We also have saved the interrupt error code, if any, and have the vector number in an easily computable form. The five steps are followed for other than an interrupt 13.

The action taken is

If an "error code" was stacked, POP it off.

1. Save the interrupt task's registers.
2. Set descriptor selectors for use.
3. Move IP, CS, and Flags to the interrupted task's stack and adjust its SP.
4. Move the MS-DOS vector to the interrupt handler's (the current) stack.
5. Restore registers saved and IRET.

If the interrupt is a "13," it will normally be either an INT nn or an IRET, which require that step 3 above be varied.

Check the value at CS:IP or IRET op codes. If neither, do a disaster dump. No device or 8086 interrupt occurs at this number.

If an INT nn—Fetch the nn value. Step IP by 2 on the stack. If nn is other than 00, we set nn*4 as the vector pointer and join the "normal" steps at step 3. If nn is 00, copy the V86 CS, AX and DX to the CX, AX, and DX in the Supervisor TSS. Then CALL the Supervisor task and on return continue at Step 5.

If an IRET—Move the flags, CS and IP from the V86 stack to this stack, adjust the V86 SP, and go to Step 5.

- We need to check if it's an INT or IRET, so we must get V86 CS as a descriptor so we can check.

- The 00 Supervisor Task operates as a protected mode task in 80486 mode. The interrupt handler for the V86 task CALLs this task when it detects an INT 00. This task (included primarily for illustrative purposes) then executes the instructions pointed to by the V86 task's DS:DX. The instructions must be followed by a RET FAR instruction.

Debug support

The choice of printed output for debug rather than display output is based on the fact that errors in this level of code often causes the system to reboot. This causes your debug information to be overprinted on the screen. The following are various procedures used in debug.

- The first is a procedure to set both a descriptor in the GDT to the segment's linear address (segment value is in BX), and to load BP with the descriptor value. The caller will move it (usually) into DS, which forces the linear address to be loaded from the GDT, overriding any previously cached value.

- Put out on printer the byte in AL. *Note:* AL is destroyed, but only AL.

- Convert a hex digit on printable form and print it.

- Print the byte in AL as an ordered pair of hex digits.

- Convert the word in AX to hex and print it.

- Convert the doubleword in EAX to hex and print it.

- Put out a carriage return and line feed.

- Dump the memory at DS:AX for 16 bytes. Follow with a display and CR/LF. AX is returned pointing to the next address to dump. ES is set to the standard DS for execution.

- Get the linear address for the DS, either as an 8086 or 80486 value. Note that this decision depends on the DS value being above GDT-size for 8086, which is normally the case for this program.

- Print AX in hex, followed by a space.

- Dump all registers

- Dump a TSS and its stack (64 bytes of it). At procedure entry, CX has the TSS displacement.

- Dump the contents of the task's stack. First, we need to build a DS to map the task's SS, which can be either 80486-style or V86-style. Then dump the data.

- Dump the GDT, IDT, and all TSS's. The displacement to the TSS of interest is in CX.

- Minimum dump for trace.

80486 software

The following software is available from TAB Books, Blue Ridge Summit, PA 17294-0850.

System requirements

- A computer based on an 80486 processor.

- MS-DOS (or compatible), with at least version 3.1.

- Any standard Video Display Unit.

- To assemble source: Microsoft *Macro Assembler*, Borland *Turbo Assembler* or compatible software.

- Memory: much less than 256K.

- Printer, hooked up to the "normal" IBM printer address.

Diskette contents

VIRT86L.ASM	The source for the 80386 virtual 8086 monitor.
VIRT86L.EXE	The executable link edited object of the ASM file.
VIRT86L.LST	The assembly listing of the ASM file.
VIRT86L.XRF	The cross reference of the above assembly.
DOINST.ASM	The source for an example of a program that uses the VIRT86L monitor to execute instructions.
DOINST.EXE	The executable link edited object of the DOINST.ASM file.
DOINST.LST	The assembly listing of the DOINST.ASM file.
DOINST.XRF	The cross reference of the above assembly.

Program listing

The following are the assembly listings and the cross reference listings for the VIRT86L and DOINST programs. These listings will print on a printer with either a 132 character width or one with the ability to "condense" and print on an 8½ by 11 inch paper.

Sample runs

Load your system. When you get the system prompt, place the diskette into your floppy drive. In our system, we only have one floppy drive; however, we have the programs on Drive C, the hard disk, so all the prompts in the following will be "C>".

The system prompts will be shown. Your responses are italicized.

RUN #1—Running the 80486 program.

C> *VIRT86L*

Virtual 8086 mode is established! Enter G(go) or D – *G*

C>

Note: Now you are in Virtual 8086 mode. MS-DOS is under control of the 80486 program VIRT86L. You can do whatever MS-DOS commands you wish. To get out of this mode, you must reboot your system, generally with the CNTL-ALT-DEL keys.

RUN #2—In this sample, answer "D" at the prompt and get a dump.

C> *VIRT86L*

Virtual 8086 mode is established! Enter G(go) or D – *D*

Note: The dump you get prints a block of hexadecimal characters, divided by blank lines. Prior to dumping, verify the port addresses for your parallel printer. The sections are

- The stack used for the INT00 interrupt handler.
- The normal stack for the program.
- Registers.
- Dump Control Segment.
- Global Descriptor Table and elements of the Interrupt Descriptor Table.
- The TSS for the V86 INT00 Interrupt Handler.
- The stack for the TSS of #6, above.
- The TSS switched out of to enter V86 mode.
- The stack for #8, above.
- The TSS for the Virtual 8086 mode.
- The stack for #10, above.

- The stack being used by the caller of the dump.

RUN #3—The next is if you go into VIRT86L and run the DOINST program while under V86 mode.

C> *VIRT86L*

Virtual 8086 mode is established! Enter G(go) or D – G

C> *DOINST*

Note: This gives you a dump. The sections are

- The registers.
- The dump control segment.
- The Global Descriptor Table and elements of the Interrupt Descriptor Table.
- Dump Control Segment.
- Global Descriptor Table and elements of the Interrupt Descriptor Table.
- TheF TSS for the V86 INT00 Interrupt Handler.
- The stack for the TSS of #6, above.
- The TSS switched out of to enter V86 mode.
- The stack for #8, above.
- The TSS for the Virtual 8086 mode.
- The stack for #10, above.
- The stack being used by the caller of the dump.

If you type "DOINST" at the "C>" while outside of control of the VIRT86L program, you will get a "Divide Overflow" error.

```
              PAGE    59,132              ; Set page depth and width
              .MODEL  SMALL               ; MODEL first gives 16 bit
                                          ; segment size.
              MASM51                      ; Recognize Microsoft Macro
                                          ; Assembler 5.1 formats
              .486P                       ; Indicate 80486 privileged
                                          ; instruction set.
; c.1987, 1988, 1990 Don Brumm and Penn Brumm
;  VIRT86L.ASM
; This program sets up an 80486 task and then does a task switch
; to a virtual 8086 (V86) task.  From the V86, a return and stay resident
; exit is made to MS-DOS.  I/O and I/O interrupt masking is left up to
; MS-DOS.
;
; Most interrupts are reflected to the MS-DOS interrupt handlers.
; IRET and INT nn instructions cause an interrupt 13.  IRET is emulated.
; INT nn interrupts are also, with the exception of INT 00, which is used
; to test instructions.
;
;
; Step 1:
;   Define macros for the 80486 conversions and repetitive setup
;   instructions used in the program.
;
;
;
; Convert an 8086 segment register value to a linear address
;
segadr        MACRO   segr
              sub     EAX,EAX             ; Clear whole register
              mov     AX,&segr            ; Get segment register
              shl     EAX,4               ; Get as an address
              ENDM
;
; Set TSS linear address into a descriptor
;
settssa       MACRO   reg,tss,seg
              lea     E&reg&X,&tss        ; Get displacement to TSS
              add     E&reg&X,EAX         ; Get a linear address in register
              mov     seg&.base_l,reg&X   ; Set low 16 bits of linear address
              SHR     E&reg&X,8           ; Shift bits 16-23 to H
              mov     seg&.base_m,reg&H   ; and set mid range.
              ENDM
;
; Convert an 8086 segment to a linear address in a segment descriptor
;
```

```
segcvt     MACRO   segr,segm
           segadr  segr
           mov     segm&.base_l,AX      ; Set supv base of data
           shr     EAX,8                ; Get it in AH
           mov     segm&.base_m,AH      ; Put it in midrange byte
           ENDM
;
; Step 2:
;    Describe data structures used by the program.  (The TSS is
;    described within the body of the data in order to allow use
;    of data references for its initializations.)
;
;    Define the descriptor.  The fields and their sizes are described.
;
desc       struc
limit      dw      0                    ; Offset of last byte
base_l     dw      0                    ; Low 16 bits of 32 bit addr
base_m     db      0                    ; Bits 16-23
access     db      0                    ; Access priv
gran       db      0                    ; Granularity and Limit
base_h     db      0                    ; Bits 24-31 of the Base
desc       ends


;
; Describe the stack of the L0 interrupt handler for the V86 mode task.
;    (Note that the description is 'upside down' because it is used
;      as a data area which addresses from low to high, not a stack.)
;
stkdef     struc
oldip      dw      0                    ; Low 16 bits of EIP
           dw      0                    ;
oldcs      dw      0                    ; CS value
           dw      0                    ;
oldfl      dw      0                    ; Low 16 bits of EFLAGS
           dw      0                    ;
oldsp      dw      0                    ; Low 16 bits of ESP
           dw      0                    ;
oldss      dw      0                    ; SS value
           dw      0                    ;
oldes      dw      0                    ; ES value
           dw      0                    ;
olddds     dw      0                    ; DS value
           dw      0                    ;
oldfs      dw      0                    ; FS value
           dw      0                    ;
oldgs      dw      0                    ; GS value
```

```
            dw      0
stkdef      ends

            PAGE
;
; Step 3.
;  Define the segmented structure of the program.
;
; We chose a simple model with a single real segment, because it
; is easily converted to a .COM file.
;
; The program operates by establishing a protected mode environment
; and a virtual 8086 task segment, then returning to MS-DOS in the
; virtual 8086 task.  The continued execution of MS-DOS is monitored
; by the protected mode interrupt handler.  An interface to execute
; instructions in protected mode is provided using INT 00.
;
            .CODE
            ASSUME  DS:_TEXT, ES:_TEXT, SS:_TEXT
;
; Step 4:
;   Declare the stack and data space
;
            DB      2000h DUP(?)        ; Provide stack space


;
; Step 5:
;   Define the Global Descriptor Table's (GDT) space
;
gdt_def     desc    <>                      ; The first one is a dummy.
;                                             It can be used as a null.
;
;   Level 3 empty LDT
;
ref_l3      desc    <7,0,0,11100010b,0,0> ; p,3,type 2 limit=7
refl3       equ     ref_l3-gdt_def+3
;
;   Level 0 empty LDT
;
ref_l0      desc    <7,0,0,10000010b,0,0> ; p,0,type 2 limit=7
refl0       equ     ref_l0-gdt_def
;
;   Dynamic data reference used in Interrupt Handler
;
```

436   Appendix E

```
ref_d       desc    <0FFFFh,0,0,10010010b,00001111b,0>   ; Data
ref_dta     equ     ref_d-gdt_def
;
;   Dynamic data reference used in dump TSS
;
ref_dd      desc    <0FFFFh,0,0,10010010b,00001111b,0>   ; Data
ref_dtad    equ     ref_dd-gdt_def
;
;   Reference to real location zero for MS-DOS interrupt vectors.
;
ref_zer     desc    <0FFFFh,0,0,10010010b,00001111b,0>   ; Loc zero
ihzero      equ     ref_zer-gdt_def
stk_data    desc    <0FFFFh,0,0,10010010b,00001111b,0>   ; Stack as data
stkdata     equ     stk_data-gdt_def
            desc    <0,0,0,10010110b,0,0>  ;stack
ref_0       desc    <sz486t-1,0,0,10001001b,00000000b,0> ; 80486 Task
ref0d       equ     ref_0-gdt_def
ref_1       desc    <sz486t-1,0,0,10001001b,00000000b,0> ; 80486 Task
ref1d       equ     ref_1-gdt_def
v86_0       desc    <szv86t,0,0,11101011b,00000000b,0>   ; V86 Task
v860d       equ     v86_0-gdt_def+3
;
;
;   Descriptors for use by interrupt handlers
;
sup_c       desc    <0FFFFh,0,0,10011010b,00001111b,0>   ; Code
supcd       equ     sup_c-gdt_def                        ; DPL=0, nonconforming
                                                         ; Readable
;
sup_d       desc    <0FFFFh,0,0,10010010b,00001111b,0>   ; Data
supdd       equ     sup_d-gdt_def                        ; DPL=0, writeable
;
sup_s       desc    <0,0,0,10010110b,00000000b,0>        ; Stack
supsd       equ     sup_s-gdt_def                        ; Expand down,
                                                         ; Writeable
;
;
;   Descriptors for use by instruction execution task
;
exe_c       desc    <0FFFFh,0,0,10011010b,00001111b,0>   ; Code
execd       equ     exe_c-gdt_def                        ; DPL=0, nonconforming
                                                         ; Readable
;
exe_d       desc    <0FFFFh,0,0,10010010b,00001111b,0>   ; Data
exedd       equ     exe_d-gdt_def                        ; DPL=0, writeable
```

```
;
exe_s     desc    <0,0,0,10010110b,00000000b,0>      ; Stack
exesd     equ     exe_s-gdt_def                      ; Expand down
                                                     ; Writeable
;
;   End of the GDT
;
gdt_size  equ     $-gdt_def
;
; Step 7:
;   Define the Interrupt Descriptor Table's (IDT) space.
;   The addresses are initialized as part of the setup.
;   The selector is that of the supervisor code descriptor.
;
          .SALL
idt_def   equ     $
          REPT    256
          desc    <0,supcd,0,8Eh,0,0>
          ENDM
idt_size  equ     $-idt_def
;
; Step 2A:
;   This section describes a Task State Segment (TSS).  Some of the
;   field names, have a "t" prefix to keep from using the
;   standard 80486 system name.  (This description is here because
;   it contains references to the descriptors just defined.)
;
tss_d     struc
back      dw      0                   ; Back link to any previous TSS
          dw      0                   ; Reserved
esp0      dd      400h                ; SP for level 0 interrupt
ss0       dw      supsd               ; and SS.
          dw      0                   ; Reserved
esp1      dd      400h                ; Level 1 interrupt handler's stack
ss1       dw      supsd
          dw      0                   ; Reserved
esp2      dd      400h                ; Level 2 interrupt handler's stack
ss2       dw      supsd
          dw      0                   ; Reserved
tcr3      dd      0
teip      dd      0                   ; Instruction Pointer
teflags   dw      2                   ; EFLAGS
          dw      0
teax      dw      0                   ; AX for init
          dw      0
tecx      dw      0                   ; CX for init
```

```
                dw       0
tedx      dd       0
tebx      dd       0
tesp      dd       1000h
tebp      dd       0
tesi      dd       0
tedi      dd       0
tes       dw       supdd            ; Extended Segment selector
          dw       0                ; Reserved
tcs       dw       supcd            ; Code Segment selector
          dw       0                ; Reserved
tss       dw       supsd            ; Stack Segment selector
          dw       0                ; Reserved
tds       dw       supdd            ; Data Segment selector
          dw       0                ; Reserved
tfs       dw       0                ; F segment selector
          dw       0                ; Reserved
tgs       dw       0                ; G segment selector
          dw       0                ; Reserved
tldt      dw       refl0            ; Local Descriptor Table (LDT)
          dw       0                ; Reserved
          dw       0                ; Reserved
iomap     dw       104              ; Displacement to I/O Map base
tss_d     ends
;
; Step 8:
;    Define the Task State Segments (TSS)
;
;    This task gets control on an INT 00 from the virtual 8086 mode task.
;    It runs as a level 0 protected mode task.
;
supv      tss_d    <>               ; Space for supv task
sz486t    equ      $-supv
;
;  This task is swiched out of to start the virtual 8086 task.
;
supv2     tss_d    <v860d>          ; Task switched out of
;
;    This is the TSS for the virtual 8086 task, under which
;    MS-DOS will execute.
;
v86       tss_d    <>               ; Define v86 task state segment
          dw       4096 dup (0)     ; I/O bit map of 8K, all bits=0
                                    ; allow I/O to devices 0000 - FFFF.
szv86t    equ      $-v86
          dw       -1               ; A byte of all 1s ends the I/O map
```

Instructions used in protected mode and a sample program   **439**

```
            PAGE
;
;
; Some local data and work areas.
;
dtsize      dw    0                  ; Size of descriptor table
dtload      dd    0                  ; Address of descriptor table
intcd1      dw    0                  ; Pop1 if int code stored
intcd2      dw    0                  ; Pop2
;
; Debug dump controls: A 1 in a byte enables trace entries,
;                       2 causes a normal dump to be taken,
;                       3 causes a disaster dump to be taken, and
;                       0 enters the quiet zone of no output.
;
debugf      db    0                     ; Prior to entry of protected mode
debugf0     db    0                     ; Ihcommon entry point
debugf0a    db    0                     ; and exit
debugf1     db    02                    ; Int 13 entry
debugf1a    db    0                     ; and INT nn exit,
debugf1b    db    0                     ; IRET exit as well as all others.
retdisp     dw    0                     ; Address of interrupt handler call
;                                         (See int_hand0 and its write up.)
dsaddr      dd    0                     ; Address of data area
dumpcal     dw    0                     ; Address of call to dump for debug
success     db    'Virtual 8086 mode is established!',10,13
            db    'Enter G (go) or D (dump)- $'
newline     db    0dh,0ah,'$'
endad       db    0
datasiz     equ   $-gdt_def+15       ; size of data area
;
; Define displacement into stack for interrupt handler
;
ihspv       equ   1800h              ; Initial value of SP
ihspn1      equ   ihspv-size stkdef  ; No interrupt code on stack
ihspn2      equ   ihspn1-4           ; Interrupt code stored
            PAGE
;
;   Set segment descriptors (we're in real mode).
;
segsetup:
            mov   AX,CS               ; Set segment address into AX
            mov   SS,AX               ; Set SP to 2000h
            mov   SP,2000h
            mov   DS,AX               ; Set DS
```

```
            mov     ES,AX                    ; and ES


;
; Step 9:
;   Build and set segment descriptors for use by 80486 task.
;
            cld                              ; Force direction of strings
                                             ; from low to high (up).
            cli                              ; Set interrupts off
;
; Step 9A:
;   Convert various segment registers into linear addresses in
;   80486 descriptors
;
            segcvt  DS,sup_d                 ; Set Data Segment
            segcvt  CS,sup_c                 ; and Code Segment
            segcvt  SS,sup_s                 ; Set Stack Segment
            segcvt  SS,stk_data              ; As a Data segment, too.
            segadr  DS                       ; Get DS as a linear in EAX
            mov     dsaddr,EAX               ; Save it for later use
;
; step 9B:
;   Set interrupt handler displacements in their descriptors.
;   We count on the fact that the descriptors and handlers are
;   each generated in a group so they are adjacent within their group.
;
            lea     BX,idt_def.limit         ; Set index to displacement[0]
            lea     AX,int_hand0             ; get first displacement,
            mov     CX,256                   ; and set count.

fillihd1:
            mov     [BX],AX                  ; Set the displacement
            add     AX,4                     ; then step it by its size.
            add     BX,8                     ; Step the descriptor index too.
            loop    fillihd1                 ; Do it 256 times.

            segadr DS                        ; Get DS as a linear in EAX
;
; Step 9C:
;   Convert linear address of data areas for segment descriptors
;   such as TSS descriptors and LDT descriptors.
;
            settssa D,supv,ref_0             ; Point selector to supv
            settssa D,supv2,ref_1            ; Point to supv 2
            settssa D,v86,v86_0              ; Point to V86 TSS
```

```
          settssa D,gdt_def,ref_l3    ; Point l3 ldt at null of gdt
          settssa D,gdt_def,ref_l0    ; l0 ldt too

;
; Step 10:
;   Set the segment selectors in the 80486 TSS for Interrupt Handlers
;
          mov      supv.tcs,supcd      ; Set code descriptor
          mov      AX,supdd            ; Get the data segment selector
          mov      supv.tds,AX         ; and set in the TSS data
          mov      supv.tes,AX         ; and set in the TSS extra
          mov      supv.tfs,AX         ; and set in the TSS FS
          mov      supv.tgs,AX         ; and set in the TSS GS
          mov      supv.tss,supsd      ; Set stack selector in the TSS
          mov      AX,refl0            ; Get LDT pointer
          mov      supv.tldt,AX        ; and set the LDT pointer
          mov      supv2.tldt,AX       ; in both supervisor TSSs
;
; Step 11:
;   Set the Code, Stack, and EFLAGS Registers
;
          sub      EAX,EAX             ; Clear EAX
          mov      AX,01200h           ; Get SP value (SS has 2000h)
;                                      80486 gets lower 1800h
          mov      supv.tesp,EAX       ; and set in the TSS
          mov      AX,offset instexe   ; Get the code to exec
          mov      supv.teip,EAX       ; Set in the TSS
;
;   An EFLAGS register of 0002 is fine, so we leave it as is.
;
          mov      supv.ss0,supsd       ; Set lev 0 SS for interrupt
          mov      word ptr supv.esp0,800h ; Set an SP value too
;
          mov      supv.ss1,supsd       ; Set lev 1 SS
          mov      word ptr supv.esp1,800h ; Set an SP value too

          mov      supv.ss2,supsd       ; Set lev 2 SS
          mov      word ptr supv.esp2,800h ; Set an SP value too
;
; Step 12:
; Set up the virtual 8086 TSS.
;   Set descriptor values into the Virtual 8086 task state segment (TSS).
;   In this case, we duplicate the environment of the real mode 8086 that
;   is now running into the V86 TSS.
```

```
        mov     AX,DS                   ; Get DS in AX
        mov     v86.tes,AX              ; Set for V86 execution
        mov     v86.tds,AX              ; in all data segment pointers.
        mov     v86.tfs,AX
        mov     v86.tgs,AX
        mov     AX,SS                   ; Get SS value of current stack
        mov     v86.tss,AX              ; and set it.
        mov     AX,CS                   ; Get CS value
        mov     v86.tcs,AX              ; and set it too.
;
; Set the level 0 interrupt handler stack segment selector and pointer.
;   We really only need Level 0 but set L1 and L2 for completeness.
;   We also set only the low 16 bits of ESP because we know that the
;   upper 16 bits will allways be zero.
;
        mov     v86.ss0,supsd           ; Set lev 0 SS
        mov     word ptr v86.esp0,ihspv ; Set an SP value too
;
        mov     v86.ss1,supsd           ; Set lev 1 SS
        mov     word ptr v86.esp1,1600h ; Set an SP value too

        mov     v86.ss2,supsd           ; Set lev 2 SS
        mov     word ptr v86.esp2,1400h ; Set an SP value too
;
;   Set register values needed to continue in 8086 mode (IP and SP)
;
        sub     EAX,EAX                 ; Ensure top is clear
        mov     AX, offset resume       ; Get the resume address
        mov     v86.teip,EAX            ; and set it
        mov     AX,SP                   ; Get the SP value
        mov     v86.tesp,EAX            ; and set it
;
;   Set the EFLAGS in the TSS so it will execute in V86 mode.
;
        mov     v86.teflags,0011001000000010b ; Set low 16 bits
;           Flag Names ====> NIOODITSZ A P C
;                                  PL
;
        mov     v86.teflags+2,0000000000000010b ; and the high 16
;           Flag Names ======>              AVR
;                                           CM
;   VM is on, IOPL = 3 and Interrupts are enabled.
;
        mov     v86.iomap,sz486t        ; Set displacement to I/O table
```

```
;
;   Set the LDT value in the V86 TSS
;
            mov     v86.tldt,refl3      ; set level 3 ldt
;
; Step 13:
;   Set up 80486 registers to run in protected mode.
;
;   Set the GDT and IDT Registers in the 80486 CPU
;
            mov     EAX,dsaddr          ; Load 32 bit address
;
;   Use the DS linear address to get both the GDT and IDT register values.
;   Set the GDT value into memory first.
;
            sub     EBX,EBX             ; Clear EBX
            lea     EBX,gdt_def         ; Get displacement to GDT
            add     EBX,EAX             ; then linear address of GDT
            mov     dtload,EBX          ; Plug that value in
            mov     dtsize,gdt_size-1   ; and the size of table.

            LGDT    FWORD PTR dtsize    ; Load the table parms


;
;   Then load the IDT value into memory.
;
            sub     EBX,EBX             ; Clear EBX
            lea     EBX,idt_def         ; Get displacement to IDT
            add     EBX,EAX             ; then linear address of IDT.
            mov     dtload,EBX          ; Plug that value in
            mov     dtsize,idt_size-1   ; and the size of table.

            LIDT    FWORD PTR dtsize    ; Load the table parms


;
; Step 14:
;   The 80486 environment is set.
;   Now transfer into Protected Mode.
;
            mov     EAX,CR0             ; Move CR0 into EAX
            or      AL,1                ; Set protected mode
            mov     CR0,EAX             ; then move it back.
            jmp     localx              ; Clear pipelined decode queue
localx:
;
```

```
;   We are now executing in protected mode
;
            mov     AX,refl0            ; Point to empty LDT desc
            lldt    AX                  ; and set LDT
;
;   Debug aid
            cmp     debugf,0            ; Is dump wanted?
            je      skip01              ; No - skip it

            call    edump               ; Get what is necessary
            call    newln               ; Do cr/lf
skip01:

            mov     AX,supdd            ; Get 486 data descriptor
            mov     DS,AX
            mov     ES,AX
            mov     FS,AX
            mov     GS,AX               ; into all data segments.
            mov     AX,supsd            ; Get 486 stack descriptor
            mov     SS,AX
            db      0eah                ; Do a far jump to set CS
            dw      godoit-_TEXT,supcd


;
;   Step 15:
;     At this point all descriptors are of 80486 form, even CS.
;
;     Now set the Nested Task (NT) flag and go to the V86 task
;
godoit:
            mov     CX,ref1d            ; Get value for task register
            ltr     CX                  ; and set it.
            pushfd                      ; Push EFLAGS
            pop     EAX                 ; Get them into EAX
            or      AH,40h              ; Set the nested task flag
            push    EAX                 ; Push EFLAGS again
            popfd                       ; then get them into flags reg
;
;   Now transfer to the Virtual 8086 (V86) mode using an IRET.  The
;   back chain in our TSS and the nested task flag cause the transfer.
;
            iret                        ; and transfer to V86


;
;   Step 16:
```

```
;   We are now executing in virtual 8086 mode. The code issues a message
;   and wait for a capital G (for Go) from the keyboard.  When received,
;   the code continues by executing the DOS exit-but-remain-resident
;   call.
;
;   The result is that from entry here, MS-DOS runs as a virtual
;   8086 task.  Entry to protected mode can be effected by an INT 00.
;
resume:
resumed     equ   resume-_TEXT
            cld                             ; Normal direction
  resloop:
            lea   DX,success               ; Point to the message
            mov   AH,9                      ; Set write code
            int   21h                       ; Let DOS put it out.
            mov   AH,1                      ; Get a keyboard char
            int   21h
            push  AX                        ; Save the character
            lea   DX,newline                ; Point to new line string
            mov   AH,9                       ; Set write code
            int   21h                        ; Call DOS
            pop   AX                         ; Get char back
            cmp   AL,'G'                      ; Have a "Go"?
            je    todos                      ; Yes - off to DOS
            cmp   AL,'D'                      ; Want a dump?
            jne   resloop                    ; No, try again
            mov   debugf0,3                   ; Fforce a dump next int
            jmp   resloop                     ; Go try again

todos:
            lea   DX,totalsize+20fh          ; Point to top address
            shr   DX,4                        ; Convert to paragraphs
            mov   AH,31h                       ; Set stay resident
            int   21h                          ; Assume we are done
;
; The above transfer to MS-DOS leaves us in memory.  (This is both
; fortuitous and planned, because real control of the CPU is in the
; hands of the rest of this program!)
;
; The code to this point could now be overlayed - its purpose is now
; completed.
            PAGE
;
; SUPPORT CODE
; 1.
```

```
;
; Generate the initial entry points for the interrupt handlers.
; These entries have a correspondence with the 8086 interrupt
; vector table.  They are the same length (4 bytes) and the
; return address from the call is used to generate the proper
; displacement into the table.  (At this point, we have CS and
; our SP/SS to work with.)
;
int_hand0:                         ; Initial displacement
        REPT    256                ; Interrupts 0-255
        call    ih_common          ; A 3-byte call
        iret                       ; A 1-byte iret
        ENDM
; 2.
;
; Handle all interrupts and traps.
; The handler here reflects the interrupt to MS-DOS.  The action
; taken is simply:
;                   0) If an 'error code' was stacked, pop it off.
;                      (If we were handling interrupts here, we would
;                      examine and use the error code.)
;                   1) Save the interrupted task's registers and
;                   2) Set descriptor selectors for use here.
;       For other than interrupt 13
;                   3) Move IP, CS, and Flags to the interrupted task's
;                      stack and adjust its SP.
;                   4) Move the MS-DOS vector to the interrupt handler's
;                      (our current) stack.
;                   5) Restore registers saved and IRET.
;
;       Interrupt 13 will normally be either an INT nn or an IRET which
;           require that step 3 above be varied.
;                   3) Check the value at CS,IP for INT or IRET op codes
;                      if neither, do a disaster dump - No device or 8086
;                      interrupt occurs at this number.
;
;                   3-INT) Fetch the nn value, step IP by 2 on my stack.
;                      If nn is other than 00 we set nn*4 as the vector
;                      pointer and join at step 3.
;                      If nn is 00 we copy the v86 CS, AX, and DX to
;                      CX, AX, and DX in the supv TSS.  We then call
;                      the supv task and on return continue at step 5.
;
;                   3-IRET) Move the flags, CS and IP from the v86 stack
;                      to our stack, adjust the v86 SP and take step 5.
```

```
ih_common:
        push    AX                      ; Save one register
        mov     AX,supdd                ; Get data addressability
        mov     DS,AX
        pop     AX                      ; SP now points to return of the
;                                         interrupt entry's call here.
        pop     retdisp                 ; Get it off the stack into a save area.
        cmp     SP,ihspn2               ; Is there an int code on the stack?
        jne     ihcommn                 ; No - don't mess with it.
        pop     intcd1                  ; Get the interrupt code's first and
        pop     intcd2                  ; second word off stack.
;
;  The above provides us with a known stack format.  We have also saved
;  the interrupt error code, if any, and have the vector number in easily
;  computable form.  (Not bad for 8 or 10 instructions.)
;
ihcommn:
        pusha                           ; Save registers

        mov     AX,stkdata              ; Get the stack as data desc
        mov     ES,AX                   ; into ES
        mov     BX,SP                   ; Get SP into BX
        mov     AX,ES:[BX+26]           ; Load high word of EFLAGs
        and     AL,2                    ; Isolate the VM bit
        jnz     stillok                 ; If there - normal
;
;  An interrupt from other than virtual 8086 mode is treated as an
;  error in this code.  If this were a general purpose interrupt
;  handler, we would process the interrupt as a normal 80486 event.
;  However, we dump and ignore the encounter.
;
        mov     debugf0,3               ; Force dump of disaster
        mov     debugf0a,3
stillok:
        mov     DX,DS                   ; Set normal descriptor selector
        mov     ES,DX                   ; into ES.
        cmp     debugf0,0               ; Want a dump?
        je      skip02                  ; No - skip it
        cmp     debugf0,1               ; Just trace type?
        jne     fulld02                 ; No - do full
        mov     AX,retdisp              ; Get the int number
        call    mindump                 ; and trace it
        jmp     skip02                  ; Done
fulld02:
        cmp     debugf0,2               ; Normal dump desired?
        je      fulld02e                ; Yes - go dump
```

```
                mov     debugf0,0           ; Do disaster dump once
; Make sure we get extra stack for disaster
                mov     AX,stkdata          ; Get stack area again
                mov     DS,AX               ; Dump stack info
                mov     AX,780h             ; Low part first -
                mov     CX,8                ; for 128 bytes
badstk0:
                call    dumpln
                loop    badstk0             ; Get it all

                call    newln               ; Space between
                mov     AX,1780h            ; Then high part -
                mov     CX,8                ; for 128 bytes
badstk1:
                call    dumpln
                loop    badstk1             ; Get it all
                call    newln               ; and a space
                mov     DS,DX               ; Set normal descriptor selector


fulld02e:
                call    edump
skip02:
                mov     SI,retdisp          ; Get return displacement
                sub     SI,int_hand0-_TEXT  ; As a displacement
                and     SI,0fffch           ; into MS-DOS interrupt vectors.
                mov     retdisp,SI          ; Clear it for debug

                mov     AX,stkdata          ; Get stack as data selector
                mov     ES,AX               ; into ES
                mov     BX,SP               ; Get SP into BX
                add     BX,16               ; Point to IP location
                cmp     SI,13*4             ; Is this int 13
                je      isint13             ; Yes - go process special

notint13:
                mov     AX,ES:[BX].oldss    ; Get SS of V86 task
                mov     CL,AH               ; Set high byte in CL
                shl     AX,4                ; Convert desc to linear address

                shr     CL,4                ; in AX and CL
                mov     ref_d.base_l,AX     ; Set bits 0-15 in the descriptor
                mov     ref_d.base_m,CL     ; Then bits 16-23 (we ignore 24-31 heh)

                mov     CX,ES:[BX].oldsp    ; Get SP of V86 task,
                sub     CX,6                ; adjust it for fake interrupt,
                mov     ES:[BX].oldsp,CX    ; and put it back.
```

```
        mov     BP,ES:[BX].oldip    ; Get interrupted IP,
        mov     DI,ES:[BX].oldcs    ; CS,
        mov     AX,ES:[BX].oldfl    ; and flags.

        mov     DX,ref_dta          ; Get descriptor
        mov     DS,DX               ; into DS
        xchg    BX,CX               ; Put v86 SP into BX & save stack disp

        mov     [BX],BP             ; Stack IP,
        mov     [BX]+2,DI           ; CS, and
        mov     [BX]+4,AX           ; flags on v86 stack.

        and     AX,0fcffh           ; Clear interrupt and trap flags
        mov     BX,ihzero           ; Get zero base descriptor selector
        mov     DS,BX               ; as DS
        mov     BX,SI               ; Index into the vector table
        mov     BP,[BX]             ; Get vector's IP
        mov     DI,[BX]+2           ; and CS.

        mov     BX,CX               ; Get stack displ back
        mov     ES:[BX].oldfl,AX    ; Set flags,
        mov     ES:[BX].oldip,BP    ; IP, and
        mov     ES:[BX].oldcs,DI    ; CS on my stack.

rejoin:
        mov     DX,supdd            ; Get data addressability
        mov     DS,DX
        mov     ES,DX
        cmp     debugf0a,0          ; Is an exit dump wanted?
        je      skip03              ; No - bypass it
        cmp     debugf0a,1          ; Just a trace?
        jne     fulld02a            ; No - do full
        mov     AX,BP               ; Get the to address
        call    mindump             ; Trace it
        jmp     skip03              ; Done
fulld02a:
        call    edump

        mov     AX,stkdata          ; Get stack as data selector
        mov     DS,AX               ; into DS.
        mov     BX,ihspn1           ; Set offset to PL0 stack area
        mov     AX,[BX].oldss       ; Get SS of V86 task,
        mov     BX,[BX].oldsp       ; and SP.
        mov     DS,DX               ; Restore DS
        mov     CL,AH               ; Prepare to set
        shr     CL,4
```

```
            mov     ref_d.base_m,CL      ; bits 16-23
            shl     AX,4                 ; then
            mov     ref_d.base_l,AX      ; bits 0-15 of address in descriptor.
            mov     AX,ref_dta           ; Get descriptor's selector
            mov     DS,AX                ; into DS.
            mov     AX,BX                ; Set SP as displacement
            mov     CX,4                 ; Prepare to dump
dumpit380:
            call    dumpln               ; Put it out 16 at a time
            loop    dumpit380

            mov     AX,supdd             ; Get normal DS value back
            mov     DS,AX                ; into DS

            call    newln                ; Do cr/lf
            cmp     debugf0a,3           ; Doing a disaster dump?
            jne     skip03               ; No - leave as is
            mov     debugf0a,0           ; Shut it off
skip03:
            sub     AX,AX                ; Get a zero
            mov     DS,AX                ; for DS and
            mov     ES,AX                ; ES.
            popa                         ; Restore all regs
;
; Because we choose to use 16-byte operand sizes, we need a 32-bit
; IRET size to recognize a switch back to virtual 8086 mode.
            iretd


;
; 3.
;
; int 13 - we need to check if INT or IRET, so we must get v86 CS as
;          a descriptor so we can check.
;
isint13:
            mov     AX,ES:[BX].oldcs     ; Get CS in AX
            mov     SI,ES:[BX].oldip     ; Put IP in SI (for LODSB index)
            mov     CL,AH                ; Prepare to compute mid
            shl     AX,4                 ; Get descriptor as low 16
            shr     CL,4                 ; and get mid 8 bits
            mov     ref_d.base_l,AX      ; Set low 16
            mov     ref_d.base_m,CL      ; and mid 8 bits of linear for CS
            mov     AX,ref_dta           ; Get just-built descriptor's sele
            mov     DS,AX                ; into DS
            cld                          ; Ensure that SI will increment
            lodsb                        ; Get faulting op code
```

Instructions used in protected mode and a sample program   451

```
            cmp       AL,0cfh              ; Is it an IRET?
            je        prociret             ; Yes - go emulate it
            cmp       AL,0cdh              ; Is it INT nn?
            je        procint              ; Yes - emulate it
;
; This is unexpected - force dump
;
            mov       DS,DX                ; Set normal data desc
            call      edump                ; Take a dump now
            mov       debugf0a,3           ; Force dump on way out
            mov       SI,13*4              ; Set normal displacement
            jmp       notint13             ; and join normal interrupt


;
; 4.
;
; INT nn processing
;
procint:
            lodsb                          ; Get nn
            mov       ES:[BX].oldip,SI     ; Set new IP on stack
            mov       DS,DX                ; Set normal DS
            mov       AH,0                 ; Clear high byte of AX
            add       AX,AX                ; Get nn*2
            add       AX,AX                ; and nn*4
            mov       SI,AX                ; as interrupt vector
            jnz       notint13             ; Normal if it isn't int 00
;
; A request to execute an instruction has been issued.
; Copy the caller's DS, AX and DX to the supv TSS as param pointers.
;
            mov       AX,ES:[BX].oldds     ; Set DS into supv's CX
            mov       supv.tecx,AX
            mov       CX,BX                ; Save pointer into stack
            mov       BX,SP                ; Get pointer to registers
            mov       AX,ES:[BX+14]        ; Get caller's AX to supv's AX
            mov       supv.teax,AX
            mov       AX,ES:[BX+10]        ; and DX too.
            mov       word ptr supv.tedx,AX
            mov       BX,CX                ; Restore normal index
;           call      ref0d:0              ; Call 80486 task for handling
            db        09ah
            dw        0,ref0d
            jmp       rejoin               ; We just return in line for int 00
;
; 5.
```

```
;
; IRET processing -
;
prociret:
            mov     DS,DX                   ; The V86 CS is no longer used
            mov     AX,ES:[BX].oldss        ; We need the ret from v86 stack
            mov     CL,AH                   ; So - compute the descriptor
            shr     CL,4
            shl     AX,4
            mov     ref_d.base_l,AX         ; Bits 0-15
            mov     ref_d.base_m,CL         ; and bits 16-23
            mov     CX,ES:[BX].oldsp        ; Get V86 SP
            mov     AX,ref_dta              ; Get v86 SS
            mov     DS,AX                   ; as my DS
            xchg    BX,CX                   ; Set v86 SP into BX
            mov     AX,[BX]                 ; Get ret IP,
            mov     SI,[BX+2]               ; CS, and
            mov     DI,[BX+4]               ; flags.
            add     BX,6                    ; Adjust the SP
            xchg    BX,CX                   ; and put it into CX.
            mov     ES:[BX].oldsp,CX        ; Now put the values on my stack
            mov     ES:[BX].oldip,AX
            mov     ES:[BX].oldcs,SI
            mov     ES:[BX].oldfl,DI
            jmp     rejoin                  ; Join exit/return


;
; 6.
;
;       This code operates as a protected mode task in 80486 mode.  The
;       interrupt handler for the v86 task calls this task when it detects
;       an INT 00.  This task (which is a task primarially for illustrative
;       purposes) then executes the instructions pointed to by the v86 task's
;       DS:DX.  The instructions must be followed by a RET FAR instruction.
;
;       The interrupt handler stores the DS and DX values into the TSS
;       prior to calling the task.
;
instexe     PROC
instexb:
            cmp     debugf1,0               ; Is a dump wanted?
            je      SHORT skip04            ; No - bypass it
            cmp     debugf1,1               ; Just trace?
            jne     SHORT fulld04           ; No - do full
            mov     AX,0e0dh                ; Get the int number
            call    mindump                 ; Trace it
```

```
           jmp     SHORT skip04        ; Done
fulld04:
           call    edump               ; Get the data
skip04:
           push    EAX                 ; Save control info
           sub     EAX,EAX             ; Clear a register and
           mov     AX,CX               ; copy the descriptor to it.
           sub     ECX,ECX             ; Clear ECX, too
           mov     CX,DX               ; Get code displacement in ECX
           shl     EAX,4               ; Get descriptor as a linear
           add     EAX,ECX             ; and the code's linear address.
           mov     exe_c.base_l,AX     ; Set low 16 bits into the code,
           mov     exe_d.base_l,AX     ; data, and
           mov     exe_s.base_l,AX     ; stack descriptors.
           shr     EAX,8               ; Get bits 16-24 in AH
           mov     exe_c.base_m,AH     ; Set mid 8 bits into the code,
           mov     exe_d.base_m,AH     ; data, and
           mov     exe_s.base_m,AH     ; stack descriptors.
           mov     BX,exedd            ; Set data selector in BX
           mov     CX,exesd            ; and stack into CX.
           pop     EAX                 ; Restore caller's AX
;          call    execs:0             ; and call the code
           db      09ah
           dw      0,execd
           jnz     SHORT skipdmp       ; If nonzero is returned - skip;
           call    edump               ; else, dump my environment
skipdmp:
           mov     AX,supdd            ; Get my data selector
           mov     DS,AX               ; and ensure next entry is ok
           mov     ES,AX
           iret                        ; return to v86 caller
           jmp     instexb             ; to the start
instexe    ENDP
           PAGE


;
; DEBUG SUPPORT
;
;      The choice of printed output for debug rather than display output
;      is based on the fact that errors in this level of code often cause
;      the system to reboot.  This causes one's debug information to be
;      visable only as an after-image on the retina.  I need more lasting
;      data (as do most of us).
;
```

```
getdsv      PROC
;
;          Proc to set both a descriptor in the GDT to the segment's linear
;          address (segment value is in BX) and to load BP with the
;          descriptor value.  The caller will move it into (usually) DS,
;          which will force the linear address to be loaded from the
;          GDT (overriding any previously cached value).
;
            push    EAX
            sub     EAX,EAX              ; Clear EAX
            mov     ref_dd.base_h,AH     ; Clear high 8 of address
            mov     AX,BX                ; Get segment register
            shl     EAX,4                ; Get linear address of segment
            mov     ref_dd.base_l,AX     ; Set low 16 bytes
            shr     EAX,8                ; and get bits 16-23 in AH
            mov     ref_dd.base_m,AH     ; into descriptor.
            mov     BP,ref_dtad          ; Get value of the selector
            pop     EAX
            ret
getdsv      ENDP


printc      PROC
;
;       Print the byte in AL
;       Note: Only AL is destroyed
;
            push    CX                   ; Save regs used
            push    BX
            push    DX
            mov     DX,03bch             ; Get port address (data)
            out     DX,AL                ; Print the byte
            mov     BL,10h               ; Set delay outer count
            sub     CX,CX                ; and loop count
            inc     DX                   ; Point to status port
busyl:
            in      AL,DX                ; Get status
            test    AL,80h               ; Check busy bit
            jnz     strobe               ; Not now - signal data ready
            loop    busyl                ; 64K times
            dec     BL                   ; 16 we check
            jnz     busyl                ; for busy
strobe:
            mov     AL,0dh               ; Signal printer we have data
            inc     DX                   ; Use the strobe port
```

Instructions used in protected mode and a sample program   455

```
            out     DX,AL                   ; Send that signal
            mov     CX,500                  ; Set a short delay
signl:
            push    AX                      ; Make storage reference
            pop     AX                      ; for real delay
            loop    signl
            dec     AL                      ; Set strobe bit off
            out     DX,AL
            pop     DX                      ; Restore registers
            pop     BX
            pop     CX
            ret

printc      ENDP


hexit       PROC
;
; Convert a hex digit to printable form and print it
;
            or      AL,30h                  ; Make it a number?
            cmp     AL,3ah                  ; Did we?
            jl      yes1                    ; If low - it is one
            add     AL,7                    ; Convert to A-F
yes1:
            Call    printc                  ; Print the char
            ret
hexit       ENDP

prtalx      PROC
;
;       Print the byte in AL as an ordered pair of hex digits
;
            push    AX                      ; Save register
            shr     AL,4                    ; Get high nibble
            call    hexit                   ; Put it out as hex digit
            pop     AX                      ; Get the character back,
            push    AX                      ; but save the register
            and     AL,0fh                  ; Try the low nibble
            call    hexit                   ; Print the hex digit
            pop     AX
            ret
prtalx      ENDP

prtaxx      PROC
```

```
;
;       Convert the word in AX to hex and print it
;

                push    AX                      ; Save it
                push    AX                      ; twice
                mov     AL,AH                   ; Do upper byte first
                call    prtalx                  ; Print it
                pop     AX
                call    prtalx                  ; Then the lower byte
                pop     AX
                ret
prtaxx  ENDP


prteaxx PROC
;
;       Convert the double word in EAX to hex and print it
;

                push    EAX                     ; Save it
                push    EAX                     ; twice
                shr     EAX,16                  ; Get the high word first
                call    prtaxx                  ; Print it
                pop     EAX
                call    prt16                   ; Then the lower word
                pop     EAX
                ret
prteaxx ENDP



newln   PROC
;
;       Put out a c/r and l/f
;

                push    AX
                mov     AL,0dh                  ; Put out C/R
                call    printc
                mov     AL,0ah                  ; and line feed
                call    printc
                pop     AX
                ret
newln   ENDP

dumpln  PROC
;
;       Dump the memory at DS:AX for 16 bytes - Follow with printable
;       display of the 16 bytes then C/R LF.
```

```
;           On return, AX points to the next address to dump.
;           ES is set to our standard DS for execution.
;

            push    EBX                 ; Save registers
            push    CX
            push    AX
;
;       Get the linear address for the DS either as a 8086 or 80486 value
;       Note this decision depends on the DS value being above gdtsize
;       for 8086 (normally the case for this program).
;
            sub     EBX,EBX             ; Clear dword register
            mov     BX,DS               ; Get the segment selector
            and     BX,0fff0h           ; less local and rpl flags.
            cmp     EBX,gdt_size        ; Compare to max 80486 style
            jg      do8086              ; Must be 8086 form
            or      EBX,EBX             ; Let zero selector also
            jz      do8086              ; be 8086 form.
;
; We could be wrong and make a garbage value here, but normally we're ok
;
            push    ES                  ; Save current ES
            mov     AX,supdd            ; Get standard data selector
            mov     ES,AX               ; into ES
            mov     AH,ES:gdt_def.base_h[BX] ; Get high byte
            mov     AL,ES:gdt_def.base_m[BX] ; Get mid byte
            shl     EAX,16              ; into the high half
            mov     AX,ES:gdt_def.base_l[BX] ; Then the low 16 bits
            pop     ES                  ; Restore ES
            jmp     short dolinear      ; Combine the segment
do8086:
            mov     AX,DS               ; Get descriptor in AX
            shl     EAX,4               ; Times 16 in EAX
dolinear:
            sub     EBX,EBX             ; Clear EBX
            pop     BX                  ; Get displacement
            push    BX                  ; (save for the text)
            add     EAX,EBX             ; Now we have the linear addr.

            call    prteaxx             ; Put out address
            mov     AL,' '              ; and 2 spaces
            call    printc
            mov     CX,8                ; Do 8 words
nxtword:
            mov     AX,[BX]             ; Get with bytes reversed
```

```
                add     BX,2            ; Step pointer
                xchg    AL,AH           ; Re-reverse them
                call    prt16           ; Print as hex
                loop    nxtword         ; for all 8
                mov     AL,' '          ; Get another space
                call    printc          ; and print byte
                pop     BX              ; Get pointer back
                mov     CX,16           ; Get byte count
nxtbyte:
                mov     AL,[BX]         ; Get a byte
                inc     BX              ; and step pointer
                cmp     AL,' '          ; Check to a space
                jl      isactl          ; If less - go make a dot
                cmp     AL,07eh         ; Is it too high to print?
                jng     nothigh         ; If not - use as is
isactl:
                mov     AL,'.'          ; If so - replace with dot
nothigh:
                call    printc          ; Print the char
                loop    nxtbyte         ; and loop for 16

                call    newln           ; Do cr/lf

                mov     AX,BX           ; Set return value for AX
                pop     CX
                pop     EBX
                ret
dumpln          ENDP


prt16           PROC
;
; Procedure to print AX in hex followed by a space
;
                call    prtaxx          ; Print the AX value
                mov     AL,' '          ; Follow it with a space
                call    printc          ; (put it out)
                ret
prt16           ENDP


dumprg          PROC
;
; Dump all the registers
;
                PUSH    EAX
```

```
        call    newln           ; Do cr/lf

        pushfd                  ; Save EFLAGS
        Call    prteaxx         ; Put out EAX,
        mov     EAX,EBX
        call    prteaxx         ; then EBX,
        mov     EAX,ECX
        call    prteaxx         ; then ECX,
        mov     EAX,EDX
        call    prteaxx         ; then EDX,
        mov     EAX,EBP
        call    prteaxx         ; then EBP,
        mov     EAX,ESP
        call    prteaxx         ; then ESP,
        mov     EAX,ESI
        call    prteaxx         ; then ESI,
        mov     EAX,EDI
        call    prteaxx         ; and then EDI.
        call    newln           ; Do cr/lf

        mov     AX,CS
        call    prt16           ; and then CS,
        mov     AX,DS
        call    prt16           ; then DS,
        mov     AX,ES
        call    prt16           ; then ES,
        mov     AX,SS
        call    prt16           ; then SS,
        mov     AX,FS
        call    prt16           ; then FS,
        mov     AX,GS
        call    prt16           ; then GS,
        sldt    AX
        call    prt16           ; then LDT,
        str     AX
        call    prt16           ; and task register.

        call    newln           ; Do cr/lf

        mov     EAX,CR0         ; Get CR0 and
        call    prteaxx         ; print it.
        mov     EAX,CR2         ; Get CR2 and
        call    prteaxx         ; print it.
        mov     EAX,CR3         ; Get CR3 and
        call    prteaxx         ; print it.
```

```
            sgdt    fword ptr dtsize    ; Store the GDT register,
            mov     EAX,dtload          ; get the address
            call    prteaxx             ; and put it out.
            sidt    fword ptr dtsize    ; Store the IDT register,
            mov     EAX,dtload          ; get the address,
            call    prteaxx             ; and put it out.
            pop     EAX                 ; Get EFLAGS register and
            call    prteaxx             ; put it out.

            call    newln               ; Do cr/lf

            pop     EAX
            ret
dumprg      ENDP


dmptss      PROC
;
; Dump a TSS and its stack (64 bytes of it).
;    At entry CX, has the TSS displacement
;
            push    AX                  ; Save registers used
            push    EBX
            push    ECX                 ; Save TSS displacement
            mov     AX,CX               ; Set displacement of TSS
            mov     CX,7                ; Prepare to dump 70 hex
dumpit2:
            call    dumpln              ; Put it out 16 at a time
            loop    dumpit2

            call    newln               ; Do cr/lf


;
; Now we dump the contents of the stack of the task.
;    First we need to build a DS to map the task's SS,
;         which can be either 80486 style or V8086 style.
;    Then we can dump the data.
;
            pop     EBX                 ; Get displ to this TSS
            push    EBX                 ; and save it again
            mov     CX,[BX].tss         ; Get task's SS value and the
            mov     DX,WORD PTR [BX].tesp ; task's SP (16 bit).
            mov     AX,[BX].teflags+2   ; Get the upper 16 bits of EFLAGS
            and     AL,2                ; and isolate the v86 mode flag.
            jnz     short gotss         ; If we have it in v86 form ok.
            and     CL,0f8h             ; Don't allow for local stacks.
```

```
            lea     BX,gdt_def          ; Get locaction of the GDT.
            add     BX,CX               ; Set displacement
            mov     CH,[BX].base_m      ; Get bits 17-23 in
            shl     ECX,8               ; bits 17-23 of ECX
            mov     CX,[BX].base_l      ; Get the low 16 bits in CX
            shr     ECX,4               ; and an 8086 style desc in CX
gotss:
            mov     BX,CX               ; Put in reg for proc
            call    getdsv              ; BP has descriptor just built
            mov     DS,BP               ; Set as DS
            mov     AX,DX               ; Set the SP value
            mov     CX,4                ; Set count
dumpiSS:
            call    dumpln              ; Put it out 16 at a time
            loop    dumpiSS

            mov     BX,supdd            ; Get std DS back
            mov     DS,BX               ; into DS

            call    newln               ; Do cr/lf

            pop     ECX                 ; Restore registers saved
            pop     EBX
            pop     AX
            ret
dmptss      ENDP


edump       PROC
;
;
;       Dump the GDT, IDT, and all tss's
;       The displacement to the tss of interest is in CX.
;
            pop     dumpcal             ; Set call addr in mem
            push    dumpcal             ; Get it back on stack
            push    AX                  ; Save AX
            push    BX                  ; BX
            push    CX                  ; CX
            push    DX                  ; and DX

            call    dumprg              ; Print Registers first

            call    newln               ; Do cr/lf
            lea     AX,dtsize           ; Point to debug data
            call    dumpln              ; and dump it.
```

```
                call    dumpln
                call    newln
                lea     AX,gdt_def                 ; Set displacement of GDT
                mov     CX,(idt_def-gdt_def+31)/16 ; Prepare to dump all
dumpitg:
                call    dumpln                     ; Put it out 16 at a time
                loop    dumpitg

                call    newln                      ; Do cr/lf
                lea     CX,supv                    ; Point to supv TSS
                call    dmptss
                lea     CX,supv2                   ; Point to supv2 TSS
                call    dmptss
                lea     CX,v86                     ; Point to v86 TSS
                call    dmptss

                call    newln                      ; Do cr/lf

                mov     CX,6                       ; Prepare to dump
                mov     AX,SP                      ; from SP and
                mov     BX,SS                      ; SS
                mov     DS,BX
dumpit30:
                call    dumpln                     ; Put it out 16 at a time
                loop    dumpit30

                mov     AX,supdd                   ; Get normal DS value back
                mov     DS,AX                      ; into DS

                call    newln                      ; Do cr/lf

                pop     DX                         ; Restore registers
                pop     CX
                pop     BX
                pop     AX
                ret                                ; Return
edump           ENDP

mindump         PROC
;
; Minimum dump for trace without too much inteference
;
                shl     EAX,16                     ; Move AX to high EAX
                pop     AX                         ; Get return addr
                push    AX                         ; Back on stack
```

```
            call    prteaxx         ; Put it out
            call    newln           ; Space a line
            shr     EAX,16          ; Get AX back
            ret
mindump     ENDP
totalsize:
            END     segsetup
```

```
            PAGE    59,132
            .486P
            MASM51
;
;  Test-bed program for code to be executed in 80486 protected
;  mode.  The VIRT86L program is assumed to be running the MS-DOS
;  system as a virtual 8086 task.  The INT 00 escape is used to
;  to gain linkage in protected mode at 'goback'.
;
code        SEGMENT para 'CODE' USE16
            ASSUME  CS:code, DS:code, SS:code
            org     100h
            db      256 dup (0)
startex:
            mov     SP,startex-code   ; Set an SP value.
            lea     DX,goback         ; Set displacement to code.
            mov     CX,CS             ; Get a value
            mov     DS,CX             ; for our DS (we use CS).
            int     0                 ; Invoke protected mode call.
;
;  A real program might have other things to do here.  Feel free to
;  do whatever is necessary or desirable.
;
            mov     AH,4ch            ; Set 'terminate' code
            int     21h               ; and end via MS-DOS call.
orgpt       equ     $-startex+15 and 0fff0h
            org     startex+orgpt     ; Align on a para boundry
;
;  Define the protected mode routine.  (Again, this is expandable to
;  suit whatever is needed.)
;
goback:
;
;  At entry, the code segment points here.  The value in BX is a
;  selector for a data descriptor that points here.  The value in
;  CX is a selector for a stack segment that also points here.
;
;  On return from the code here, we want the original DS, SS, and SP
;  values in effect.  If we set a zero flag, the code takes a dump
;  as it exits.
;
            mov     SI,SS             ; Save SS of monitor
            mov     DI,SP             ; and the SP also.
            mov     DX,stackwk-goback ; Set an SP for myself
            mov     SS,CX             ; Set our passed SS
            mov     SP,DX             ; and our new SP.
```

```
            push    DS                      ; Now save DS
            mov     DS,BX                   ; and set our DS value


            pushad                          ; Save the extended registers
            pushfd                          ; and the EFLAGS
;
; Execute whatever instructions are desired here
;
            mov     BX,CS                   ; Get my code segment desc
            verr    BX                      ; Check if I can read it
            pushf                           ; Stack flags, then put in
            pop     WORD PTR DS:[datawd1-goback]  ; a safe place
            verw    BX                      ; Check if I can write it
            pushf                           ; Stack these flags, too
            pop     WORD PTR DS:[datawd2-goback]  ; and to data area
;
; Make sure the stack is clear here.
; Reverse the entry code to restore the proper environment for our
; return.
;
            popfd
            popad                           ; Our stack is now back
            pop     DS                      ; Restore DS
            mov     SS,SI                   ; Restore SS
            mov     SP,DI                   ; and SP
;
; Set a zero condition code to get a dump. Set non-zero to avoid one.
;
            mov     AL,1                    ; Set a proper value in AL
            or      AL,AL                   ; and set the condition code
            retf
            ret
;
; Allow space for some data here
;
            ALIGN   4
datawd1     dw      0
datawd2     dw      0
datawd3     dw      0
datawd4     dw      0
datadbl1    dd      0
datadbl2    dd      0
            dw      256 dup (?)
stackwk     equ     $
code        ENDS
            END     startex
```

Glossary

absolute address The fully defined address by a memory address number.

access time The interval between a request for data or information from the memory unit and its actual availability to the processing unit.

accumulator One or more registers for the storage of immediate results and operands in the Arithmetic-Logic Unit (ALU).

active elements Those components in a circuit that provide gain, or control direct current flow, such as transistors and diodes.

adder Switching circuits that combine binary bits to generate the sum and carry of those bits.

address Information identifying individual storage locations or words in a memory unit.

address decoder A circuit that converts the 80486 address into chip-select signals sent to the bus control logic.

address decoding Condensing an address on the bus into a single signal, which either selects or disables a particular device and sets the current number of wait states for that device.

address latch A circuit that maintains its contents for a specified period of time. Latches are used to maintain the I/O address for the duration of a bus cycle.

address space The total area accessible to a program.

address translation Converting a selector and offset into a physical address.

addressing mode The specification of an operand in an instruction.

alphameric Alphabetic, numeric, and special characters.

ALU See *Arithmetic-Logic Unit.*

American Standard Code for Information Interchange (ASCII) A binary encoding scheme using seven bits to represent alphabetic characters, numbers, and special symbols.

analog An item that represents something else. For example, a meter movement that indicates a voltage value on a scale.

AND gate A circuit that forms a logic gate whose output is a 1 only when all its inputs are 1. The gate output for all other conditions is a 0.

anode The lead on a diode or other device that receives positive voltage. This is opposed to the other lead, the cathode, that receives negative voltage.

architecture An orderly organization of subsystems to satisfy overall system objectives.

Arithmetic-Logic Unit (ALU) A unit that performs all the arithmetic and logic operations in a microprocessor.

ASCII See *American Standard Code for Information Interchange.*

assembler A software program that translates assembly language into binary machine language.

assembly language A symbolic notation for writing machine instructions.

asynchronous operations A mode of operation for interacting systems in which each system is independent of the internal timing constraints of every other system.

bar A sign that denotes the inverse, or complement, of a function. It is written as a line over the function or value.

base address The physical address of the start of a segment.

BCD See *Binary Coded Decimal.*

benchmark A program used to test and evaluate the performance characteristics of different systems.

bias A constant added to the true exponent of a real number to obtain the exponent field of that number's floating-point representation in the FPU.

biased exponent The exponent as it appears in a floating point representation of a number.

bi-directional A term used to describe signal-transmission lines that can transmit signals in either direction.

binary A term used to describe the base-two number system.

Binary Coded Decimal BCD. A coding scheme in which every decimal digit from 0 to 9 is represented by its equivalent four-bit binary number.

binary point The counterpart of the decimal point, but it exists in floating-point binary numbers. Each binary digit to the right of the binary point is multiplied by an increasingly negative power of 2.

bistable multivibrator A flip-flop.

bit A digit in the binary number system. It is a "made up" word, taking the "b" from binary and the "it" from digit.

bit field A contiguous sequence of bits. A bit field may begin at any bit location of any byte and may contain up to 32 bits in the 80486.

Bits Per Second (BPS) A common measure of the rate of flow of information between digital systems.

bit string A contiguous sequence of bits. A bit string may begin at any bit position of any byte and may contain up to $2^{32}-1$ bits, in the 80486.

Boolean approach To impose the condition that all logic statements, reasons, facts, and so on, are either true or false.

bootstrap A technique for starting up the operations of a computer system from a very small program in its memory.

BPS See *Bits Per Second*.

buffer Storage elements such as registers or memory locations for the temporary storage of information prior to its use by the intended system, such as a peripheral device.

bus A collection of signal transmission lines.

bus command A signal directing that a particular operation be performed on the bus.

bus cycle A single transfer of information on the bus.

bus driver A source of electrical current used to maintain or transmit signals along a bus.

byte A collection of eight adjacent bits.

C3-C0 The four condition code bits of the FPU status word. These bits are set to certain by the compare, test, examine, and remainder functions of the FPU.

cache A buffer type of high-speed memory filled at medium speed from main memory. Cache memory is the fastest portion of the overall memory storing only the data that the processor may need in the immediate future.

cache flush An operation that marks all cache lines as "invalid."

cache hit A request for access to memory in which the needed information can be read from the cache. (Opposite of a *cache miss*.)

cache line The smallest unit of storage that can be allocated in a cache. The internal cache of the 80486 has a line size of 128 bits.

cache line fill An operation that loads an entire cache line using multiple read cycles to main memory.

cache miss A request for access to memory that requires actually reading main memory. (Opposite of a *cache hit*.)

call gate A gate descriptor for invoking a procedure with a CALL or JUMP instruction.

cancel To remove a binary 1 from a flip-flop. Also, the process of removing a binary number from a register.

cathode The lead on a diode or other device that receives negative voltage. See also *anode*.

Central Processing Unit (CPU) This consists of the microprocessor, the Arithmetic Logic Unit, various registers, and control and timing circuits.

character This general term refers to all alphameric punctuation marks, mathematical operators, alphabetic characters, and the coded representation of such symbols.

chip A small piece of semiconductor material containing miniaturized electronic circuits; an integrated circuit.

chop In the FPU, to set one or more low-order bits of a real number to zero, yielding the nearest representable number in the direction of zero.

clear/reset This process sets all relevant data to binary zero.

clock A generator of periodic electrical pulses that control the timing of electronic switching circuits in computers. Clock speed is limited by the response time of the ICs used in the system. All other things being equal, the faster the clock frequency, the more functions that can be performed in the same amount of real time.

CMOS See *Complementary Metal Oxide Semiconductor.*

code A means of representing information in digital form by assigning a specific pattern of bits to each item of information.

code segment An address space that contains instructions; an executable segment. The type of information held in a segment is specified by its segment descriptor.

comparator A component that compares two binary numbers.

compile To translate a high-level language program to the desired machine-level set of program steps. A compile is done via the required language compiler.

compiler A program that translates high-level language source code into machine language.

Complementary Metal Oxide Semiconductor (CMOS) A combination of a p-channel and an n-channel transistor that creates a fast, low-power electronic switch. CMOS is a technology for fabricating electronic components.

condition codes The four bits of the FPU status word that indicate the results of the FPU's compare, text, examine, and remainder functions.

conforming A property of a segment indicating that each procedure in that segment will move outward to the ring of its caller when it is called.

context switch See *task switch.*

control bus That part of a bus that transmits control and status signals among support chips and a processor.

control register In the 80486, these registers hold data of machine states of a global nature. They are called CR0, CR1, CR2, and CR3. The low-order 15 bits of CR0 are called the Machine Status Word, for compatibility with the 80286.

control transfers In the 80486, transfer of control is done by use of exceptions, interrupts and by the instructions CALL, JMP, INT, IRET, and RET. A "near" transfer goes to a place within the current code segment. "Far" transfers go to other segments.

control word A 16-bit FPU register that the user can set to specify the modes of computation the FPU is to use and the exception interrupts that are to be enabled.

controller That element or group of elements in a computer system that directs a series of operations and sends the proper signals to other computer circuits to carry out.

coprocessor An auxiliary processor that operates in coordination with the CPU, allowing architectural capabilities which, in view of the limitations of contemporary technology, could not otherwise be provided. Co-processors furnish the hardware to perform functions that would otherwise be performed in software. In addition, they extend the instruction set of the main processor.

counter   A device capable of changing state in a specified sequence on receiving appropriate input signals.

Current Privilege Level (CPL)   The privilege level of the program that currently is executing. In general, CPL can be determined by examining the lowest 2 bits of the Code Segment (CS) register.

cycle time   A fixed time interval.

cycle stealing   A channel controller or multiplexer of the interface system may "steal" a memory cycle-time to transmit a word from the external data storage medium into main memory or vice versa.

data   Facts, symbols, numbers, letters, or anything that can be represented as binary bits on a computer.

data bus   That part of a bus that transfers data among the support chips and a processor.

data segment   An address space containing data. The type of information held in a segment is specified by its segment descriptor.

data structure   An area of memory defined for a particular use by hardware or software, such as a page table or task state segment (TSS).

debug registers   In the 80486, there are six programmer-accessible registers: DR0-DR3, DR6 and DR7. DR0-DR3 specify the four linear breakpoints. DR4 and DR5 are reserved by Intel. DR6 displays the current state of the breakpoints, and DR7 is used to set the breakpoints.

decoder, binary   A combination of logic gates that converts any binary number into a decimal number.

delay   The slowing up of the propagation of a pulse, either deliberately to prevent inputs from changing while clock pulses are present, or un-intentionally as caused by transistor rise-and-fall time, pulse-response characteristics.

denormal   A special form of floating-point number. On the FPU, a denormal is defined as a number having a biased exponent of zero.

descriptor   An 8-byte quantity specifying an independently protected object.

descriptor cache   See *shadow register*.

Descriptor Privilege Level (DPL)   A field in a descriptor indicating how protected the descriptor is. The DPL is the least privileged level at which a task may access a particular descriptor and access the segment associated with that descriptor.

descriptor table   An array of segment descriptors. There are two kinds of descriptor tables: the Global Descriptor Table (GDT) and an arbitrary number of Local Descriptor Tables (LDTs).

digit   A single decimal number, 0 through 9.

digit, binary   A single binary number, 0 or 1.

digital circuit   A semiconductor configuration that operates as a switch. Also called a *binary circuit*.

DIP See *Dual In-line Package*.

direct addressing Specifying a memory location by an address embedded in an instruction.

Direct Memory Addressing (DMA) A technique for transferring data in or out of memory without disturbing the program being executed by the processing unit.

discrete circuit An electronic circuit comprising separate individually manufactured and assembled transistors, diodes, resistors, capacitors, and other components.

displacement A 16-bit value specified in an instruction and used for computing address offsets.

display A list of pointers to the stack frames of the procedure in which the currently executing procedure is enclosed.

DMA See *Direct Memory Addressing*.

double extended IEEE Std 754 term for the FPU's extended format, with more exponent and significand bits than the double format and an explicit integer bit in the significand.

double format A floating-point format supported by the FPU. It consists of a sign, an 11-bit biased exponent, an implicit integer bit, and a 52-bit significand; a total of 64 explicit bits.

doubleword A 32-bit quantity of memory.

DPL See *Descriptor Privilege Level*.

DRAM See *Dynamic Random Access Memory*.

DRAM controller A component that handles the details of interfacing to dynamic random access memory.

driver An element coupled to the output stage of a circuit to increase its power capability or fanout.

Dual In-line Package (DIP) The container in which a chip resides. This refers to the double, parallel rows of pins that connect the resident chip to the circuit board.

dump Recording the system's memory contents on an external medium, such as magnetic tape.

Dynamic Random Access Memory (DRAM) Random access memory that must be periodically refreshed in order not to lose data.

editor A program used to manipulate a source program in an interactive manner.

effective address The address produced by addressing-mode calculations. A base register, scaled index, and displacement may be used in the calculations.

Effective Privilege Level (EPL) The EPL is the least privileged of the RPL and DPL.

emulate To create the machine language instructions of one processor for another by means of microprogramming.

environment The 14 or 28 bytes (depending on addressing mode) of FPU registers affected by the FSTENV and FLDENV instructions. It encompasses the entire state of the FPU, except for the eight registers of the FPU stack.

Error Correcting Codes (ECC) A parity-bit check allowing the detection of erroneous bits in a code word.

error value See *exception value*.

exception A condition occurring when an instruction violates the rules of normal operation.

exception pointers In the FPU, the indication used by exception handlers to identify the cause of an exception.

exception value A special value produced by an instruction if it causes a masked exception.

execution time Time required by a microprocessor to execute a machine-language instruction. Execution time varies from one instruction to another.

expand down A property of a segment that causes the processor to check that, in all accesses to that segment, offsets are greater than the segment's limits. Used for stack segments.

expand up A property of a segment that causes the processor to check that all accesses to that segment offsets are no greater than the segment's limit. Generally, all segments other than stack segments have this property.

explicit cache See *shadow register*.

exponent A number that indicates the power to which another number is raised.

extended format The FPU's implementation of the double extended format of IEEE Std 754. Extended format is the main floating-point format used by the FPU. It consists of a sign, a 15-bit biased exponent, and a significand with an explicit integer bit and 63 fractional-part bits.

fall time The decay time of the trailing edge in a pulse waveform.

fan-in The total number of inputs to a particular gate or function.

fan-out The total number of loads connected to a particular gate or function.

far pointer In the 80486, a 48-bit logical address of two components: a 16-bit segment selector and a 32-bit offset.

fault An exception reported at the instruction boundary immediately before the instruction that generated the exception.

fetch To obtain or secure information from a memory unit.

flag bit A single bit indicating one of two mutually exclusive conditions or states.

flat memory organization An address space in the 80486 that consists of a single array of up to 4 gigabytes. The 80486 maps the 4 gigabyte flat space onto the physical address space by address translation mechanisms.

flip-flop A circuit with two and only two stable states.

floating-point operand A representation for a number expressed as a base, a sign, a significand, and a signed exponent. The value of the number is the signed product of its significand and the base raised to the power of the exponent.

Floating-Point Unit (FPU)   The part of the 80486 processor containing the floating-point registers and performing the operations required by floating-point instructions.

flush   See *cache flush*.

gate   The simplest logic circuit. Its output voltage will be high or low depending on the states of the inputs and the type of gate that is employed. Generally, four types of gates exist: a call gate, a trap gate, an interrupt gate, and a task gate.

GDT   See *Global Descriptor Table*.

general register   One of the 16-bit registers: AX, BX, CX, or DX.

glitch   A false digital pulse.

Global Descriptor Table (GDT)   A table in memory containing descriptors for segments shared by all tasks.

Global Descriptor Table Register (GDTR)   In the 80486, this register holds the 32-bit linear base address and the 16-bit limit of the Global Descriptor Table.

graphics   Pictorial display of data.

handshaking   A colloquial term describing a method of data transfer among asynchronous devices.

hang-up   The inability of a flip-flop to be triggered from a pulse command.

hard-wired logic   Logic design using a number of nonprogrammable chips as the logic elements.

hertz (Hz)   Cycles per second.

hit   See *cache hit*.

IC   See *Integrated Circuit*.

IDT   See *Interrupt Descriptor Table*.

immediate operand   A constant contained in an instruction and used as an operand.

implicit integer bit   A part of the significand in the single real and double real floating-point formats that is not explicitly given. In these formats, the entire given significand is considered to be to the right of the binary point.

indefinite   A special value returned by floating-point functions when the inputs are such that no other answer makes sense. For each floating-point format, one quiet NaN is designated as the indefinite value.

index register   One of the 16-bit registers: SI or DI. Generally, an index register holds an offset into the current data or extra segment.

index   A number that accesses a table. An index is scaled (multiplied by shifting left) to account for the size of the operand. The scaled index is added to the base address of the table to get the address of the table entry.

indirect addressing   Accessing a memory location by first fetching the desired address from some other memory location or register.

inexact   IEEE Std 754 term for the FPU's precision exception.

infinity   A floating-point result with greater magnitude than any integer or any real number.

initialization   The step that sets certain counters and clears certain registers in preparation for a following task.

instruction   A single step in a program, or a single line of code.

Instruction Pointer (IP)   A register containing the offset of the instruction currently being executed. A selector for the segment containing this instruction is stored in the CS register. In the 80486, the instruction pointer (EIP) is a 32-bit register containing the offset address of the next sequential instruction to be executed. The low-order 16 bits of EIP are the IP.

instruction prefetch   Reading instructions into the processor from sequentially higher addresses prior to execution; a technique for overlapping the execution of instructions.

instruction register   A register in the microprocessor that stores the current instruction being executed.

instruction set   The set of all machine-language instructions that can be executed by a processor.

integer   In the 80486, a signed binary numeric value contained in a 32-bit doubleword, a 16-bit word, or an 8-bit byte. The sign bit is located in bit 31 of the doubleword, in byte 15 of the word, and in bit 7 of the byte.

integer   A number (positive, negative, or zero) that is finite and has no fractional part.

integer bit   A part of the significand in floating-point formats. In these formats, the integer bit is the only part of the significand considered to be to the left of the binary point.

Integrated Circuit (IC)   A complex electronic circuit fabricated on a single piece of semiconductor material.

interface   A common boundary between two systems across which information is exchanged.

interleaving   A technique for improving the performance of computer memories. Successive memory locations are assigned to different banks, cycling through the available banks. Then the concurrency offered by multiple banks is fully exploited when accessing memory locations in sequence.

internal cache   A cache memory on the processor chip. The 80486 has 8K bytes of internal cache memory.

interrupt   To suspend execution of the current program on a processor in order to service one or more peripheral devices. Also a *forced call*, not appearing explicitly in a program triggered by an exception, by a signal from a device external to the processor, or by a special interrupt instruction.

interrupt controller   A component prioritizing multiple interrupt requests.

Interrupt Descriptor Table (IDT)   A table in memory indexed by an interrupt number and containing gates to the corresponding interrupt handlers.

Interrupt Descriptor Table Register (IDTR)   This register points to a table of entry points for interrupt handlers. In the 80486, the register holds the 32-bit linear base address and the 16-bit limit of the Interrupt Descriptor Table.

interrupt distributor An interrupt handler provided by the operating system that transfers to a different user-supplied interrupt handler depending on which task is interrupted.

interrupt gate A gate descriptor that invokes an interrupt handler. An interrupt gate differs from a trap gate only in its effect on the IF flag. An interrupt gate clears the flag (disables interrupts) for the duration of the handler.

interrupt handler A procedure or task called in response to an interrupt.

interrupt latency That elapsed time before an interrupt request is serviced.

interrupt procedure A procedure called in response to an interrupt.

interrupt task A task activated in response to an interrupt.

interval timer A component that interrupts the processor after a period of time elapses. Software can set the time period and specify whether the timer should interrupt repetitively or stop after the first instance.

invalid Unallocated. Invalid cache lines do not cause cache hits. Valid cache lines have been loaded with data and may cause cache hits.

invalid operation The exception condition for the FPU covering all cases not covered by other exceptions. Included are FPU stack overflow and underflow, NaN inputs, illegal infinite inputs, out-of-range inputs, and inputs in unsupported formats.

I/O permissions bit map The mechanism that allows the 80486 to selectively trap references to specific I/O addresses. The Permissions Bit Map resides in the Task State Segment (TSS). The map is a bit vector, and its size and location in the TSS are variable. The 80486 locates the map by means of the I/O Map Base field in the fixed portion of the TSS.

IP See *Instruction Pointer*.

jump An instruction causing a transfer of control from one part of the program to another.

labels Identifying statements or numbers that describe flip-flop or logic-gate positions.

Large-Scale Integration (LSI) A technique for fabricating a large number of integrated electronic circuits on a small piece of semiconductor.

Last-In-First-Out (LIFO) A method by which the last item placed in a stack or unit is the first one to be processed.

latch A component that memorizes its current input on command. Also, a feedback loop in a symmetrical digital circuit, such as a flip-flop, for retaining a state.

LDT See *Local Descriptor Table*.

LIFO See *Last-In-First-Out*.

linear address space Address space that runs from 0 bytes to the maximum physical address that a processor can address. In the case of the 80486, the linear address space runs up to 4 gigabytes.

local address space The collection of segments accessible through a task's LDT.

Local Descriptor Table (LDT)   A table in memory containing descriptors for segments that are private to a task.

Local Descriptor Table Register (LDTR)   This register holds the 16-bit selector for the Local Descriptor Table.

lock   In a multiple processor system, a signal from one processor that prevents the others from accessing memory. The processor has exclusive use of the memory until it stops sending the signal.

logic diagrams   Drawings that show how flip-flops and gates must be connected to perform specific computer functions.

logic gates   An electronic circuit that performs a logic operation, such as OR.

logic levels   One of two possible: 0 or 1.

logical address   A logical address in the 80486 consisting of a selector and offset. The selector points to some segment's descriptor, which includes a segment's linear base address. The offset tells how far into the segment the required byte is.

long integer   An integer format supported by the FPU and consisting of a 64-bit two's complement quantity.

long real   An older term for the FPU's 64-bit double format.

looping   Executing a fixed set of instructions over and over.

LSI   See *Large-Scale Integration*.

machine language   A format for coding instructions as binary codes that can be directly interpreted by a processor.

Machine Status Word (MSW)   A register containing a bit for controlling the mode (real versus virtual) and bits that control the processor's execution of WAIT and ESC instructions.

mask bit   A bit that covers up or disables some condition.

masked   A term that can apply to each of the six FPU exceptions (I, D, A, O, U, and P). An exception is masked if a corresponding bit in the FPU control word is set to one. If an exception is masked, the FPU will not generate an interrupt when the exception condition occurs; it will instead provide its own exception recovery.

masked exception   An exception producing an exception value rather than an interrupt.

masking   A means of examining only certain bits in a word. This is usually done by ANDing the word with a mask containing 1's in the desired bit locations.

memory   A medium for storing programs and data.

memory management   The facilities for mapping the address space of a task into the available memory.

memory-mapped input/output   A technique whereby a peripheral device masquerades as a memory location.

memory unit   The part of a computer that stores information such as instructions and operands.

memory passing   A technique for inter-task communication in which data is transmitted from one task to another.

Metal Oxide Semiconductor (MOS) A technique for manufacturing field-effect transistors in which the flow of charge inside a semiconductor material is controlled by means of the electrical potentials of metal electrodes attached to the surface.

microprocessor Central Processing Units (CPUs) built into chips by means of VLSI technology.

microprogram A sequence of micro-instructions that can be directly related to the very basic operations of a processor.

miss See *cache miss*.

mnemonic A symbolic name, particularly used for opcodes.

MOS See *Metal Oxide Semiconductor*.

MSW See *Machine Status Word*.

multiplexing Distributing and sharing a common resource among several users.

multiprocessing Using more than one processor in a system.

multitasking The creation and use of multiple tasks on a computer.

NaN An abbreviation for "Not a Number," a floating-point quantity that does not represent any numeric or infinite quantity.

NAND Logic function that produces the inverted AND (*not*-AND) function.

N-channel MOS (NMOS) The same as MOS, except that the majority of carriers in the semiconductor material are negatively charged.

near pointer In the 80486 a 32-bit logical address. A near pointer is an offset within a segment.

negative edge gating A circuit response as the control signal goes from high to low.

NMI See *Nonmaskable Interrupt*.

NMOS See *N-channel MOS*.

Nonmaskable Interrupt (NMI) A signal to the processor from an external device indicating that a problem has arisen or is imminent.

NOR The logical negation of the OR function.

NOR gate An electronic circuit that forms a logic gate and whose output is a 1 only when all inputs are 0.

normal The representation of a number in a floating-point format in which the significand has an integer bit one, either explicit or implicit.

normalize To convert a denormal floating-point representation of a number to a normal representation.

NOT A Boolean logic operation denoting negation.

Not-a-Number (NaN) An exception value produced by the numeric processor in response to a masked invalid operation exception.

not present In a virtual-memory, a segment on disk but not in main memory.

null selector A selector in which all bits are zero (0).

object program The numeric, machine language output of an assembler.

offset A quantity specifying the position of a byte within a segment.

opcode The part of an instruction that specifies the operation to be performed, as opposed to the items upon which the operation is performed.

operand Data operated on arithmetically or logically by a processor.

OR A logic operation that produces a 1 at the output if at least one input is a 1.

ordinal An unsigned binary numeric value contained in a byte, a 16-bit word, or a 32-bit doubleword.

overflow A floating-point exception condition in which the correct answer is finite but has magnitude too great to be represented in the destination format. Do not confuse this kind of overflow (also called numeric overflow) with stack overflow.

P-channel MOS (PMOS) Same as MOS except that the majority of the carriers in the semiconductor material are positively charged.

packed BCD A packed byte representation of two decimal digits, each in the range of 0 through 9. One digit is stored in each half-byte. The digit in the high-order half-byte is the most significant.

packed decimal An integer format supported by the FPU. A packed decimal number is a 10-byte quantity, with nine bytes of BCD digits (i.e., 18 BCD digits) and one byte for the sign.

page A set of consecutive bytes. Pages begin on 4K boundaries. Paging divides programs into multiple uniform sized pages that have no direct relationship to the logical structure of a program.

page fault In the 80486, the processor will issue an Interrupt 14 if it finds one of the two following conditions: the current procedure does not have enough privilege to access the indicated page, or the page-table entry or page-directory needed for the address translation has a zero in its present bit (i.e., the page is not currently loaded from auxiliary storage).

page frame A 4K unit of contiguous addresses of a physical memory. The page frame address specifies the physical starting address of a page; the low-order 12 bits are always zero.

page table An array of 32-bit page specifiers. The table itself is a page and contains 4 kilobytes of memory, or up to 1K 32-bit entries.

paging A form of memory management simulating a large, unsegmented address space using a small, fragmented address space and some disk storage. Paging provides access to data structures larger than the available memory space by keeping them partly in memory and partly on disk.

parallel A technique for processing binary data in which all bits are acted upon simultaneously.

parameter An item transmitted to a procedure by its caller.

parity An indication of whether a number of 1's in a number is even or odd.

passive elements Elements without gain, such as resistors, inductors, or capacitors.

peripheral device An electronic device connected to the processor. Peripheral devices communicate to the processor by means of input and output instructions, interrupts, or memory-mapped input/output.

physical address A number transmitted to the memory hardware in order to specify the location of a memory access.

PICU See *Priority Interrupt Control Unit.*

PIO See *Programmable Parallel Input/Output.*

PMOS See *P-channel MOS.*

physical address The mechanism that actually selects the memory where a required byte is located. Physical address differs from linear address only when paging is in effect.

pointer An address used by software and consisting of a selector and offset. In real mode, pointers are real addresses; in virtual mode, they are virtual addresses.

pointer register One of the BP or BX registers. Generally, a pointer register holds an offset into the current stack segment.

polling A technique for identifying the source of an interrupt signal by periodically interrogating each external device.

port A chip through which peripheral devices are connected to a microprocessor.

position-independent code Code that will execute properly regardless of whether it is placed in memory.

positive-edge gating A circuit that responds as control signals go from low to high.

positive logic Logic operations in which the more positive voltage represents the 1 state.

precharge A period of dormancy required between accesses to a dynamic random access memory (DRAM) chip.

precision The effective number of bits in the significand of the floating-point representation of a number.

precision control An option, programmed through the FPU control word, that allows all FPU arithmetic to be performed with reduced precision. Because no speed advantage results from this option, it's only used for strict compatibility with IEEE Std 754 and with other computer systems.

precision exception An FPU exception condition that results when a calculation does not return an exact answer. This exception is usually masked and ignored and is used only in extremely critical applications.

prefix A byte preceding the opcode of an instruction. It specifies that the instruction should be repeated, locked, or that an alternate segment should be used.

priority Refers to a precedence relationship applied to simultaneous occurrences.

Priority Interrupt Control Unit (PICU) A device that arbitrates the priority of simultaneous interrupt requests.

privilege level A number in a predetermined range indicating the degree of protection or degree of privilege.

procedure A portion of a program performing a particular function that may be used at several points in the program.

process See *task.*

processor cycle A unit for measuring instruction execution time.

program counter A register in a processor that stores the address of the next instruction to be executed.

program locality The principle explaining that programs tend to access memory near the most previous access. Program locality enables cache memory to be as effective as it is.

Program Status Word (PSW) A special register that keeps track of the address of the next instruction to be executed and often stores other status flags.

Programmable Array Logic (PAL) Integrated circuits that can be programmed to perform specific logic functions. A PAL device consists logically of a programmable AND array whose output terms feed a fixed OR array.

Programmable Parallel Input/Output (PIO) Interface circuitry.

Programmable Read-Only Memory (PROM) A read-only memory whose contents are generally set just after fabrication and then not changed.

protected virtual address mode A mode of operation in which the processor offers multitasking, advanced protection facilities, and virtual memory.

pseudo-descriptor A 48-bit memory operand accessed when a descriptor table base register is loaded or stored.

pseudozero One of a set of special values of the extended real floating-point format.

quadword A 64-bit operand. The CDQ instruction can be used to convert a doubleword to a quadword. A quadword held in the EDX and.EAX registers may be the dividend used with a doubleword divisor.

Quiet NaN A floating-point NaN in which the most significant bit of the fractional part of the significand is one. By convention, these NaNs can undergo certain operations without causing an exception.

RAM See *Random Access Memory*.

Random Access Memory (RAM) Read/write memory.

Read-Only Memory (ROM) Memory in which information is stored during or immediately after fabrication and not changed later.

ready list A list of tasks waiting to use the processor.

real Any finite value (negative, positive, or zero) that can be represented by a (possibly infinite) decimal expansion.

real address An address consisting of selector and offset in real address mode.

real address mode A mode of operation in which the processor closely mimics the behavior of a "lower level" chip in the chip family (for example, an 80386 mimic of an 8086).

real time operation An operation in which a processor, interacting with an external process, executes its program concurrently with the evolution of the external process.

re-entrant code Code allowing the program to be interrupted during execution.

refresh The process of reading and then writing back a cell of a dynamic random access memory (DRAM).

register Fast, temporary-storage locations, usually in the processor itself.

rendezvous A method for synchronizing two tasks. The first to reach the synchronization point waits for the other.

Requested Privilege Level (RPL) A field in a selector indicating the degree of "trust" or privilege a program has in the selector. RPL is determined by the least two significant bits of a selector.

reset A signal causing computer hardware to reinitialize itself, a part of system initialization.

restartable An instruction is restartable after suffering a partial exception if, after removing the cause of the exception, the program may be correctly continued by re-executing the instruction.

rise time The time required for the leading edge of a waveform to proceed from 10 percent to 90 percent of maximum amplitude points.

ROM See *Read-Only Memory*.

RPL See *Requested Privilege Level*.

scatter read Reading a block of data into noncontiguous locations in memory.

segment A region of memory, in a range of 1 byte to the maximum that can be handled by the processor. Also refers to units of contiguous address space.

segment descriptor table A memory array of 8-byte entries containing descriptors. An 80486 descriptor table may contain up to 8192 descriptors.

segment register One of the registers: CS, DS, ES or SS.

segmented memory organization An address space consisting of up to 16,383 linear address spaces up to 4 gigabytes each. The total space, as viewed by a program in the 80486, can be as large as up to 2^{46} bytes (64 terabytes).

selector A quantity that specifies a segment.

semaphore A variable shared between tasks or processors and used for synchronization. A zero means proceed; a non-zero means wait.

serial data The data available as a series of bits occurring one after the other in a single file.

set-associative A form of cache organization in which the location of a data block in main memory constrains but does not completely determine its location in the cache. An n-way set-associative cache allows data from a given address in main memory to be cached in any of n locations. In the 80486, both the Translation Lookaside Buffer (TLB) and the internal cache have a four-way set-associative organization.

shadow register A hidden register associated with a visible register. A shadow register holds the descriptor corresponding to the selector in the associated visible register.

shift The process of moving data from one place to another.

short integer An integer format supported by the FPU consisting of a 32-bit two's complement quantity.

short real An older term for the FPU's 32-bit single format.

shutdown The quiescent state from which the processor may be awakened by a reset or nonmaskable interrupt.

signature The particular reference signal of a given circuit.

sign extension Conversion of data to a larger format, where empty bit positions are filled with the value of the sign. This conversion preserves the value of signed integers. For unsigned integers, see *zero extension*.

signaling NaN A floating-point NaN that causes an invalid-operation exception whenever it enters into a calculation or comparison, even an unordered comparison.

significand The part of a floating-point number that holds the most significant nonzero bits of the number. The significand is comprised of an integer bit and a fraction. The integer bit is implicit in the single format and double format.

simulator A program that simulates a processor on a different computer or processor.

single extended A floating-point format that provides greater precision than single. It also provides an explicit integer bit in the significand.

single format A floating-point format that consists of a sign, an 8-bit biased exponent, an implicit integer bit, and a 23-bit significand; a total of 32 explicit bits.

single stepping Executing a program one instruction at a time and pausing after each instruction. This is generally a means by which programmers determine the effect of a line of code.

software A comprehensive set of computer programs and associated documentation.

SRAM See *Static Random Access Memory*.

stack A buffer whose information is generally accessed in a LIFO manner. See also *LIFO*.

stack fault A special case of the invalid-operation exception, indicated by a one in the SF bit of the status word. This condition usually results for stack underflow or overflow in the FPU.

stack frame Storage for the values of a procedure's local variables corresponding to a particular invocation of the procedure.

stack pointer A register that stores the memory address of the top (last-in) element of a stack in memory.

stack segment A data segment that holds a stack. A stack segment may be expand-down, which allows the segment to be resized toward lower addresses. The type of information held in a segment is specified in its segment descriptor.

state The condition of an input or output of a circuit concerning whether it is a logical 1 or logical 0.

Static Random Access Memory (SRAM) Random access memory in which data is retained indefinitely, unless the power is turned off.

status word A 16-bit FPU register that can be set manually but is usually controlled by side effects to FPU instructions. The status word contains condition codes, the FPU stack pointer, busy and interrupt bits, and exception flags.

string A contiguous sequence of bytes, words, or doublewords. A string may contain from zero bytes through $2^{32} - 1$ bytes (or 4 gigabytes in the 80486).

strobe   A signal to a latch to memorize its current input. The output of the latch will be the memorized value, even if the input changes until another strobe signal occurs.

supervisor mode   The privilege level applied to operating system pages. A program executing at privilege level 0, 1, or 2 is in supervisor mode.

swapping   Moving a segment from disk to memory (swapping in) or from memory to disk (swapping out).

synchronous   Operation of a switching network by a clock-pulse generator. All circuits in the network switch simultaneously, and all actions take place synchronously with the clock.

system clock   The fundamental time signal in a system.

system initialization   A series of operations performed by a combination of software and hardware when power is first applied to a computer system or if the reset switch is used.

tag   The part of a cache line that holds the address information determining if a memory operation is a hit or miss on that cache line.

tag word   A 16-bit register automatically maintained by the FPU. For each space in the FPU stack, it tells if the space is occupied by a number; if so, it tells what kind of number.

task   A defined function that is unique within the computer. Tasks are also referred to as *processes*.

task dispatching   Selecting a task and running it.

task force   A group of related tasks sharing the same Logical Descriptor Table (LDT).

Task Register (TR)   This register points to the information needed by the processor to define the current task.

Task State Segment (TSS)   A segment holding the contents of a task's registers when the processor is executing another task.

task switch   Changing from one task to another.

temporary real   An older term for the FPU's 80-bit extended format.

test card   A troubleshooting aid for comprehensive check-out of all input/output functions.

test registers   Registers TR6 and TR7 are used to control testing of the CAM (content addressable memory) in the Translation Lookaside Buffer.

time-slicing   A technique allowing several tasks to share a computer. The computer switches from one task to another, never staying with a single task for longer than a very small, fixed time.

toggle   To change a binary storage element to its opposite value.

Top   The 3-bit field of the status word that indicates which FPU register is the current top of stack.

transcendental   One of a class of functions for which polynomial formulas are always appropriate, never exact for more than isolated values.

transfer of control   The condition brought about when instructions are executed in sequence starting at some new location instead of executing the instruction stored after the current instruction in memory.

Translation Lookaside Buffer (TLB)   A cache that translates linear addresses to physical addresses. The TLB is a four-way, set-associative memory. The TLB testing mechanism is unique to the 80486, and may not be implemented in the same way in future Intel processors.

trap   An exception reported at the instruction boundary immediately following the instruction that generated the exception.

trap gate   A gate descriptor that invokes an exception handler. A trap gate differs from an interrupt gate only in its effect on the IF flag. Unlike an interrupt gate, which clears the flag (disables interrupts) for the duration of the handler, a trap gate leaves the flag unchanged.

trigger   A timing pulse used to initiate the transmission of logic signals through the appropriate signal paths. Also, the input pin on a flip-flop.

true   A true condition is the statement for a logic 1 in Boolean algebra.

TSS   See *Task State Segment*.

unbiased exponent   The true value that tells how far and in which direction to move the binary point of a floating-point number's significand.

underflow   An exception condition in which the correct answer is nonzero but is too small to be represented as a normal number in the destination floating-point format.

Universal Synchronous/Asynchronous Receiver Transmitter (USART)   A mechanism used by a processor to communicate with a device using a serial data format.

unload   To remove information in massive quantities.

unmasked   A term that can apply to each of the six FPU exceptions (I, D, A, O, U, and P). An exception is unmasked if a corresponding bit in the FPU control word is set to zero. If an exception is unmasked, the FPU will generate an interrupt when the exception condition occurs.

unnormal   An extended real representation in which the explicit integer bit of the significand is zero and the exponent is nonzero. The FPU does not support this format.

USE16   An assembly language directive for specifying 16-bit code and data segments.

USE32   An assembly language directive for specifying 32-bit code and data segments.

user mode   The privilege level applied to application pages. A program executing at privilege level 3 is in user mode.

valid   Allocated. Valid cache lines loaded with data may cause cache hits.

vectored interrupt   A technique of interrupt processing in which each interrupt specifies the address of the first instruction of its service routine.

virtual address   An address consisting of selector and offset in protected virtual address mode.

virtual memory   A technique for running programs larger than the available physical memory. Pieces of the program area stored on disk and are moved into memory only as necessary. This movement is automatically performed by the operating system and is invisible to the program.

virtual mode　See *protected virtual address mode*.

Very Large-Scale Integration (VLSI)　An abbreviation for a chip containing more than 1,000 gates.

wait state　An extra processor cycle added to the bus cycle in order to allow for slower devices on the bus to respond.

word　A machine-dependent unit of storage that is generally the width of the data bus or internal registers.

word integer　An integer format consisting of a 16-bit two's complement quantity.

back　A form of caching in which memory writes load only the cache memory. Data propagates to main memory when a write-back operation is invoked.

write-through　A form of caching in which memory writes load both the cache memory and main memory.

zero divide　An exception condition in which floating-point inputs are finite but the correct answer has infinite magnitude, even with an unlimited exponent.

zero extension　Conversion of data to a larger format where empty bit positions are filled with zero. This conversion preserves the value of unsigned integers. For signed integers, see *sign extension*.

Bibliography

Ashborn, Jim. "Intel Microprocessors: A Tradition of Innovation." *Solutions* (November/December 1985): 8–9.

___. "MULTIBUS II Adds Punch to 80386-Based Designs." *Solutions* (November/December 1985): 10.

Augarten, Stan. *Bit by Bit.* Ticknor & Fields: New York, NY, 1984.

_____. *State of The Art.* Ticknor & Fields: New York, NY, 1983.

Carr, Joseph J. *Microprocessor Interfacing.* TAB Books: Blue Ridge Summit, PA, 1982.

Chorafas, Dimitris N. *Microprocessors For Management.* Petrocelli Books: New York, NY, 1984.

Ciarcia, Steve. *Ciarcia's Circuit Cellar.* McGraw-Hill Book Company: New York, NY, 1984.

Cluley, J.C. *Computer Interfacing and On-Line Operation.* Crane Russak: New York, NY, 1975.

Coli, Vincent J. "Introduction to Programmable Array Logic." *Byte* (January 1987): 207–219.

Evanczuk, Stephen. "Intel's 486 Announced: Integrates FPU and MMU." *High Performance Systems* (April 1989).

Fawcette, James E. "80386: The Megabyte Manager." *PC World* (February 1986): 238–243.

Frederiksen, Thomas M. *Intuitive IC CMOS Evolution.* National Semiconductor Corporation: Sunnyvale, CA, 1984.

Freedman, Robert A. "Getting Started with PALs." *Byte* (January 1987): 223–230.

Glorioso, Robert M. and Fernando C. Colon Osorio. *Engineering Intelligent Systems.* Digital Press: Bedford, MA, 1980.

Graham, Neill. *Introduction to Computer Science.* West Publishing Co.: New York, NY, 1979.

Hayes, Norman M. "Chip Set Geared To Unix Simplifies High-End Designs." *Computer Design* (January 1, 1986): 65–72.

Hindin, Harvey J. "32-bit Parts and Architectures Vie for Attention." *Computer Design* (January 1, 1986): 49–61.

Intel Corporation. *i486 Microprocessor Data Sheet.* Intel Corporation: 1990.

_____. *i486 Microprocessor Hardware Reference Manual.* Intel Corporation: 1990.

_____. *i486 Microprocessor Product Brief Book.* Intel Corporation: 1990.

_____. *i486 Microprocessor Programmer's Reference Manual.* Intel Corporation: 1990.

_____. *Microprocessor and Peripherals Handbook.* Intel Corporation: 1983.

Lau, Edwin J. *Performance Improvement of Virtual Memory Systems.* UMI Research Press: Ann Arbor, MI, 1982.

Lewis, Peter H. "32-bit Chip: Powerhouse in the Wings." *New York Times* (August 29, 1985)

_____. "Now, an Era of Software Harmony." *New York Times* (April 1989)

Markhoff, Nicolas. "Complete Systems Now Possible with 32-bit Chip Sets." *Computer Designs* (July 1, 1985): 77–89.

McGrievy, D.J. and K.A. Pickar. *VLSI Technologies Through the 80s and Beyond.* IEEE Computer Society Press: Silver City, MD, 1982.

Mead, C. and L. Conway. *Introduction to VLSI Systems.* Addison-Wesley: Reading, MA, 1980.

Middleton, Robert G. *New Handbook of Troubleshooting Techniques.* Prentice-Hall: Englewood Cliffs, NJ, 1984.

Monds, Fabian. *The Business of Electronic Product Development.* Peter Peregrinus Ltd., on behalf of the Institution of Electrical Engineers: London, UK, 1984.

Phillips, David. "Mainframe Tricks Raise Performance of 32-bit Micros." *Computer Designs* (July 1, 1985): 95–103.

Pooch, Udo W. and Rahul Chattergy. *Designing Microcomputer Systems.* Hayden Book Company: Rochelle Park, NJ, 1979.

Rafiquzzaman, Mohamed. *Microprocessors and Microcomputer Development Systems.* Harper and Row: New York, NY, 1984.

Shires, Glen. "80386 Cache Design." *Solutions* (November/December 1985): 12–27.

Short, Kenneth L. *Microprocessors and Programmed Logic.* Prentice Hall: Englewood Cliffs, NJ, 1981.

Startz, Richard. *8087/80287/80387 for the IBM PC and Compatibles.* Brady Books: 1988.

Theaker, Colin J. and Graham R. Brookes. *A Practical Course on Operating Systems.* Springer-Verlag: New York, NY, 1983.

Thomplait, Cliff. "Memory Management Boosts Efficiency of Powerful Micros." *Computer Design* (July 1, 1985): 105–109.

Thompson, Roger and Anil Uberoi. "Processor Offers Code Compatibility, VAX-Like Architecture." *Computer Design* (January 1, 1986): 76–80.

Tseng, Vincent, Ed. *Microprocessor Development and Development Systems.* McGraw-Hill Book Company: New York, NY, 1982.

Zaks, Rodnay. *From Chips To Systems.* Sybex: Berkeley, CA, 1981.

Index

80486 Programming

If you are intrigued with the possibilities of the programs included in *80486 Programming* (TAB Book No. 3577), you should definitely consider having the ready-to-run disk containing the software applications. This software is guaranteed free of manufacturer's defects. (If you have any problems, return the disk within 30 days, and we'll send you a new one.) Not only will you save the time and effort of typing the programs, the disk eliminates the possibility of errors that prevent the programs from functioning. Interested?

Available on 5¼" disk requiring 256K, an 80486-based processor, MS-DOS (at least 3.1), and an appropriate assembler source at $29.95 plus $2.50 shipping and handling.